MCGRAW-HILL RURAL ACTIVITIES SERIES

W. A. Ross, *Consulting Editor*

Developing Farm Woodlands

McGraw-Hill

RURAL ACTIVITIES SERIES

W. A. Ross, *Consulting Editor*

[Other books in process]

Developing Farm Woodlands

JOHN FREDERICK PRESTON

*Formerly Forest Inspector, U.S. Forest Service
and Chief, Forestry Division, U.S. Soil Conservation
Service. Author of* Farm Wood Crops

McGRAW-HILL BOOK COMPANY, INC.

NEW YORK   TORONTO   LONDON

DEVELOPING FARM WOODLANDS

II

THE MAPLE PRESS COMPANY, YORK, PA.

Preface

THIS BOOK has been written to provide farmers and students of agriculture simple but complete instructions for woods operations that will produce a profitable woodland enterprise as a part of the farm business. The steps in the process are equally applicable to many small woodlands. The economics that govern forestry, as well as other operations, however, often do not permit nonfarm woodland owners profitably to take certain steps in developing a woodland that are entirely feasible and profitable for farmers. This difference, due to the economics of the farm setup, is inherent in farm forestry and gives farmers considerable advantage in growing and marketing forest products. Nevertheless, other owners of relatively small forest properties will find the steps outlined in this book technically applicable and, if consistently carried out, they will result in an increasingly profitable woods enterprise.

Limitations will always be found in the usefulness of any book. This one attempts to cover all types of forest found in the continental United States. The operating steps as given follow basic principles of silviculture and logging practice. They are the results of research as given in the many publications of the forest experiment stations of the U.S. Forest Service and of the state experiment stations. Practices often must be modified because of peculiar local conditions, especially the presence of epidemic tree diseases or insects. For example, the depredations of the spruce-bud worm in the North, of the "little leaf" disease of pine in the South, or of bark beetles anywhere may force a heavy cutting when normally a light cut or a thinning would be recommended.

The operating steps outlined in this text are applicable under most normal conditions. If followed, they will build up the resistance of the forest trees to all attacks of diseases or insects. Vigorous, healthy trees are the best insurance against losses due to disease and insects. Sometimes things seem to go wrong in spite of the use of the best-known practices. This was true when the chestnut blight took all of our eastern chestnut. It is equally true of unusual storm damage. Now we have the oak-wilt disease that is threatening our eastern hardwood forests. The outcome of the attack of this new and little-known disease is still in doubt. The defense against it, and against others, is determined by research. Local foresters and experiment stations are available for advice in such matters.

This is primarily an operations book. It deals with methods of doing things to make a better woods, such as planting trees, weeding, thinning, pruning, and methods of cutting and marketing. Management is involved in all of these, but it is emphasized chiefly in connection with the discussion of cutting practices and in the chapters where specialized management to produce profitable crops of maple sap, Christmas trees, and naval stores is discussed. Some technical terms will have to be used and understood by the reader. Their meaning will often be explained in the text, and a glossary of terms will be found in the appendix. It is assumed that the reader is acquainted with the common names of forest trees in his locality and that he can recognize these trees in the woods. This is essential to the success of the forest manager. Many state foresters publish books giving descriptions and pictures of forest trees, or they will refer the inquirer to a suitable tree guide. The American Forestry Association also publishes a book describing and picturing all important trees in the United States.

One purpose of this book is to take the mystery out of farm forestry. Farmers and agricultural leaders have long shied at forestry practices as something beyond and outside the realm of agriculture. Yet, after 200 years of farming, forests remain as sizable woodland fields on at least half of American farms. Farm management of woodland fields is no more difficult than is pasture management. Even relatively small incomes from the woods will raise the standard of living on a million or more farms. Forestry on the farm is simple and entirely feasible for farmers to learn and to practice. They will learn its methods only by practice. The simplicity of the methods of growing wood as a farm crop, as set forth in this book, will, it is hoped, encourage farmers to grow wood on fields best suited to that crop.

The author is particularly indebted to the following men for helpful reviews of parts of the manuscript: A. C. McIntyre, Soil Conservation Service, Upper Darby, Pennsylvania; K. E. Barraclough, Extension Forester, Durham, New Hampshire; Fred E. Winch, Jr., Associate

Professor of Forestry, Cornell University, Ithaca, New York; Dr. W. C. Bramble, Professor of Forestry, Pennsylvania State College, State College, Pennsylvania; W. W. Simonds, Extension Forester, State College, Pennsylvania; E. P. Farrand, Extension Forester, State College, Pennsylvania; Kenneth B. Pomeroy, Southeastern Forest Experiment Station, Lake City, Florida; Dr. R. N. Gaiser, Central States Forest Experiment Station, Columbus, Ohio; T. B. Plair, Soil Conservation Service, Portland, Oregon; H. C. Mitchell, Soil Conservation Service, Forth Worth, Texas; and Dr. J. D. Diller, Division of Forest Pathology, U.S. Department of Agriculture, Beltsville, Maryland.

The following were very helpful in suggesting material and supplying illustrative material: Floyd M. Callward, Extension Forester, Storrs, Connecticut; Prof. P. W. Robbins, Michigan Agricultural College, East Lansing, Michigan; A. M. Sowder, Extension Forester, Washington, D. C.; Stanley S. Locke, Soil Conservation Service, Milwaukee, Wisconsin; J. A. Gibbs, Soil Conservation Service, Spartanburg, South Carolina; C. Svendby, Soil Conservation Service, Albuquerque, New Mexico; A. E. Ferber, Soil Conservation Service, Lincoln, Nebraska; F. B. Trenk, Extension Forester, Madison, Wisconsin; L. J. Prater, Photographic Unit, U.S. Forest Service, Washington, D.C.

My sincere thanks to these men and to many others who have helped in the preparation of this volume.

JOHN F. PRESTON

Contents

Editor's Foreword

AMERICA is a land of vast timber resources. Some of the timber has been used wisely but a great deal of it has been carelessly and wastefully handled until recent years. Two world wars have drawn heavily on our timber and have been responsible for a greater realization on the part of the American people of its real value.

The modern concepts of timber as a renewable resource and of timber as a crop mean much to the farmer. Small tracts of timber and wood lots on farms now provide an important source of income along with field and forage crops. Increase in timber values and the invention of suitable machinery and equipment for harvesting timber from small plots are responsible for increased activity.

Developing Farm Woodlands is a fine contribution to agricultural and forest literature, and to the training of prospective and present farmers. It gives practical advice and directions for doing important jobs that are so essential to the successful handling of small acreage woodlands for profit. Written against a background of fruitful experience, this volume contains the kind of assistance and guidance long sought by the small timber grower.

The author of *Developing Farm Woodlands*, John F. Preston, is a native of Missouri. He attended the University of Michigan receiving first an A.B. degree and later the degree of M.S.F. Mr. Preston was employed by the U.S. Forest Service from 1907 to 1925 as Forest Supervisor, Assistant Regional Forester and Forest Inspector. From 1936 to 1946 he was Chief of the Forestry Division, Soil Conservation Service. For eleven years the author was Forester for the Hammermill Paper Company.

From the author's broad background of practical experience comes this appropriate volume designed to assist the modern young and adult farmer with tree crop problems. May it serve well its purpose.

W. A. Ross

This Pennsylvania woodland has been selectively cut. There is promise of future harvests through good management. (*Soil Conservation Service*.)

Introduction

Wood is a Farm Crop. The growing of wood as a farm crop, a woodland enterprise as part of the farm business, is a conception that has had a long struggle for recognition. In spite of the fact that farmers own 30 percent of the privately owned commercial forest land of the United States and that nearly 25 percent of the farms east of the Mississippi River are in woodland, farmers have been slow to recognize the necessity and the feasibility of growing wood as a farm crop.

TABLE 1. OWNERSHIP* OF COMMERCIAL FORESTS IN THE UNITED STATES

Region	Public forests; Federal, state, county, municipal	Farm woodlands	Other, private ownership	Total all ownerships
North: New England, Middle Atlantic, Lake, Central, Plains...	30,725	61,010	78,486	170,321
South: South Atlantic, Southeast, West Gulf..................	16,238	69,060	97,968	183,266
Pacific Northwest.............	26,447	3,334	16,423	46,204
West: California, Northern Rocky Mountains, Southern Rocky Mountains.................	42,661	5,654	12,938	61,253
Total.....................	116,071†	139,058	205,915	461,044

* Ownership given in 1,000-acre units.
† National forests only, 73,512.

As a result, thousands of farms have been abandoned where a large proportion of the farm area could never profitably produce any crop other than forest products. Failure of the forest to contribute its share of farm income, failure of the farmer to "farm the forest," doomed such farms from the beginning. Most of the woods income in such cases has gone to the stumpage buyer, especially the "lump sum" buyer. He prospered but the farmers went broke.

1

Woodlands Are a Logical Source of Farm Income. Farm forestry can make the difference between a farm income so low that the farmer cannot survive and one that makes the farm a going concern. The truth is that our agricultural philosophy and teaching have not included wood products in the list of approved farm crops. The basic truth that farm forests can be managed and wood grown as a farm crop, thus enabling the nonarable land to assist the arable land in

Fig. 1. Only large trees produce high-grade products (Texas).   (*Soil Conservation Service.*)

producing a farm income, has never been fully grasped in all the history of American agriculture. Now, in the last half of the twentieth century, there is a hope, even a prospect, that the production of forest products will become part of the farmer's business.

One reason is the growing scarcity and high price of forest products, especially the better products that come from large trees. This fact does not help the owner of a forest so badly mistreated in the past that it will produce, now, only low-grade products. It does, however, create the incentive to manage the low-grade forest so as to convert it into one capable of producing more valuable products. If this can be done through present cutting practices that pay small returns, the undertaking is worth while. Farmers have a better opportunity to do this than any other class of forest-land owners. Some of the advantages that farmers enjoy in growing a wood crop are indicated in Table 2.

Farmers are in a position to take advantage of forest-growing opportunities because of their ownership of 30 percent of the privately owned commercial forest land of the United States. Their forest lands are accessible to market. A little cooperation among farmers in marketing wood products, a little resistance to pressure to sell at low prices, born of the knowledge of their strategic position, and a little confidence in their own ability as growers of an essential natural resource will enable them to get profits from their woods. At the same time they can gradually build up the productive capacity of their woodlands and increase the output of wood, in both volume and quality.

The Future Demand for Forest Products in the United States Is Assured. The market for wood products follows the law of supply and demand. The United States uses more than half the lumber, more than half the paper, and two-fifths of all forms of wood consumed in the world. Yet it has only 9 percent of the world's forest area. Russia has 21 percent; the British Commonwealth of Nations, 21 percent; Brazil, 13 percent. The balance is divided among 50 other nations.

Even more important to the forest grower is the fact that the forests of the United States, according to the U.S. Forest Service, are being drained of saw logs at a rate twice as fast as they are being replaced by growth. To the forest owner who manages his woods for saw-log products, that is additional assurance of a future market.

Wood Is an Essential Natural Resource. This is emphasized by the demands of war. Wood products must be obtained to prosecute a war. Farm woodlands, because of their accessibility and the relatively simple problem of recruiting labor, are always called upon to assist in meeting the demand. The difficulty is to find woodlands capable of producing the products needed. Also, it has been difficult to get many farmers with productive woodlands to cut them without destroying the younger trees—the growing stock. The lessons of the past clearly indicate that the growing of wood as a farm crop, developing a good woodland and its careful management, will pay farmers who undertake the business. The reforestation of lands chiefly valuable for tree crops is also clearly indicated to be profitable. In this case, the profits are necessarily deferred. Actually the returns may

TABLE 2. SOME ADVANTAGES FARMERS ENJOY IN GROWING WOOD CROPS

Items of cost or management practices	For the farmer	For the nonfarm owner of forests
Low-grade products	A farm market exists for posts, fuel, poles, rough logs, corduroy, and lumber. The sale of such products will often at least pay wages.	Such products must be sold. If a limited market exists or none at all, cutting to improve the stand can proceed very slowly. A labor return only does not justify an operation.
Worthless trees occupying valuable growing space	Farmers, because they are cutting usable products and because most farm woodlands are small, can cut or girdle or poison such trees at small expense.	To get rid of such trees requires considerable investment in labor, often impracticable.
Weeding in very young stands to free best species. Pruning.	For same reasons as above, and because otherwise idle time is sometimes available, farmers can carry out such operations.	A worth-while operation for any forest owner who wants to develop a good woods, but it is an investment that few owners are willing to make.
Planting trees	Farmers can buy seedlings and transplant them in garden rows, thus producing better stock for field planting at a considerable saving.	Must buy planting stock suitable for immediate planting or go to the expense of operating a nursery if the property is large enough to justify the investment.
Intensity of forestry practices	Many farmers have a seasonal surplus of labor sufficient to do all woods work that would be beneficial.	Each woods operation usually has to pay for itself directly. This often precludes intensive silviculture.
Period of return or the time between cuts on any given area	A short period of return, usually 5 years, appears desirable for the larger farm woods, divided into 5 compartments. One compartment can then be worked each year. In smaller woods, some cutting may be done over the entire woods each year.	A longer period of return, often 10–20 years, for economic reasons, is favored by many forest owners. For small properties, this makes annual cutting impracticable.
Volume taken per cut (closely related to period of return)	By utilizing farm labor and power, not otherwise utilized, farmers can afford very small volumes annually.	A minimum of 2 cords or 1,000 board feet per acre is usually considered essential.
Control of amount to cut. Regulation of the growing stock and distribution of size classes.	Farmers can safely use rules of thumb at first. By practice they will soon learn to depend on individual judgment.	Skilled technicians must be employed to control the growing stock more or less precisely.
Interest on woods capital. Taxes on forest land and some items of fixed expense or overhead.	These items of cost are present whether or not the woods produce an income. For practical purposes they may often be disregarded in calculating the returns from forest operations.	These items must always be included and deducted from the gross income of the forest.

come in the form of increased value of the whole farm before the new forest is large enough to produce forest products.

Wood Can Be a Profitable Farm Crop. Experience in many parts of the country shows that a reasonably good farm woods will produce annual products on a sustained-yield basis valued at from $5 to $15 or more per acre. It depends upon the intensity of management, the local wood markets, and the productiveness of the forest soil. This is not stumpage (the value of standing trees) but products at the roadside, cut and sold as are other farm crops. In terms of returns per hour for labor, the figures usually run from $1 to more than $2 per man-hour, based on a dollar worth approximately 100 cents. It is worth noting that many woodlands in the early stages of management, even where only low-grade products such as pulpwood, posts, and fuel, can be obtained, will pay worth-while wages for labor expended in producing the products. The per acre per year returns are not large until the woodland is developed to the point where the annual crop consists in part of high-grade products such as saw logs, veneer logs, poles, piling, or specialty products.

Some Examples of Farm-woods Income. The figures given in these examples are not directly comparable because of differences in bookkeeping. They are, however, illustrative of the returns possible, usually in the first stages of management. Two small forests in Wisconsin have been cut under the direction of the state extension forester.

Wausaukee pine forest, 40 acres, first annual improvement cutting. Mostly pulpwood and fuel removed. Hourly wages $1.01.

An oak forest of 55 acres at Dundee, same kind of cutting but part of the products were saw logs. Hourly wages earned $1.21.

A second-growth Douglas fir farm woodland in western Washington. Ten acres of thick, straight pole timber averaging 100 cords per acre. First cutting removed 9 cords per acre, mostly pulpwood. Hourly wages $2.38.

An eastern Washington farmer works in his pine woods when he has time in the winter. He sells pulpwood, boat fender poles, fence posts, and fuel. He earns $1.50 an hour for his labor, *plus the going price for stumpage*. He leaves a healthy, well-stocked stand to produce future harvests at regular periods.

A Southern Appalachian forest of 302 acres, managed by the Southeastern Forest Experiment Station. The forest contains average to poor timber, flatland to upland hardwood, pine, and old-field pine. Report covers results of a strictly improvement cutting for 3 years (1946 to 1948). It shows that a farmer harvesting his wood crop and practicing good forest management can pay all his carrying charges, earn 3 percent interest on his investment, and receive from $0.64 to $1.38 per hour for his labor.

Report from the Farm Forestry Forty in southern Arkansas; second-growth loblolly and shortleaf pine mixed with hardwoods. It has been cut annually for 12 years according to the best practices to improve the stand. Growth in 1937 was 256 ft. b.m. (feet board measure) per acre per year in trees 12 in. and up. In 1949 the growth was 391 ft. b.m. The average cut for a 12-year period (1938 to 1949) was 308 ft. b.m. For the 12 years, the average value of products per acre per year cut and delivered at the market was $15.81; at the woods landing, this amounts to about $12. The net returns for labor, after deducting taxes, fire protection, 4 percent interest on the investment, and other out-of-pocket expenses, was $1.67 per hour or, on the basis of delivery of products at woods landing, about $1.25 per hour.

A farmer in Huron County, Michigan, has managed 15 acres of hardwood containing an average stand of 5,500 ft. b.m. per acre. Management has been for saw logs, fuel, and maple sap. The results, shown by the record for 20 years, have averaged $215.75 annually or about $14.38 per acre per year.

A farmer in Missouri has worked 40 acres of oak-hickory woods for 38 years. On the basis of stumpage values, he has averaged $3.63 per acre per year. Values of cut products at the woods landing would be at least twice this amount.

A farmer in Montcalm County, Michigan, has managed for 43 years his 31-acre woods for logs, fuel, maple sap, and special products. He does all cutting and skidding himself and usually cuts only when he has an order for the products. The average net annual income, above wages, has been about $500 or about $16 per acre.[1]

Table 3 is a summary of records of woods income during a period of 2 to 6 years in 1940 to 1945 from 89 farm woodlands in Indiana, Iowa, Michigan, Minnesota, and Ohio.

The high-income farms were mostly those which had a sugarbush as part of the woodland. The range of income in this group was from $3.86 to $66 per acre per year. It is worth noting that if the items

[1] A letter to the author from R. G. Auble, farm forester, Grand Rapids, Michigan.

taxes and interest, which are questionable, are eliminated, the low-income group would show net returns per acre of $0.73 and net return per hour of labor of $0.63. The same figures in the other two columns would, of course, also be substantially increased.

The records given in the foregoing paragraphs usually reflect the income obtainable in the first stages of management where the chief

TABLE 3. SUMMARY OF WOODS INCOME

Item	High income, 25 farms	Medium income, 39 farms	Low income, 25 farms
Area in average farm, acres.........	246	192	272
Average area in managed woods, acres	42	30	58
Capital value of woodland growing stock and equipment............	$3,718.00	$1,236.00	$1,524.00
Net return* per acre..............	$8.50	$1.92	$0.23
Actual rate of interest earned on capital, percent..................	12.6	7.6	2.1
Return per hour of labor..........	$1.33	$0.67	$0.26

* Gross income minus expenses for labor, equipment, depreciation, taxes, and interest (3 percent).

purpose is to build a forest capable of producing larger income in the future.

Success of Forestry on the Farm. This depends upon the extent to which the farmer becomes the manager of his own woods. There are many ways to learn the business of managing a forest, including a great deal of public assistance, that will be mentioned later. Forestry is an action program. Woodlands are developed by use of the ax and saw. They are easily destroyed by the same tools. Whether they are developed into profitable undertakings or destroyed depends upon the knowledge and the purpose of him who directs the man with the ax and saw.

The process of development is to start with what is on the ground, cut what is fit to use or sell, leave the thrifty immature trees to grow. Increase the density of stocking where it is too thin by planting or natural reproduction. Thin out patches of trees where they are too crowded. Destroy worthless trees or brush that constitute weeds, preventing good trees from growing. Gradually develop a stand of all sizes of trees scattered throughout the forest but not necessarily on each acre. This is what foresters know as the growing stock—the capital stock of the woods. Once it is achieved, the effort of management is to maintain it.   The cutting is then from the top (the large trees) and from below—thinning and weeding plus pruning.   The result is the maximum yield of wood products in quantity and quality of which the soil is capable.   If the farmer, guided by the goal of full

Fig. 2. A good farm woods capable of producing a satisfactory income (Arkansas).   (*Soil Conservation Service.*)

stocking and a complete growing stock, cuts annually the products that are available for use or sale, he will begin to get part of his farm income from his woods.   He will begin to depend upon his woods for annual revenue.   He will watch the results of his cutting and note its effect upon his growing stock.   He will learn the best practices for his woods by the mistakes that he makes.   His skill in developing his woodland will increase as he continues to cut.   His knowledge of markets and how and what to sell will also increase from year to year. He will, in short, become a woodland manager, a practical practicing

forester.   He will be growing wood as a farm crop, and he will find
it both interesting and profitable.

The chapters which follow will tell farmers and students of agriculture, how and how much to cut, how to plant and do most of the
things required in developing a farm woodland.   Once a farmer
starts doing these things, he will soon know, by practice, more about
how to develop his woods than any forester can tell him.   That is
because growing wood as a farm crop is as much of a farm job as it is a
forestry job.

1. Growing Trees as a Farm Crop

THIS CHAPTER is primarily concerned with farms that include lands now covered with forest trees and which might be so managed as to grow trees or wood as a farm crop. What are the points to be considered before deciding to add wood to the list of farm crops? To grow wood successfully as a crop requires that the land be dedicated to that use for a considerable time. Most forest trees require 50 or more years to mature. This does not mean that income from an existing woods or even from a newly planted stand must be postponed for that period. It does mean that the land use is tied down for long periods of time.

It is essential that a farmer consider carefully the advantages and the disadvantages, to him and his farm business of undertaking to grow a wood crop on specified areas of his farm. The business of growing wood as a farm crop will not be successful unless the farmer is wholeheartedly in favor of it. He must be willing to learn the details of management and be willing to work at it regularly. He must be willing to work his forest soil intensively, to grow the most timber and the highest-quality products of which it is capable. Natural advantages make this kind of management practicable. Less intensive management will be unfair to his woodland enterprise and will give him a return directly related to the time and effort that he gives to his woodland. Further discussion of these and other points to be considered in deciding whether or not to undertake the business of growing wood as a farm crop appears in this chapter in connection with the following activities:

1. Comparing the Relative Capability of Land for Tree Growing and for Other Crops
2. Protecting the Woods
3. Getting Better Acquainted with the Woods
4. Sizing up the Labor, Equipment, and Market Angles
5. Using Aids Available in Forestry
6. Weighing Other Factors Involved
7. Making the Final Decision

Not all farmers will find a farm-woodland enterprise worth while on their particular farms. They may have no forested land at all or only minor patches along streams. Land may be more valuable as part of the pasture, as protection for livestock, than for timber production. A particular farm may have no open land chiefly valuable for growing trees and hence suitable for reforestation. The farm may be so situated that it does not need the protection of tree windbreaks to stop winds, collect snow, and to temper the cold of winter or the heat of summer. In such cases there is no forestry problem—no need to consider the growing of trees as a farm crop.

However, on farms that have forested land not clearly more useful for livestock protection or some other nonforestry purpose, the usefulness of trees as a farm crop should be studied. Where winds blow free, causing dust storms and wind erosion, and where soil moisture is at a premium, a series of tree windbreaks around the homestead and the crop fields will be helpful. This will be a job of tree planting, protection, and management where the income is in the form partly of fuel and posts, but mostly in indirect and intangible values. How to start tree windbreaks is included in Chap. 2. Later management presents special problems not within the scope of this book. Other reforestation projects, such as planting trees to produce fence posts on high-grade land, are included in Chap. 2. Their later management becomes part of the steps to develop any farm woodland.

1. Comparing the Relative Capability of Land for Tree Growing and for Other Crops

Not all land can be used profitably or permanently as cultivated fields, pastures, or meadows. Millions of acres of eroded slopes and abandoned fields on farms testify to this truth. If pioneer farmers had been able to classify land before clearing, according to soil characteristics, slope, and erodibility, many land-use mistakes would have been avoided. As a matter of fact, a great many present-day farmers are repeating the mistakes of their forefathers in attempting to convert land now in timber to uses for which it is wholly unsuited. Some forested land on farms is clearly of a type that safely could be converted to plow or pasture land.

It is therefore important to know the capability of the land now in forest growth, whether it is good timber or cutover or brush land.

Farmers in soil-conservation districts (and that includes most of them) can get a soil survey of their farms through application to the supervisors or directors of the district or through the county agent. The results of a soil and land analysis may show that all forested land on the farm is clearly best suited for timber growing or possibly could be used for pasture. It may also show that some areas now in forest

Fig. 3. Cultivated field ruined by erosion. Shows some natural reproduction but this process is too slow. This field should be planted (Arkansas). (*Soil Conservation Service.*)

occupy a land-capability class which means that the land could be used for row crops. In other words, it is inherently good land suitable for corn, cotton, or other intensive use.

You may find that you have three types of land in forest: land clearly unsuited to uses other than trees; land valuable for timber growing but which, if cleared, plowed, fertilized, and seeded, could be made into pasture; land chiefly valuable for crops other than trees. Of course, in addition, there might be open land in such poor condition that you would decide to reforest it (Fig. 3). One could hardly decide not to keep the first class in trees. The second class would usually be left in tree growth if the decision is to grow wood as a farm crop. However, if the area in the first class was considerable or if there was a dire need for additional pasture, it might be wise to convert the acres in the second class to pasture. Make such a decision only after considering prospective wood values that must be sacrificed as well as the costs of conversion. Consider also the possibilities of intensive measures to improve existing pastures or the purchase of additional lands already in pasture. Either of the latter two alternatives often proves to be cheaper.

Forest land in the third class is in an entirely different category. There is no question of its suitability or its usefulness for raising valuable row or forage crops. There would be, of course, the expense of getting rid of the timber. This might be done by selling all merchantable timber on the stump, or a farmer might cut it himself and sell logs and other products, thus producing enough income, or more than enough, to pay for preparing the land for the plow. On the other hand, if the farm already has sufficient plow or forage land to meet farm requirements, it may prove to be more profitable in timber. If the timber is immature, one answer is to protect it, perhaps thin it for pulpwood, fuel, posts, and other minor products, and let it grow until the best trees reach merchantable saw-log size. That amounts to a decision to grow wood as a crop on the land and to manage it for that purpose for a limited time—the time required to grow the pole timber to saw-log size. In the meantime you as a grower can begin to realize the possibilities of timber income from such land. You are then in a better position to decide whether a wood crop or some other farm crop would best serve your purpose. Good land will produce better wood crops than poor land. It will also respond to intensive management more quickly and more abundantly than poor land. A great many well-managed and productive farm woodlands occupy high-class farmland. There is, therefore, no compelling reason why this class of land cannot profitably be managed to produce good timber crops.

Thus the inherent capability of the land is the first hurdle for any farmer to get over before deciding to grow wood as a farm crop. You know how good or how poor your forest land is for competing crops and, in the light of that knowledge, you must decide what specific areas you wish to dedicate to growing a wood crop. The kind of woods management to be undertaken depends upon a study of other factors still to be discussed.

2. Protecting the Woods

A fundamental requirement of good woods management is the protection of the forest property against agencies that will destroy it or reduce its productiveness. These agencies are usually fire, grazing animals, wind, insects, and disease. Unless there is a reasonable prospect of reducing to a minimum these destructive forces, a profitable wood crop cannot be grown. Let's look at them.

Controlling Fires. Fires may destroy the forest trees entirely or do only negligible damage. It depends upon the nature of the forest, the weather conditions at the time of the fire, and the machinery for combating fires. Controlled fires, set at the proper season, to burn slash, to rid the forest of worthless brush, or for some other silvicultural purpose, are sometimes used by the forest manager. Their use will be mentioned later (Fig. 157).

Wildfires occur at times when the forest floor and the vegetation are dry. The damage, even from a ground fire, is considerable. A ground fire burns litter which contains nitrogen for the soil and which makes humus that is an important part of forest soils. It destroys young trees. It injures thin-barked trees, allowing spores of wood-destroying fungi to enter. It dries the soil and exposes it to drying winds, thus depleting the soil moisture. Fortunately, on the great majority of farm woodlands, protection from fire is not difficult. The woods are often separated from or surrounded by cultivated fields or pastures. Usually simple measures, such as fire lines and roads, and quick action with handy tools to stop fires that may start are the only steps required (Fig. 4).

In some localities, however, forest fires are a community problem, either because the general sentiment favors annual burning of the woods or because no organized effort has been made to get at and eliminate the causes of fires or to maintain an organization for the detection and fighting of fires. Where farm woodlands are parts of large wooded areas, such as the coniferous forests of the West and South, individual farmers are often powerless to prevent fires from destroying or doing serious damage to their woodlands. Under such conditions, state fire districts, or sometimes cooperative fire districts by private timberland owners, are organized. The individual forest owner pays his share of the cost of protection, either as taxes or as an assessment against his property. Fire-protection costs rarely run more than 5 cents per acre per year.

Study local fire conditions and decide whether or not you can successfully protect woodlands from serious damage by fire. Fire protection is one of the musts of growing wood. Investments of time and money in the development of the woodland are not worth while if the productive power of the forest soil is to be reduced by recurring fires. It is even less worth the effort if severe fires are allowed to destroy the growing stock.

Controlling Grazing. Grazing in hardwood forests is equally as destructive as ground fires. One reason why fires are generally not

Fig. 4. Fire line through a hardwood forest along property line (Arkansas). (*Soil Conservation Service.*)

much of a menace in most farm woodlands in the hardwood forest types is that such a large percentage of them are grazed by domestic animals. Grazing undoubtedly reduces the danger of fire because the vegetative ground cover is so reduced that there is little left to burn. Such a cure for the fire disease, however, is a drastic remedy. Continued heavy grazing of hardwood forests can and often does completely destroy the forest. Meanwhile, the forage values obtained are small compared to open pastures (see Fig. 5).

With fire and grazing absent, it is not possible to wipe out a hardwood forest by cutting. Stumps will sprout and seedlings will start to grow. In time a new forest will replace the old. Ordinary recurring ground fires will reduce the density and the productiveness of a hardwood forest, but they will not completely destroy it. Grazing the hardwood forest, according to studies made by Den Uyl and Day, first removes the reproduction or young growth, which may provide one season's forage for a limited number of animals. The shrubs and saplings then begin to disappear as a result of browsing and trampling. A grazing line appears at a point where animals can no longer reach the foliage, and grass begins to cover the ground beneath the trees. Further grazing injures the roots of the larger trees, and stag-headed

Fig. 5. Heavily grazed hardwood forest (Indiana). There is no future for this woodland until young growth becomes established. (*Soil Conservation Service.*)

trees begin to appear. As these die, fall, or are cut for use, the woodland becomes more open, and more extensive areas of grass develop. Gradually, deterioration continues until the trees are gone and grass or weeds cover the ground. It is difficult to revive the woodland after the grazing line has developed. Up to this time, the removal of the livestock will permit young growth to become established and forest conditions again to prevail. The growth rates of the older trees as well as the quality of lumber produced have been seriously impaired, and many years will elapse before normal growing conditions will be restored.

Even moderate grazing is harmful. The trampling compacts the soil, giving it less moisture-holding capacity and destroying the favorable conditions for the growth of soil bacteria, earthworms, and microorganisms upon which soil fertility depends. Unfortunately, grazing animals find the reproduction of the better species of trees, such as white ash, sugar maple, yellow poplar, basswood, red and white oak, more palatable than others, for example, scrub oak, hawthorn, blue beech, dogwood, ironwood, sweet gum, papaw, and persimmon. Grazing aids the establishment of weed species and thus prevents the right kind of woodland development.

As the owner of a hardwood farm woodland, decide that you can and will prevent all grazing of domestic animals. At the same time be prepared to cope with the added risk of fire damage incident to the cessation of grazing. These are musts if the woodland to be developed is to produce worth-while crops.

Grazing in *coniferous woodlands* or in stands of *mixed hardwood* and *conifers* is in a little different category. In the pure or nearly pure coniferous forests of the South and West, dual use of the land for grazing and timber production is successfully practiced. Grazing is beneficial if controlled so that only the forage (from grass, weeds, and browse) is consumed by the animals. It reduces the fire hazard and does only minimum damage to the forest soil. This is because grazing animals, unless forced to do so by lack of other more palatable forage, do not eat coniferous growth. Hence moderate grazing does not interfere with the establishment and growth of young conifers (usually pine, Douglas fir, larch, cedar, or spruce). Probably the trees would grow faster and the forest would produce more timber without grazing, but this has not been proved. On the great expanses of forest land, the advantages of dual use are so great that foresters accept it and more or less shut their eyes to the possible disadvantages. On relatively small woodlands, the owner should watch the results of the dual-use system and reduce the intensity of grazing use or eliminate it entirely if it is interfering with the chief purpose of timber growing.

In mixed stands of hardwood and conifers, where the conifers are the preferred species, moderate grazing reduces the hardwood young growth and gives the conifers a better chance to survive. Such conditions occur mostly in the South up to and a little north of the Mason and Dixon line. Heavy, continuous grazing can do great damage to the soil and to coniferous reproduction. This would nullify the potential benefits of the grazing. Control the intensity and periods of woodland grazing. In other words, use grazing as a helpful tool in promoting the growth of coniferous trees at the expense of hardwoods. Where that is important in the plan of woodland development, make full use of it.   Like the ax, it may be used and withdrawn at the discretion of the forest manager.   Often it is a rapid, cheap, and satisfactory way of accomplishing a silvicultural result (see Fig. 6).

Generally domestic animals, in the order of severity of grazing dam-

FIG. 6. Grazing in mixed conifer-hardwood forest enables pine seedlings to grow while inferior hardwoods are killed (Virginia).   (*Soil Conservation Service.*)

age likely to be done to the forest, are listed as follows—horses, goats, sheep, cattle, hogs.   The grazing of cattle in southern forests is considered to be permissible if properly controlled.   Exclude all other domestic animals.   The ranging of hogs in longleaf pine forests of the South and in shelter belts and windbreaks in the Great Plains and in the West is recognized as harmful.   Do not permit it.   In other types, the moderate grazing of hogs may not be objectionable.   Such use sometimes may prove helpful in preparing the ground for natural reproduction.

Protecting Trees from Insects, Diseases, Wind. Lengthy pages might be written about these enemies of the forest. Descriptions and pictures of the more common indications of trouble could be included, but it is doubtful that this would be of much help to the practical forest manager. A list of references is included for those who wish to study this phase of the management problem.

Discussion of various phases of these forest enemies will be found later in this text in connection with specific steps in the development program. In general the best defense against them is to maintain a healthy stand of mixed species. A thrifty growing stand will best resist most attacks of insects or disease and will suffer least from wind or ice damage. If you undertake to grow wood as a farm crop, you will be cutting in the woods every year. Watch for signs of disease or insect attack and cut affected trees. Remove windfalls promptly. These are the sanitary measures useful in the fight against insects, disease, and wind.

Occasionally something may appear that requires special measures. When this occurs, call upon the state forester, the nearest farm forester, or the county agent for help. In the meantime, there is rarely any reason to hesitate about undertaking a farm-woodland enterprise because of the presence of wood-rotting or insect-attacking enemies in the woods. More or less of this is always present. Under normal operating conditions involved in growing wood as a farm crop, you need have no fear of any great loss due to such agencies.

3. Getting Better Acquainted with the Woods

It is important to know rather precisely what kind of woods you have before undertaking a farm-woodland enterprise. In this way you will avoid any wrong impressions of the immediate income that may be obtainable. So, let's look at the woods critically and see just what condition they are in and judge the possibilities of management from evidence obtained. In the following paragraphs, the things to look for are given and analyzed.

The *forest types* are perhaps the first consideration. More often than not, the farm woodland can be classified as one of the better forest types—hardwoods, pine, Douglas fir, mixed hardwood and pine. But it may be that your woodland is scrub pine—jack pine of the North or Virginia pine of the Middle Atlantic states—or post and blackjack oak or one of the swamp types.   It is plain that if the type is poor, the income from management will be less than if it is a good type.

The *forest site* is likewise important.   Even with the better types, there is a difference in the productiveness of the soil, known in forestry terminology as "site."   Any farmer will recognize the poorer types mentioned above as generally associated with poor sites.   This is not always true, however, since some poor types, like scrub pine, gray birch, and popple, are temporary types.   They are essentially pioneer or nurse crops occupying the ground due to past fires, insect attack, wrong cutting practices, storm, or some other cause.

Old fields once cultivated, abandoned, and restocked with inferior species are in this class.   Such temporary types are usually explained by deterioration of the soil (site), by erosion, burning, or exposure. If nature is not interfered with or is aided by management, such temporary types, as soon as the soil is built up by the nurse crops, will be followed by the original types which they replaced.

Many farmers recognize such differences in site as bottom-land hardwoods, north slopes with maple, beech, birch, white pine, and hemlock, or coves, where yellow poplar thrives. These are the best sites capable of maximum wood production.   Some sites are best classified by the height growth of the trees.   When trees grow or will grow to maximum heights for the species, they live in good productive soil.   Therefore, judge the site partly by the topography and partly by the record of present or past tree growth.   This will indicate the productiveness of the site.   This statement is true for forested areas still covered by forest growth.   For an open area, to be planted to trees, the site may be one that originally grew excellent hardwood or conifers, but in the transformation from original forest to open land, the site has so deteriorated that now only a nurse crop will grow. More about this in the next chapter.   By these signs judge whether your particular farm woodland is located on a naturally productive soil and will respond readily to a development program or whether it is on a less productive site and will, therefore, produce less abundantly.

The *species, sizes,* and *distribution* of trees now growing in the woodland are another factor that determines how long must be the period of waiting before really worth-while income can be obtained.   In forestry language, this is the way to judge the growing stock.   If past treatment has continually removed the best species, the best trees, and left the worst, the woods will be made up largely of inferior species and poor specimens of good species. In the north woods, there will be too many beech, too many ironwoods and hornbeams, perhaps too many hickories. Too much of the ground space is thus occupied by weeds at the expense of the better oaks, maple, basswood, ash, and white pine or hemlock.

In the mixed stands the pine may be subordinated to less desirable hardwoods. In pure conifer types, hardwood brush may be preventing the reproduction of conifers, and the pine stand may be made up only of small-sized trees left by the last logger.

On the other hand, the woods may contain desirable trees from 4 to 18 in. d.b.h. (diameter breast high, 4½ ft. above the ground) and up. The distribution over the area may be good. If, in addition, there is abundant reproduction of the better species wherever sufficient light reaches the forest floor, you may congratulate yourself because of an excellent growing stock (Fig. 62).

Examine the *present condition* of the woods critically because this indicates at once some of the first steps to be taken in management. If there is a lack of reproduction of the best species, is it due to past grazing of the woods or to fire, or is it because the overhead canopy is too dense? How far up the scale of size classes is the absence of young growth pronounced? Prolonged grazing or annual burning will often result in a stand with no young trees smaller than 6 to 8 in. d.b.h. This means that adverse conditions have prevailed for a period represented by the length of time required to grow trees from seedlings to 6 to 8 in. d.b.h. The first step in management in such a stand is to change the conditions which have caused destruction of the young growth, and wait for natural reproduction or start planting. Cutting, of course, will proceed but always with an eye to its effect on the establishment and growth of the young stand. A woods that has no foundation of young trees is unstable. Continuous production is not assured until they are established. Proceed cautiously with cutting.

In addition to watching for the prevalence of good and inferior species in all size classes, look also at the form and signs of defect in the stand. Unsound, deformed, crippled specimens will occupy growing space needed by thrifty young trees. An improvement cutting, as the first step in management, is indicated by the presence of these and of "wolf" trees and inferior species (Fig. 7). Straight sound stems and good thrifty crowns are characteristics of trees which should form the growing stock.

What *forest products* are available in the woods now?   Saw logs?
Poles or piling?   Black walnut or white oak logs from trees 20 in. in
diameter and up?   Old-growth Douglas fir, or pine or spruce?   It is
not likely that there will be many trees in this class, but if there are,

Fig. 7. A 16-in. beech tree ruined by fire scar and subsequent rot (Pennsylvania).   (*Soil
Conservation Service.*)

seek some professional advice before cutting.   There are high values
in these woods.   More likely, however, only an occasional tree will be
found fit for one or more saw logs, and a great many others fit only for
pulpwood, small poles, or fuel.   Are such products salable locally?
Whatever kind of woods you have, you will have to start your management program with what you find in the woods.

The *accessibility* of the woods to markets is an important factor.
Fortunately, most farm woodlands are reasonably well situated from
the standpoint of getting products to market.   A few short stretches of

permanent road may be needed to facilitate marketing of products. However, some farm woodlands, usually large ones, have difficult access problems.   Some expensive road and bridge building may be required.   This fact will have an important bearing upon the kind of management practicable.   Annual cutting in the woods and selling of products at the roadside or at the mill or shipping point, under the direct supervision of the farmer, is the best way to make farm woodlands contribute worth-while amounts to farm income.   This is what is meant in the expression "growing trees (or wood) as a farm crop."

In large woodlands where the cost of making them accessible is heavy, a commercial sale of stumpage may be forced.   In order to pay for the permanent improvements, it may be necessary to make a heavy cut of merchantable products.   Make this cut as small (in volume or area) as possible in order to pay for the improvements.   Where this condition exists, call in a consulting forester to examine the timber and arrange for a commercial sale.   Make clear to the forester what is wanted—namely, the smallest cutting that will pay for the roads and bridges needed to operate later on an annual cutting budget.

4. Sizing Up the Labor, Equipment, and Market Angles

To conduct logging operations efficiently and profitably requires good labor, good equipment, and the ability to market the products not usable on the farm.   Consider and weigh these matters carefully.

Labor is usually available on the farm at off seasons for other crops. Numerous studies of farm economics have pretty well established the fact that most farms have some labor available for use in the woodlands.   It is chiefly a question of whether or not to utilize it in that way.   In many cases, farmers and their regular farm help can do all of the work.   Sometimes exchange of labor among neighboring farmers will solve the problem.   In managing the larger woodlands, hired help is often needed.

Woods work is considered dangerous, especially to the uninitiated. All reasonable precautions must be taken to avoid accidents and to render first aid if they occur.   In some states, farmers or others who conduct woods operations must take out industrial insurance to protect themselves and their employees against loss of time and expenses when accidents occur.   The state forester will be able to inform you about the law and the cost of industrial insurance.   It is certainly advisable to inquire about this matter in advance of using hired labor in the woods.

How much labor will be required? For a sustained-yield operation in an average farm woodland—in other words, where the farmer is growing trees as a farm crop—experience indicates that about ½ man-day per acre per year is required to cut the products representing the annual cutting budget. For a 40-acre woods with a fair stand of some saw logs, pulpwood, posts, and fuel to cut, this would amount to 20 man-days a year. Actually the figures for a poor woods indicate about ¼ man-days and for a good woods 1 man-day per acre. The work would include cutting wood for home use and for sale and the time required for felling, bucking, and skidding logs, cutting and stacking pulpwood, fuel, and posts. Where woods operations include weeding, thinning, pruning, and release cutting, in addition to products usable or salable, the man-days would be increased.

From the standpoint solely of products for use or sale, the man-days are, of course, related to the volume of products.   In felling and bucking small saw logs (say from trees 16 to 18 in. d.b.h.), from 1 to 1½ man-days is required for each 1,000 ft. log scale.[1] Skidding with a team of horses a distance of 200 to 300 ft. will require one day for 2,000 to 4,000 ft. b.m. (feet board measure) log scale. Pulpwood, not peeled, will require about 1 man-day per cord; pulpwood, peeled and stacked, about 1¼ man-days per cord. Fuel in 4-ft. lengths, cut and stacked, will require from ½ to 1½ man-days per cord, depending on whether cut from softwood or hardwood, stems or limb wood, the species, and ground conditions. Posts will require 1 man-day for about 50, but this varies considerably.

The *equipment* needed for getting out wood products from average farm woodlands is not very extensive or expensive. The tools required are axes, saws, wedges, chains or grabhooks, and, of course, power units—horses or tractors. Wheel tractors are usable for skidding logs where the ground is level or nearly level and not too rough. Ordinary farm trucks will haul the smaller products, but logs are better handled in trucks designed for that use. Further discussion of logging equipment and methods will be found in Chap. 6. For the present purpose, it is sufficient to say that there is nothing complicated or difficult about processing wood products from the average farm woodland. Some old-growth trees of pine or Douglas

[1] For pine trees of fair size as little as 4 man-hours of labor is required.

fir or, in some cases, high-grade black walnut require heavy equipment or skills that farmers do not, as a rule, possess (Figs. 8 and 9). Stumpage sales or contract logging to move such products are then indicated.

The *market* for the products that the farmer finds in his woods should be investigated if he is not already familiar with it. The opportunity

FIG. 8. White oak trees 40 to 60 in. d.b.h. in virgin forest (Illinois). (*Soil Conservation Service.*)

to sell logs almost always exists. Sometimes there is pressure from buyers to sell stumpage rather than logs at the skidway or delivered at the mill. This usually is a temporary situation and need not give the farmer much concern. The demand for saw logs is sufficient that a little resistance on the part of sellers, and especially a little cooperation, will soon change the pattern of buying.

The market for more abundant and less valuable products, such as pulpwood, mine timbers, railroad ties, acid wood, or fuel, is worth looking into. A visit to the county agent, letters to the state foresters and to wood-using plants within truck-hauling distance of the farm will supply general information about the possibilities of marketing these products. Established markets for a wide range of forest products make the prospect of return from a woods business look encouraging. Markets for wood, however, have a way of changing, usually for the better. It is seldom that a producer is wholly satisfied with the existing wood market. Often a market for some products has to be developed. More about this in a later chapter. If some

FIG. 9. Old growth hemlock (Pennsylvania). (*Soil Conservation Service.*)

markets exist for the inferior products, more can be located as the farmer gets better acquainted with the business of growing and selling forest products.

5. Using Aids Available in Forestry

In the foregoing paragraphs, you have been advised to seek the aid of professional foresters or of public agencies. Perhaps it would be well to elaborate a little on this subject.

The *farm forester* is a publicly employed professional forester whose sole duty is to aid farmers and other woodland owners in the application of forestry practices. Primarily, as their title indicates, their responsibility is to farmers. These men are usually assigned to specific districts. As a rule, they work under the direction of the state forester, but, in some states, under the State Extension Service. Unfortunately, there are not enough of them to aid all farmers, but those who seek their help will eventually receive it. They will assist farmers in learning what to do and how to do it, but they do not undertake to do the work. Their advice is helpful to those farmers who want to learn to manage their own woods, especially to those who seek to grow wood as a farm crop.

The *county agricultural agent* will know where the nearest farm forester is located and will assist farmers in getting in touch with him. He may also be able to help farmers himself, especially in problems of marketing wood products.

The *extension forester* (sometimes there is more than one) in the state is also available to help farmers in forestry work. His field is primarily general educational work to interest farmers in the practice of forestry, but he does give advice when he can about the management of specific woodlands. The county agent will write to the extension forester and give him the request for help of an individual farmer. This would usually be the practice where no farm forester is available.

The *state forester* in most states undertakes to assist farmers who ask for help, either through one of the farm foresters or through a staff forester who has a state-wide assignment. In some states, the state forester will assign a forester to mark timber for cutting and assist in finding a buyer for merchantable timber. For this service, a small fee is charged to cover part of the cost to the state.

The soil conservation district has available agricultural technicians who assist farmers in planning a farm conservation program including the woodlands. Often their help in the woodlands is a little sketchy, but if a farmer is interested, he will be able to benefit by their advice. The district supervisors can always get forestry help to farmers who apply for it. The *Soil Conservation Service*, which works primarily with the districts, maintains a staff of forestry specialists who are assigned to help farmers where there is a demand for such services. This is usually where state agencies are unable to meet the need.

Finally, *consulting foresters* are now available throughout the nation. They are not yet licensed by the state, but any who are recommended by the public agencies and especially those approved by the supervisors of the local soil conservation district will be qualified and reliable. Consulting foresters are private foresters who make their living assisting woodland owners in all phases of forestry, such as planting trees, estimating and marking timber, supervising cutting operations, or locating wood markets. They charge fees, usually at a rate per day for small jobs or a percentage of the gross sales of wood products for managing a woodland. As already pointed out, farmers who have large woodlands suitable only for commercial stumpage sales, or those who have a large volume of high-grade timber, will find the services of consulting foresters well worth while. Unless there are special problems, however, you can usually get enough help from the publicly employed foresters. Especially is this true if you have undertaken to manage your own woodland business and seek only advice on the best ways of doing it. An absentee woodland owner or a farmer incapable of handling his own woods operation will find the services of consulting foresters very satisfactory and financially profitable.

Under the general classification of consulting foresters, there are a number of forestry agencies operating in various parts of the United States primarily interested in promoting better forestry practices. Often they are sponsored by wood-using industries. They offer various degrees of service from educational work, demonstrations on the ground, to a complete consultation service. Sometimes the service is free; sometimes a small charge is made. Most such agencies confine their services to owners of small woodlands.

Examples of such forestry agencies are the Southern Pulpwood Association in the South, the American Walnut Association in the Middle West, Trees for Tomorrow, Inc., in the Lake states, the New England Forestry Foundation, Cash Crops, Inc. (at last accounts operating in New England, the South, and the Far West), and many others. The county agent or the state forester will be able to supply information about this source of help available in a particular locality.

6. Weighing Other Factors Involved

Sometimes things not directly connected with the business of making a profit will affect the decision to maintain and develop a woods.

The *sale value* of the farm is important because no one knows when conditions will arise that will make a sale advisable or necessary. A woods is an asset to any farm; the better the woods, the more helpful it is in adding something to the total farm value. A well-developed woods, especially one with a record of annual income, even if only a return for labor expended, is a very positive farm asset. Many prospective buyers look for a farm that is interesting. They want a place to enjoy as well as one from which to make a living. A woods is a bit of the primeval scene that appeals to human sentiment. This phase of farm-woodland values should not be overlooked.

Fig. 10. Picking raspberries from a wildlife area of Nebraska. (*Soil Conservation Service.*)

The *protection* afforded by a woodland against storm, cold or hot winds, erosion, or frost damage is sometimes sufficient to justify its maintenance and development. Woodlands in the form of shelter belts of trees, either planted or natural, are perhaps most valuable in these ways, but any woodland has such values. Protection of livestock, protection against erosion if the woods cover steep slopes, tempering of the winds that blow across the homestead or the garden, are values difficult to evaluate but none the less real. Look at these attributes of your woodland. They may be worth many times more than any values the land could produce if used for other crops than wood.

The *wildlife* that is associated with a good farm woodland is one of the intangible values. It may be the deciding factor in the mind of the buyer of the farm when you want to sell. The small wild creatures—squirrels, raccoons, opossum, skunk, bobwhite or quail, innumerable birds—make their homes in and near the woods. They do if it is a protected, cared-for woods. A grazed or a burned woods is almost barren of wildlife. Birds feed largely on insects, many of which destroy farm crops. Boys like to hunt squirrels and rabbits. Everybody enjoys the blossoms and the fruits found in the woods. These are values worth keeping.

7. Making the Final Decision

The foregoing pages stress the advantages to the farm economy of a farm-woodland enterprise. At the same time, some of the discouraging features are not overlooked. The things that influence the decision to keep and to develop a farm woodland have been enumerated at some length. It has been done in order that you may have before you all of the factors to be considered before you make a final decision about what to do with your woodland. As already mentioned, a piece of land to be devoted to the growing of trees is a long-range venture, if it is to be a success. The development program in the average farm woodland will require from 20 to 30 years before realizing the full benefits of the productive power of the soil. It is, therefore, a farm enterprise not to be undertaken unless the farmer is wholeheartedly in favor of it; unless, also, he is prepared to give his wood crop at least as much thought and attention as he gives other farm crops; unless he develops a growing stock by careful attention to details of management over a sufficient period to allow the full power of nature to work for him.

There are *two kinds of management* possible. One is the commercial type where the development is based solely on silvicultural requirements of the forest and on forest economics. The woodland is protected and developed and wood is cut in accordance with farm needs and the limitations of the market. No cutting is done except that which will clearly pay a profit on the operation, *now*. Usually, but not necessarily, this results in stumpage sales at intervals of 5 to 10 years or even at longer periods. Some cutting for home-use material may be done annually or biennially as needed. This may be the only kind of management practicable for an absentee farm owner or for the nonfarm woodland owner.

This kind of management represents good forestry practice and, from the standpoint of the forester, it is to be approved. It will give many of the benefits of a good farm woodland already enumerated. It is not, however, the kind of management that fits into farm economy. It is not the best farm forestry because it puts the wood crop on a different basis from most other farm crops. The farmer does not learn how to manage his own woods because the application of practices is too infrequent. He must depend upon the logger and the visiting forester to manage his woods. In short, his woods business is in addition to but not a part of his farm business. He is not growing wood as a farm crop.

The second kind of management is intimately tied in to farm economy. The work in the woods is done by the regular farm help or by labor employed by the farmer. Wood products are made and sold at the farm or at the buyer's mill or shipping point. Cutting proceeds every year. A woods operation becomes a farm habit. The annual income from the sale of wood products becomes a dependable part of the annual farm income. Because of the annual woods operation and the availability of labor, much silvicultural development work that does not immediately show a profit will be done. The farmer can afford to speed the development of his growing stock. He practices more intensive silviculture than a commercial forest owner finds possible. His reward comes in a better forest in a shorter time. His annual income will increase as his forest improves. This is growing wood as a farm crop. It is forestry integrated with the farm business.

It is not always possible to operate a farm woods as above indicated. At least at first it seems to be impossible. That is because commercial forestry or destructive logging has had control of the market for so long. Times are changing, however, and farmers can speed the change by refusing to sell except under conditions favorable to the farm economy.

Some concessions to the existing order will have to be made. Cuts at intervals of 2 to 5 years may be required in order to accumulate sufficient volume to negotiate sales of products. There is little doubt, however, that if farmers want to sell products on an annual basis in small lots, the markets will make the adjustment required. It is the job of the farm foresters and agricultural leaders to work with buyers and consumers to help farmers sell products in a way that fits farm economy. It can be done. The compromises that may at first be necessary should not be allowed to blot out or blur the goal to be reached. Actually, the goal has already been reached in many regions. It is the way to successful farm forestry. It is the way in which farmers can become managers of their own woodlands. It is the way that forestry will become firmly established as a part of agriculture. It is the way to grow wood as a farm crop.

Fɪɢ. 11. Salvage of wind-thrown trees in a red-spruce forest in Maine. In this case, the volume and rate of cutting was forced by Nature. (*Soil Conservation Service.*)

The farmer's decision to grow wood as a farm crop has been made. That is the assumption and the premise of this text. If this is true, then the chapters that follow will assist the farmer and the student of farm forestry to learn the principles to be applied in the application of the various steps in the development program. They will likewise assist those interested in commercial forestry, although many desirable steps of a farm wood-crop program are not possible of application in commercial forestry.

SUPPLEMENTARY ACTIVITIES

1. Visit a farm woodland, preferably one of small size (10 to 40 acres). Walk through it systematically in parallel lines. If a hand compass is available, use it to keep the lines straight. Note the following points:

a. The type of timber. Is it hardwood? Mixed hardwood and conifers? Pure or nearly pure conifers? Is all or part of it swamp or bottom land or high ground?

b. Principal species. Oak, hickory, maple, cedar, yellow poplar, pine, spruce, Douglas fir, and larch.

c. Sizes of trees. Smallest size: seedlings and young trees 2 to 6 in. d.b.h. Larger sizes 8 to 20 in. and larger. Use calipers, a diameter tape, or an ordinary tape to check sizes. If the latter, measure the circumferences at breast height and divide by 3. This will be the approximate diameter.

d. Distribution of sizes. Are the different diameters (size classes) fairly well distributed over the area? If not, where are the gaps? A few sample plots of $\frac{1}{10}$- or $\frac{1}{5}$-acre size tallying the sizes found is a good way to get a picture of size distribution. Instructions for taking sample plots will be found in Chap. 6.

e. Effect of past practices. *Grazing.* Grazing in hardwoods causes absence of seedlings of the best species, sometimes of all species. If long continued, trees up to 6 to 8 in. are absent or very scarce. The soil is compact; more or less grass is present. Grazing in conifer types or mixed types may be beneficial if not too heavy.

Fire. Look for fire scars on larger trees at the base. Look for presence or absence of reproduction and for forest litter on the ground.

Insects. Bark beetles are indicated by sawdust and pitch tubes on bark. Sometimes recently killed trees are found with needles all brown.

Wind. Presence of windfalls. Is the forest open so that winds dry out the soil?

f. General condition of forest. Look at the soil. Dig into it a little. Is it hard and compact or loose and crumbly? The latter is characteristic of good hardwood soil. Most pine soils are harder. What about soil moisture?

Look at the trees. Are they thrifty and with good crowns? How about the stem (boles). Trees growing close enough together prune themselves; if too far apart the lower limbs persist. Clean, straight boles are desirable.

Look at the young trees. Are they overtopped by competing brush or weed species?

Look for open spaces. Are the woods too open? Is all the growing space utilized?

2. Make report on your findings.

a. Describe briefly what you have found.

b. Is this a good woodland which will respond to management?

c. What steps in management can you suggest to develop this woodland?

Protection: What is needed?

Cutting products: What kind are available?

Release cutting: Is it needed?

Tree planting: Why and when?

Pruning: What trees, what sizes?

Thinning: Would any usable products be obtained?

2. Starting a Farm Forest

FARMERS have two general objectives in starting forests. The first is the control of erosion by wind or water or both. The second is the growing of trees for the sake of the products they produce, chiefly wood, sap, or Christmas trees.

In the management of erosion-control forests, the production of wood products necessarily is subordinate to the main purpose of controlling erosion. Such forests create conditions especially favorable to wildlife, and this by-product normally can be obtained without injuring their value for erosion control.

The management of erosion-control forests is not specifically covered in this text. This is because the general principles of management conform to those for other types of woodland with slight changes to meet local situations. Very conservative cutting is the general rule because of the necessity for maintaining a good crown cover.

There are many local problems, in both planting and management of erosion-control forests. If you contemplate any extensive plantings of this type, be sure to seek the advice of local foresters. Brief directions are given in this text which will give the general principles to be followed for the different types of forests involved, but these will not be sufficient to cover all local questions. A number of publications are available applicable to local areas that should be consulted. The list is too long to be included here, but local offices of the Extension Service, the Soil Conservation Service, or the state foresters will furnish most of the publications needed.

The second objective in starting a forest is to grow trees as a wood crop. The control of erosion may be important, but it is secondary to the main purpose. Sometimes forests are obtained by natural reproduction from existing woods or from seed trees left for that purpose. If natural reproduction is impossible or uncertain, the forest is started by direct seeding or by setting out seedlings—sometimes known as "artificial reforestation." Often on farms the objective of planting is to produce specialized tree crops, for example, fence posts, maple sap, Christmas trees, naval stores.   Directions for the later management of young forests for the production of maple sap, Christmas trees, and naval stores are found in Chaps. 8 to 10 of this text.   The management of young forests to produce these products is part of the development steps of any forest.   The differences are due to the limitations of management imposed by the nature of the products being grown. Parts of forests started primarily to create conditions favorable for wildlife are rarely managed independently of those for the production of wood products or for erosion control.   Wildlife benefits are obtained incidentally to the management of any forest, and the special wildlife measures are interlaced with those to produce wood products.

Probably the most important activities connected with starting a forest are those required to supplement the management of existing woods, in other words, activities where the grub hoe supplements the ax and the saw.   The planting of trees or the establishment of natural reproduction in such cases becomes one of the initial development steps in woodland management.

Whether the young growth is started by natural processes or by planting, getting the young trees established is only the first step in growing a tree crop.   In the case of tree planting, it may be only the first attempt to establish a stand because often tree planting has to be repeated because of either complete failure of the trees to grow or such a poor survival that the resulting stand is unsatisfactory.   Young growth, once established, has to be protected from both fire and grazing.   Frequently the young trees must be released from overhead shade of grass, brush, or volunteer tree growth and later thinned and pruned to enable them to grow to best advantage.   These things will be done if starting the young forest has been a part of the plan of woodland management on the farm because they are essential to sustained woodland production.   Management of existing woods is the primary consideration, and it is naturally of first importance.   Tree planting is or should be an integral part of that job.   It is part of the effort to make a larger and a better woods.   "Forestry begins with the forest,"[1] and tree planting is one of the steps in getting a forest where one does not now exist, but unless the tree planting is followed with the necessary development steps, the effort may be (and often is) a disappointment.

[1] Quoted from writings of A. C. Cline, former director of Harvard Forest.

Further discussion of the problems of starting a forest will be covered in this chapter under the following activity headings:

1. Taking Advantage of Natural Reproduction
2. Using Direct Seeding instead of Planting Seedlings
3. Planting for Erosion Control
4. Planting for Production of Specialized Tree Crops
5. Planting for Production of Wood Crops
6. Planning the Planting Operation
7. Selecting the Planting Stock
8. Preparing the Ground
9. Taking Care of Trees before Planting
10. Placing Trees in the Ground
11. Taking Care of Planted Trees

1. Taking Advantage of Natural Reproduction

In the management of existing stands, natural reproduction from seeds scattered from older trees is usually sufficient to ensure the maintenance of necessary young growth in the forest. The cutting of trees in accordance with the plan of management opens the forest canopy, giving sufficient light to allow young trees to grow. This is true only where the conditions of the forest floor are favorable to the germination and growth of young seedlings. Nature usually is successful in maintaining a satisfactory understory of young trees to replace those removed, provided the management practices are in harmony with Nature's methods. This cannot always be arranged, however, because some trees produce seed in abundance only at long intervals; often seed crops are produced when climatic conditions are unfavorable, and seedlings fail to survive. Special management measures are necessary to produce seedlings from trees that require abundance of light as opposed to those that are able to live under relatively heavy shade.

In the early stages of woodland management, past abuses such as grazing or fire may have so altered the soil conditions that it is very difficult to secure natural reproduction. For one reason or another, you may find it necessary to supplement natural reproduction by planting some or all of the trees desired. Sometimes in a formerly grazed woods, disking the ground, plowing furrows, or even the ranging of hogs for a short time will get seedlings to start naturally. In other cases, the forest manager may wish to establish trees quickly without waiting for the slower processes of natural reproduction, or he may wish to start a species that does not now grow in his woods.   In such cases, plant trees in open places in the woods, where the overhead canopy is thin, or in spots where part of the trees are to be removed after the young stand is established.   In the intensive management of small woodlands, artificial restocking with young trees is often justified

Fig. 12. Underplanting poor hardwoods with pine (Arkansas).   (*Soil Conservation Service.*)

where seed crops fail or droughts or any other cause prevent the seedlings from growing.   Planting is particularly advantageous in some hardwood stands where you may wish to introduce conifers (Fig. 12). In hardwoods, predominantly oak, often it is difficult to get satisfactory stands of young oak trees of the best species.   Refusal to accept what Nature gives means artificial planting of the species desired.

Natural reproduction is obtained partly from *stump sprouts* or *root suckers*.   In the management of post lots, this may be the sole dependence for new growth.   This is true if the forest products are cut from trees too young to produce seed and no trees are allowed to grow long enough to assume the role of seed trees.   Hardwoods readily sprout from the stump, and some species (for example, black locust) from the roots.   A very few conifers produce sprouts and normally not in sufficient quantity for dependable young growth.

Some sprout growth always appears after cutting in hardwoods, mainly from stumps of small trees. Depend on a reasonable proportion of new growth from sprouts; however, young trees produced from seed are preferable. This is because they are less likely than sprouts to become diseased, and usually they live longer. Sprouts normally grow in thick clusters and must be drastically reduced in number. There are still other problems of management of sprout forests not properly a part of this discussion. Sprouts are a legitimate and convenient means of securing natural reproduction, but trees of seedling origin give greater promise of a satisfactory forest. In management, favor young trees of seedling origin over those produced as sprouts or suckers.

2. Using Direct Seeding instead of Planting Seedlings

Since the beginning of forestry practice, experiments have been carried out to determine whether direct seeding of forest trees can be substituted for the planting of nursery-grown stock. Some success has been obtained in direct seeding, both broadcast and in prepared seed spots. Where successful, direct seeding has often proved to be less expensive than planting the young trees. Successful direct seeding is rare unless either measures are taken to protect the seed and young seedlings from rodents or rodents are poisoned before the seed is sown. These measures add to the expense. The result, in most cases, is that direct seeding of forest trees is not as satisfactory as and is more expensive than the planting of nursery-grown trees.

If direct seeding is done, prepare seed spots with a grub hoe or mattock and protect planted spots with a screen until the seedlings are well established. Even in this case, adverse weather conditions often cause failure. If conditions are favorable, too many seedlings appear in the planted spots. Thin these after the first- or second-year's growth. Altogether, direct seeding seems to have little prospect of success for farm planting. The planting of nursery stock, especially conifer stock, remains the only practical method of planting trees by artificial methods.

The *planting of nuts*, such as walnuts, hickory nuts, and acorns are exceptions to the above statement. Place the seed of these trees directly in the soil. Collect the seed as soon as it is ripe, and plant it either with a grub hoe or any other sharp-pointed tool, such as a sharp stick, or, in soft ground, by pushing the nut into the soil with the heel. On account of the depredations of rodents, it is often better to keep the nuts over the winter and plant them in the early spring. With the exception of acorns, plant only one seed in a spot. Plant acorns two in each spot. A great many acorns are ruined by weevils; store and plant only sound ones. If placed in a tub of water, the sound acorns will sink, the bad ones will float. Store nuts outdoors in moist sand, a layer of sand alternating with a layer of nuts; this is the common practice. Select a storage spot that is well drained so that the nuts will keep moist but not wet. Nature often does a good job of storing hickory nuts and walnuts in the leaves and grass underneath the trees. Where these readily can be found in early spring, a little care in selecting the best-looking nuts will furnish a satisfactory supply for planting.

3. Planting for Erosion Control

Since the primary consideration in this type of planting is to stop soil losses, the use of shrubs, grasses, and trees that are suited to the situation and the main purpose of planting is more important than usefulness of the crop either for timber products or other purposes. Often, of course, several purposes can be combined—particularly erosion control and the necessary food and cover to encourage wildlife.

Providing Shelter Belts and Windbreaks. These are long belts of trees that protect farmsteads, orchards, feed lots, and crop fields from the force of the wind. They slow the speed of the wind and lessen soil blowing to the leeward for a distance equal to about twenty times the height of the trees. A planted windbreak around the farmstead saves fuel in heating homes and around feed lots conserves feed for livestock. On crop fields, it saves soil moisture by slowing evaporation and by accumulating snow that melts slowly and permits the water to sink into the ground. The same advantages are obtained to leeward of natural forests (Figs. 13 and 14).

Plant farmstead windbreaks a distance of 75 to 100 ft. from the nearest building, usually on the north and west sides, sometimes on all four sides. Use a combination of hardwood trees, coniferous trees and shrubs in 1 to 10 rows including 1 to 2 rows of conifers (Figs. 15 and 16).

Field windbreaks are planted so as to slow prevailing winds usually on the north and west sides of cultivated fields. On the plains, 5 to

10 rows are required, usually 10 to 12 ft. apart.   Plant fast-growing hardwoods like poplar, cottonwood, and Chinese elm in the center for quick protection.   Plant slower-growing hardwoods such as hackberry, oak, or maple on both sides of the center row.   Use shrub borders to form a thick, low-growing vegetation on the windward side

FIG. 13. Shelter belt protecting field and highway.   The farmstead is protected on two sides.   (*Soil Conservation Service.*)

of the windbreak, and 2 or more rows of conifers on the lee side to complete it.   Under very dry conditions, where the precipitation gets down to 15 in. or less, trees and shrubs will not live without continuous clean cultivation.   Under such conditions, because of the high cost of maintenance, windbreaks are ordinarily planted only for the protection of homesteads (Fig. 16).

Planting to Control Sand Dunes.   Dunes occur in places where the breaking of the natural cover, either of forest or grass, exposes the underlying sand.   They may be only a few square rods in extent, or

Fig. 14. Hayfield protected by a shelter belt (North Dakota). (*Soil Conservation Service.*)

Fig. 15. Farmstead windbreak showing clean cultivation needed until crowns close (North Dakota). (*Soil Conservation Service.*)

Fig. 16. Close up of farm windbreak showing two rows of ponderosa pine and juniper, fruit trees and hackberry (Colorado).   (*Soil Conservation Service*.)

Fig. 17. Single row windbreak of Monterey pine (California).   (*Soil Conservation Service*.)

they may cover a considerable area.   Small sand blows usually can be controlled by the planting of such trees as poplar or conifers, beginning on the windward side and gradually extending the planting across the blow sand as the trees become established.   For larger sand dunes, first stop the movement of the sand by temporary measures, such as the building of slat fences across the dune and the planting of

Fig. 18. A sand dune stabilized by brush cover and planted to conifers (Michigan). (*Soil Conservation Service.*)

beach grasses to stabilize the sand.   Plant beach grasses about 18 in. apart in rows 6 to 8 ft. apart.   As a supplement to the beach grass or as a substitute for it, use brush mulch; however, this is often more expensive than grasses and slat fences.   As soon as the movement of the sand is stopped, plant trees as the permanent cover.   Such trees as cottonwood, pines, and spruces are suitable for sand-dune planting.

Planting to Control Stream Banks.   Erosion of stream banks is often the result of mistreatment of the watershed above.   After steps are taken to improve the management of the watershed, the cutting of stream banks can be stopped or at least the damage greatly reduced by a combination of engineering works and tree and shrub planting. The engineering problem is to direct the current away from spots where it is undercutting the bank.   Place logs or fallen trees along the stream, anchored to the bank; sometimes rock abutments and other means are used. Then plant vegetation to hold the bank from further soil loss; plant cuttings of willow or cottonwood close together. Add shrubs such as dogwood and similar small native shrubs. If conditions justify, place a mulch of brush on the bank held down by wire and stakes, and plant the shrubs and trees in the mulch. The object is to establish a thick growth of woody vegetation that will bend with the current. Cut the young trees if they get too large and allow them to sprout. Plant coniferous trees on the bank above the steep portion in order to control the current at high-water stages. This type of planting is a difficult undertaking. Seek local forestry advice if you have a difficult problem of stream-bank erosion.

Planting to Control Erosion on Road Cuts and Fills. This is not often a farm problem, but farmers may have to contend with it on some farm roads. First stabilize steep banks of bare soil with stakes and horizontally placed poles or with mulch held by wire very much as in the case of stream banks. Plant shrubs, vines, and grasses as permanent cover. Add plenty of fertilizer in order to get grasses to grow. Scrub pines often come in naturally, or they can be planted if their eventual height is not an obstacle.

Planting Gullies. This is distinctly a farm job. The formation of gullies in fields and pastures results from wrong methods of cultivation or from overgrazing. First remove the cause of erosion in the area above the gullies before attempting control of the gullies themselves. Gully control involves either agronomic practices or tree planting or both. Experience proves that protection is the first essential to gully control. Stop both fire and grazing. Where erosion is not too far advanced, a good stout fence to keep grazing animals out of the gullied areas and protection from fire will enable Nature to heal the gullies. It is, however, a slow process. It can be speeded up and the area made to produce some values in the form of wildlife and, eventually, wood products, if planted to trees and shrubs. The measures necessary to control gullies are the following:

1. Give the area protection from fire and grazing.
2. If possible, divert the water into other channels until vegetation is established.
3. Mulch the gullied area with limbs, brush, straw, and so forth. (This is very effective but expensive.)
4. Fertilize the soil and plant grass seed preferably with mulch added.

Grasses give quick results, but control is not as permanent as that provided by a tree cover.

5. Plant trees, preferably with mulch, on the badly eroded spots. Use black locust if you are within its natural range and the subsoil is loose and holds moisture. Place your chief dependence, however, on scrub pines which

Fig. 19. Successful planting of black locust to stabilize a large gully in Santa Cruz County, California. (*Soil Conservation Service.*)

are able to live under the poor soil conditions found in most gullies. Plant trees on the slopes and at the head of the gully. Plant shrubs and grasses in the main channel. This type of vegetation does not obstruct the flow of water but slows it down.

6. Place temporary dams of wire, posts, logs, brush, or rocks at intervals in the main watercourse. In addition, place burlap sacks loaded with grass seed, fertilizer, and soil across the channel to supplement the work of the temporary dams.

7. Build concrete structures if there is no other answer. They are, however, temporary at best and very expensive. They must be supplemented by

the planting of vegetation. Seek technical advice if the gully erosion is very severe.

Trees and shrubs eventually not only control the erosion but convert the area to productive use. Tree crops such as Christmas trees, fuel, and posts can be produced in 10 to 20 years, and later an all-purpose forest can be developed. Wildlife is an important product of most gully-control projects. Trees control erosion by the overhead canopy and the litter deposited on the ground. Tree roots are helpful, but the main control comes from the tree canopy and the forest litter. Therefore, trees are successful in controlling erosion only after the crowns close and forest conditions are established. Even then a forest cannot stop floodwaters that accumulate above the forest itself. It does prevent the accumulation of floodwaters on the forested area, but accumulated waters from above will cause erosion in the forest if the slope is steep.

4. Planting for Production of Specialized Tree Crops

Specialized tree crops include those providing fence posts, maple sap, Christmas trees, and naval stores.

Growing Fence Posts. These are often grown in special plantations known as "post lots." This is necessary where durable posts are not obtainable from the existing woodland. A large number of fence posts can be grown in 10 to 20 years by planting trees that are known to make durable posts. Since rapid growth is desired, usually such plantations are placed on the very best land, often an odd corner in a bottom-land type. In addition to furnishing posts for home use, considerable revenue can be obtained from the sale of posts. The usual species chosen are black locust, Osage orange, catalpa, red cedar, sometimes mulberry. Ordinarily only one or two species are selected and planted in pure plantations. No fertilizers are used except for black locust. This species seems to respond to the use of a fertilizer high in phosphorus. It has not been determined whether this is a purely temporary effect or whether the response is extended over a long period. Probably it merely gives the locust a boost in its early stages.

Cultivate the post plantation for a few years. Cut back volunteer growth of woody species. If it is desired to cut round posts, 4- by 4-ft. spacing is good, but if the trees are to be grown large enough to make split posts, a 6- by 6-ft. spacing is more satisfactory. Even so-called "durable" tree species are less durable if cut at the stage when little or no heartwood has formed. Regeneration of hardwood species after harvesting the first crop is by sprouts. Reduce the number of sprouts from each stump to one. Further consideration of sprout forests will be found in Chap. 6.

Producing Maple Sap. This is a farm product well worth having. If your farm is located within the natural range of hard maple, usually north of the Mason and Dixon line, a sugarbush can be planted, or extension of the existing sugarbush can be obtained from the seeds scattered by the older trees. The successful operation of a sugarbush requires a climate which in the early spring creates an alternation of warm days and cold nights. This seems to be the chief reason why the successful management of a sugarbush is limited to the northern part of the United States. Very few plantations of hard maple for the purpose of growing sugarbushes have been made, but there seems to be no reason why it will not prove to be profitable. From 20 to 40 years is required to grow hard maple to a size where it will be profitable to tap the trees. Plantations of hard maple can be made on undisturbed cutover forest land where the soil conditions are similar to those in the original forest where hard maple grew. It is often impossible to find such sites, and it is therefore necessary to choose the next best.

If old fields are to be planted to hard maple, first determine that erosion has not seriously injured the site. In other words, the degree of erosion must not have advanced to the point where the soil is hard, compact, and incapable of retention of moisture. If a fairly good soil is available, plant a nurse crop, preferably red pine or white pine at about 10- by 10-ft. spacing. Allow these trees to grow for 2 to 3 years; then plant the hard maple seedlings in between the rows of conifers. An alternative plan is to plant the maples without a nurse crop and cultivate them for several years. The first procedure, however, seems to promise the best results. The advantage of the nurse crop is not only to improve the site, but the pine trees can be harvested as pulpwood, posts, or poles before the maple trees reach the suitable size for use as a sugarbush.

Thin the planted maple trees gradually in mixture with conifers or in pure stands so that the final crop trees will be spaced about 30 by 30 ft. Considerable volunteer growth will start in the plantation; allow this to grow where it does not interfere with the growth of the maple trees. Such volunteer growth will protect the soil and act as trainers to help the maple trees produce straight stems. Further discussion of the management of sugarbushes will be found in Chap. 8.

Growing Christmas Trees. Such trees are a profitable farm crop. They can be obtained as thinnings from coniferous plantations or as surplus young trees in the managed woodland. They are often planted solely for the purpose of producing Christmas trees. There is an opportunity to grow Christmas trees in almost every part of the country. The species commonly grown are Douglas fir, balsam fir, Scotch pine, red pine, and spruce. If there is an opportunity to sell small Christmas trees or trees for ornamental plantings, the spacing can be as close as 3 by 3 ft., but ordinarily trees are spaced 5 by 5 ft. or 6 by 6 ft. A Christmas-tree plantation can be made on a piece of cutover land without previous ground preparation and without later cultivation. In this case, however, it will be necessary to conduct one or more weeding and release operations as described in Chap. 3. Normally, plantings are on open land. Christmas trees usually require some pruning or light trimming in order to yield the maximum number of trees of appropriate shape for the Christmas-tree market. Further consideration of the management of trees grown for Christmas trees will be found in Chap. 9.

Producing Naval Stores. These are products limited to the South within the natural range of longleaf and slash pine. Only these two trees have so far proved profitable for the production of naval stores— gum turpentine and rosin. Slash pine is much easier to plant and grow than longleaf, and therefore most plantations intended for eventual use in the production of naval stores are pure stands of this species. The usual type of forest plantation is made, from which thinnings for pulpwood and poles can be cut before the crop trees are large enough for the production of naval stores. Further discussion of naval stores as a farm product will be found in Chap. 10.

Strictly *wildlife plantations* usually consist of the planting of odd corners or rocky or steep slopes in crop fields, in size from a few square rods to several acres. They may also be in the form of border plantings to existing woodlands, or, in the case of large woodlands, they may be portions of the woods devoted to the production of trees and shrubs for wildlife food and cover.

Border plantings for wildlife serve a double purpose of benefiting wildlife, especially bobwhite, or quail, and many other types of birds, and at the same time serve the purpose of checking strong winds which would otherwise dry out the forest floor.   Odd-corner plantings on the farm are a means of making productive spots that would otherwise be wasteland.   Once established, management of isolated wildlife areas usually is merely fire protection.   Where the area is part of a .

FIG. 20. Shrub border at edge of a hardwood forest (Georgia).   (*Soil Conservation Service.*)

woods managed for wood products, wildlife measures, such as leaving trees and shrubs for their fruits or as nesting places, are incidental to the woodland-development program (Fig. 20).

5. Planting for Production of Wood Crops

The production of wood crops can be profitable if the planting is properly done.

Planting Cutover Land. Land not satisfactorily stocked or stocked with undesirable trees can be planted as a whole or to fill in the gaps where failures have occurred.   Sometimes it is worth while to precede the planting by the removal of shrubs or weed trees by pulling them out with tractors, by cutting, or by a combination of cutting and poisoning.   This allows a better distribution of the planted trees than would otherwise be possible.   Any trees planted on cutover land require later weeding operations discussed in Chap. 3. If the original hardwood-forest soil has not been injured by fire, grazing, or exposure, plant the best hardwoods such as oak, maple, birch, yellow poplar, basswood. If the soil has been injured, plant only conifers at a wide spacing of about 10 by 10 ft., and allow hardwoods to come in naturally. This procedure was mentioned in connection with the establishment of a sugarbush. If the original woodland was coniferous, plant only conifers on the cutover land. Ordinarily the planting of cutover land on the farm is for the purpose of supplementing what comes in naturally, of speeding up the process, and of increasing the number of the better species.

Planting Open Spots. Such areas in the woods or adjacent to the woods sometimes do not become established with young growth as rapidly as the forest manager desires. In the case of intensively managed woodlands, and that should apply to all farm woods, it is essential to make full use of the productive capacity of the soil. Open spots therefore cannot long be tolerated. In a hardwood forest, open spots may be planted to coniferous trees if it is desired to introduce these into the mixture. Whether conifers or hardwoods are planted depends not only upon the wishes of the forest manager but upon the soil conditions. If soil conditions are poor, conifers are to be preferred. Choose only those species that will grow well in the partial light that can be expected. Trees that grow best in partial light include maple, elm, basswood, Douglas fir, white pine, spruce, and balsam. (See Table 10, page 107.)

Planting Old Fields. Such sites on farms, no longer useful for row crops or pasture, offer an opportunity to grow a wood crop. They often present a difficult planting problem because of the erosion that has taken place. The best hardwood forest may have occupied the old field before it was cleared. Later use may have reduced the condition of the soil to a point where almost nothing will grow except what ecologists call "pioneer species." The topsoil now may be entirely gone with only a hard, compact subsoil remaining. On the other hand, the subsoil may be loose and friable and able to hold moisture fairly well.

The big problem, therefore, in planting old fields is the selection of species that will grow and the determination of what site preparation is needed. Rarely can old fields be planted to hardwood species with any degree of success. Black locust can sometimes be planted on soils that retain moisture and are sufficiently loose to enable the roots to take hold.   An old field that has been abandoned for several years and is covered with a very sparse growth of vegetation is a very difficult site for tree planting.   It may be covered very sparsely with poverty grass, plantain, cinquefoil, horse nettle, and similar species. Such a location probably will not grow trees successfully without some soil preparation, preferably a mulch of coniferous brush or straw.   Sites less eroded, especially those with a loose subsoil, can be planted to locust and the scrub pines, such as Virginia or jack pine, with expectation of success.   The kind of plant cover on the ground is an indication of the condition of the site.   This can be determined best locally.   If possible, have old fields examined by a local forester before attempting to choose the method of planting and the species and age class of stock to use.   In general, a heavy growth of vegetation is an indication of a fairly good site; a sparse vegetation with hard soil an indication of a very poor site, and one difficult to plant.   Brushy fields with openings having a diameter at least twice the height of the surrounding trees or brush can usually be planted without incurring much expense for later release.

Interplanting the Woods.   This is not extensively done now, but it will be done more often as the management of woodlands becomes more intensive.   This type of planting is often called "reinforcement planting."   The purpose of interplanting in the woods is to avoid the delay in getting young trees started either from lack of a seed source or from poor ground conditions for germination and survival.   Also, the purpose may be to convert to a more desirable mixture a stand composed of inferior species or to introduce one or more species not now present in the woods.   For example, the oaks produce a good seed crop very rarely, and the seed is so often ruined by weevils that it is difficult to get plentiful oak reproduction.   The problem may be a previously grazed woods where the soil has been trampled and compacted to the point where it cannot retain moisture.   Successful interplanting in such cases is difficult but will sometimes succeed if the trees are planted in plowed furrows or with a mattock, and each tree mulched with brush, leaves, or straw.   Obviously, the spacing for trees planted under the shade of forest trees will have to be adjusted to the openings available and to the plan of management, particularly plans for cutting some of the larger trees in order to give the planted seedlings needed light.

In the Lake states, a common problem is the planting of aspen stands with coniferous stock in order to convert the aspen (a temporary type) to coniferous forest. Such species as red pine, white pine, or spruce are used. As soon as the planted trees are established, the overstory must be thinned to allow at least half-light to reach the new seedlings. Some weeding may be necessary to ensure that the new trees survive the competition of brush and other vegetation.

The Division of Forest Pathology of the U.S. Department of Agriculture has introduced and studied *blight-resistant chestnuts* ever since the native chestnut was killed by the blight. Asiatic chestnuts, particularly the Japanese and Chinese species, have been found to be highly resistant to the blight, but in the Middle West, Lake states, and New England states, only certain Chinese kinds have proved winter hardy. The Division of Forest Pathology is also carrying on an active chestnut-breeding program in which the American chestnut is crossed with Chinese chestnuts. Each year numerous small plantings are made in cooperation with Federal and state foresters throughout the eastern half of the United States. The results of these experimental plantings indicate that certain Chinese and hybrid chestnuts can be planted in existing stands of hardwoods with every promise that they will grow into satisfactory forest trees.

Two methods of plantings are recommended: (1) Select a fully stocked pole-size hardwood stand on the very best site; plant 50 trees 10- by 10-ft. spacing; immediately cut, girdle, or poison all overstory woods growth 5 ft. or over in height. (2) Plant the chestnut trees in unburned and ungrazed cutover hardwood land on the best site. Use the same spacing. In this case the trees will have to be weeded and released in order to enable them to compete with volunteer growth. This cultural work will probably have to be repeated every few years (2 to 4 years) until the planted trees safely overtop the competing vegetation. Only these procedures promise success in growing the blight-resistant chestnut as a part of the hardwood forest on the farm. The value of chestnut as a farm tree is so great that these measures may be justified in order to introduce this tree to the farm woodland (Figs. 21 and 22). Anyone interested in planting chestnut should seek detailed instructions from the Division of Forest Pathology, U.S. Plant Industry Station, Beltsville, Maryland.

Planting Tree and Shrub Borders. Borders to existing woods, as already indicated, are both a silvicultural and a wildlife measure.

The silvicultural purpose is to stop the wind and thus conserve soil moisture essential not only to germination and growth of seedlings but to the growth of all trees. Management seeks to keep all woodland edges dense, either by no cutting at all or by cutting to produce

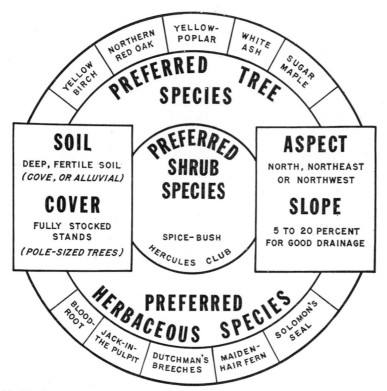

Fig. 21. Ideal site conditions for successful establishment of Asiatic chestnuts in woodlands. (*Bureau of Plant Industry, Soils, and Agricultural Engineering, U.S. Department of Agriculture.*)

sprouts and to encourage the growth of dogwood, redbud, and other shrubs native to the site. Where such measures fail, supplement by planting trees and shrubs to form a close border. Usually conifers and shrubs are used. Edges of woods next to cultivated fields are often planted to shrubs and cultivated until well established. In the Eastern states shrub species ordinarily planted for this purpose are bicolor lespedeza, bayberry, hazelnut, dogwood, high-bush cranberry, tartarian honeysuckle, snowberry, elderberry. In the Western states, squawbush, American plum, chokecherry, buffalo berry,

tamarisk, Russian olive, and Caragana are planted for this purpose
(Fig. 20).

Fig. 22. A fully stocked pole stand of hardwood photographed immediately after girdling
and planting to Asiatic chestnuts.   If the girdling is thoroughly done, little or no further
maintenance is required to enable the planted trees to grow.   (*Bureau of Plant Industry,
Soils, and Agricultural Engineering, U.S. Department of Agriculture.*)

6. Planning the Planting Operation

The actual work of putting the trees into the ground is not a difficult
or complicated job provided the different steps are well thought out in
advance.   If not well planned, some essential tools, equipment, or
material will be missing, resulting in delay that may prove embarrass-
ing and expensive.

The purpose of the planting, such as erosion control, specialized
tree crops, or wood crops, more or less indicates the species to be
planted, the spacing to be used, and often the kind of soil preparation
and the methods of planting.

The site chosen for the planting—whether good, poor, or medium;
old-field site, or more or less undisturbed soil found on cutover lands
or in forest openings—again indicates the type of planting stock,

methods of planting, and site preparation required.   As already indicated, hardwoods are suitable for planting on only the best sites, and these are ordinarily quite limited.   Use the so-called "scrub pines" on the poorest sites, and even here site preparation by means of contour furrows or by mulching is often necessary for success.   Swampland is very difficult to plant successfully.   If the swamp is continually wet, do not attempt tree planting because the techniques of successful planting of such areas have not been worked out.   If grasses (as opposed to sedges) and broadleaf weeds are present in the swamp, it is an indication (in the North) that such species as black spruce, white cedar, and tamarack may succeed.   Land subject only to spring flooding usually can be planted with such species as ash or elm.   On any wet site, however, it is well to make small experimental plantings at first before undertaking a large-scale operation.

The planting of black locust is a subject worth special consideration because this species has been widely used in planting operations, and many failures have resulted.   We now know, as a result of research, about what conditions are favorable for this species and under what conditions it should not be planted.   Black locust is a highly useful tree for the production of fence posts, for fuel, and for many other uses, but it ordinarily succeeds only under certain conditions.   The structure of the soil seems to be the most important factor, especially the subsoil.   A tight subsoil is almost always detrimental to the growth of black locust.   A dense structure lessens water absorption and moisture-holding capacity, reduces drainage and aeration, and makes root penetration very difficult.   The color of the subsoil is one indication of its condition with reference to air and drainage.   A subsoil that is red-brown or yellow-brown to yellow in color represents excellent to medium conditions.   When the color shades off to drab and yellow, and to blue, it is not favorable for locust.   Any soil which does not permit the free removal of surface water is not favorable for good locust growth.   Likewise a dry, exposed, sandy or shale ridge with excessive drainage offers a poor site for locust.   Sandy soil, however, where there is sufficient moisture, is an excellent place to grow locust.   The fertility of the soil is not as important as its physical structure.   Locust will make some growth on any soil and, from the standpoint of its use for erosion control, this is very fortunate, but if profitable returns from locust products are the first consideration in planting, select the site carefully.

Choosing the Season of Planting. This is partly a matter of the local soil and climate and partly just the planter's choice. Generally throughout the northern United States, spring planting begins as early as the frost leaves the ground and continues until the buds of the trees to be planted begin to swell, which indicates the end of the dormancy period. Unfortunately, in much of the United States the spring planting season is short—often from about Apr. 15 to May 15. On the farm, it conflicts with other important farm work. Fall planting offers a longer season and interferes less with current farm work. Fall planting, however, offers a good many risks of loss not encountered in spring planting. It can begin as soon as the trees have ceased growth for the season and the fall rains have added moisture to the soil. The chief trouble with fall planting is the winter heaving that often results. In extreme cases all of the plants are so badly heaved that they fail to live. Winter heaving is most prevalent on heavy soils and in places where the ground is not covered by a blanket of snow. On light soils or on heavier soils with broom sedge or sod cover, where heaving is not likely to give trouble, and during a favorable season, the plants have a chance to start root growth during the fall. They become well established and are in good shape for spring growth. Plant trees in the fall by placing them in the ground with the least disturbance of the natural cover. While fall planting is always somewhat more risky than spring planting, under the conditions mentioned and with some luck, the results can be more satisfactory than spring planting. In the South and portions of the West, especially on the west coast of Oregon and Washington, planting can continue most or all of the winter, and where this is possible, tree planting can be done without interference with most other farm activities.

Deciding on the Method of Planting. Planting is accomplished either by means of hand tools or by machine. Planting machines can be used only on reasonably smooth ground. For small areas and especially for rough ground or on a site full of stumps, brush, or rocks, hand planting is better than machine planting. The standard tools for hand planting are the mattock, a planting bar (Figs. 31 and 32), a spade, or a shovel. More hand planting is done with heavy mattocks or grub hoes than with any other tools. They can be used under practically all conditions, but they are most useful on rough, rocky ground and on ground with roots and heavy sod. The spade and shovel are most useful in planting hardwoods that require deeper and larger holes than conifers. The latter tools are ordinarily used for hand planting of shelter belts and windbreaks in the Plains country. A planting bar is chiefly adapted to the lighter soils and to places where no spot preparation of the ground is required. Under such conditions rapid planting can be done with the planting bar.

Machine Planting. In recent years this method is rapidly gaining favor. The principles used in planting cabbage and tobacco plants have been used in making tree planters. The chief parts of the machine are a colter to cut the ground cover, a plow to split and open the soil into which the seedlings are placed, and packer wheels that follow and compact the soil around the roots of the planted trees. There are many planting machines now on the market. The kind of planting machine most useful depends on local conditions of soil and topography. For successful machine planting, the soil into which the trees are placed must be moist but not wet. The topography and the slope must not be too rough or steep. The surface must not be covered by too many stumps and rocks and must be reasonably free of brush. The makers of some of the planting machines claim that they will operate on slopes up to 30 percent. Machines must be drawn by tractors, usually the crawler type. The rated capacity of most planting machines is 10,000 trees in 8 hr. There is little doubt that machine tree planting is satisfactory. Survival has been found to be as good and often better than with hand planting, and the cost is often only one-third of the cost of hand planting. Choose relatively small stock for machine planting, about 16 in. total length and preferably about 6 in. from root collar to the top of the tree.

From two to four men are required to run a planting machine. The four-man crew consists of one tractor driver, one planter who rides the machine, another man on the machine to feed the trees to the planter, and one man on the ground to keep the planter provided with trees and to care for the planting stock. For small jobs two or three men can carry on the work. The optimum planting sites for machines are old pastures and old fields covered with sod and with a minimum of brush and briars. Sod seems to favor survival of machine-planted trees, perhaps by retaining moisture, and of fall-planted trees by preventing winter heaving. Only one row of trees is planted at a time by a machine. Spacing between the rows is a matter of choice. The spacing between the trees planted in the row is governed by the speed of the tractor and the rhythm set by the planter. Some planting machines are equipped with adjustable wheels which enable them, on slopes, to plant on the contour (Fig. 23). Use a planting method suited to your conditions.

Spacing Trees. In a plantation this is related to the purpose of the planting. For stream-bank control, plantings are often 2 by 2 ft.

FIG. 23. Planting a seven-row farmstead windbreak with a planting machine (Nebraska). (*Soil Conservation Service.*)

For some gully-control work, the planting of shrubs is sometimes as close as 2 by 2 ft. Christmas-tree and fence-post plantations are spaced 4 by 4 ft. to 6 by 6 ft. Wider spacings, varying from 6 by 6 ft. to 10 by 10 ft., are ordinarily used for plantations intended to produce wood crops; 6 by 6 ft. may be considered the standard for most old-field plantations; 6 by 8 ft. is often used where the field is furrowed before planting, the furrows being placed 8 ft. apart and the trees 6 ft. apart in the furrows. The wider spacings, such as 8 by 8 ft., are often used for rapidly growing species, such as southern pines, and the 10- by 10-ft. spacing for cutover land where there is already some reproduction established and where volunteer growth is expected to supplement the planting. Shelter-belt and windbreak planting is usually in rows spaced 10 to 12 ft. apart. The shrub rows on the border are spaced 6 ft. apart in the rows, the larger trees 8 to 12 ft. apart. Select a spacing appropriate for your site and conditions.

The advantage of close spacing is the quick achievement of a closed canopy so desirable for erosion-control plantings. Close spacing is also desirable where the plantation in the early stages can be thinned for ornamental stock or for Christmas trees. Where early thinnings cannot be utilized, the wider spacings are used because first thinnings are not required at so early a stage. Obviously the more trees planted per acre the higher the cost for the plantation. Table 4 indicates the number of trees required per acre for various spacings.

TABLE 4. TREES REQUIRED PER ACRE FOR DIFFERENT SPACINGS

SPACING, FT.	NUMBER OF TREES PER ACRE
2 × 2	10,890
4 × 4	2,722
5 × 5	1,742
6 × 6	1,210
6 × 8	908
7 × 7	890
8 × 8	680
10 × 10	435

SHELTER BELTS

SPACING IN ROW, NO. OF FT. APART	TREES PER MILE FOR EACH ROW
6	880
8	660
10	528
12	440

Determining the Labor Requirements. Labor for tree planting varies in accordance with the number and size of the trees planted, topography, ground cover, and other conditions. The range seems to be about as follows: one man in one day of 8 hr. can plant 300 trees in rough or rocky ground with a mattock; 400 trees on smoother land, planting in holes made by a shovel, spade, or mattock; 600 to 800 trees on smooth land using the slit method of planting made with a spade or a bar or where the planting is in prepared furrows. Labor requirements for machine planting have already been set forth. Contract work for tree planting is satisfactory if reliable, experienced contractors are available.

Often soil conservation districts buy planting stock at wholesale prices and hire the planting done for cooperators at a price per thousand trees, with or without the use of a planting machine. For farmers it is often a good investment to hire tree planting done, especially if it is a spring planting job.

7. Selecting the Planting Stock

Nursery stock is produced and sold from commercial nurseries or state nurseries as either seedlings or transplant stock. Seedlings are produced from seed sown in beds and grown for one or two or sometimes three years, then lifted and shipped to the planters. This class of stock is designated as 1—0, 2—0, or 3—0, indicating that it is grown in the seedbed for one, two, or three years. To produce transplant stock which is sturdier and with a better root-top ratio, the seedlings are transferred from the seedbed at the age of one or two years and planted in long rows. Here they are held for two or three years before being shipped for field planting. This class of stock is designated as 1—2, 1—3, 2—1, 2—2 or 2—3, indicating that the plants have been held in the seedbed one or two years and grown in the transplant row for one, two, or three additional years. Transplant stock is suitable for difficult sites. Figure 24 indicates the relative size of trees grown in nurseries as seedlings and transplant stock.

For most planting of southern pines, seedling stock (1—0) is suitable and is commonly used. In the North use seedling stock two years old (2—0) for ordinary sites; for difficult sites and often for such species as spruce and balsam, which grow very slowly initially, use only transplant stock. This may be either 2—1 or 2—2. On the West Coast, Douglas fir is commonly planted as 2—0 stock. In the Plains or in other parts of the West, hardwood stock is usually 1—0, sometimes 2—0; conifers are planted as transplants either 2—1 or 2—2.

In the North and Northeast on the better sites, use such species as red pine, white pine, European larch, spruce, and balsam fir. Use white pine only in regions free of the blister rust or where the plantations are protected by the eradication of Ribes (currants and gooseberries—the alternate host of rust) within about 1,000 ft. of the plantation. On the poorer sites use Virginia pine, pitch pine, and jack pine. Hardwoods planted on suitable sites include maple, oak, ash, yellow poplar, walnut, and black locust.

In the South, most of the reforestation work makes use of the four southern pines—shortleaf, loblolly, slash, and longleaf. Ordinarily farmers do not like longleaf because of the extremely slow growth of this species in the initial stages. Some cypress is planted on moist upland sites and promises to do very well. In portions of the South, shortleaf pine is affected by the "little leaf" disease and, where it is prevalent, it is not advisable to plant this species. Hardwoods

FIG. 24. Comparative size and development of three age classes of pine nursery stock (Wisconsin). Left to right: 4-year transplant (2-2); 3-year seedling (3-0), and 2-year seedling (2-0). (*Extension Service, Wisconsin.*)

planted in the South on suitable sites are the oaks, ash, gum, yellow poplar, and cottonwood.

Cottonwood is usually planted on bottom lands. It is especially suitable for planting on farms because in addition to its commercial value for lumber, excelsior, and other uses, it is good for fuel, shade, and as a windbreak. Use it on ditch banks, in fence rows, and in other relatively unproductive farm areas. This species makes its best growth on moist loam or silty soils but grows very well on heavy clay soils along ditches and on gentle slopes bordering swamps and sloughs. Swampy sites, sloughs, or drains where planted trees frequently may be submerged for long periods are not suitable for cottonwood. Tentative recommendations for planting cottonwoods are 6 ft. apart, in rows 10 ft. apart, using one- or two-year-old seedlings and cuttings from the tops of such seedlings.   Cultivate or release the planted trees from competing vegetation during the first year.   Release is most easily done by cutting away all vegetation within a radius of about 18 in. from the tree, using an ordinary cotton-chopping hoe.   Make the first release in early May and the second late in June or July.   One man with a hoe can release from ½ to 1 acre per day where trees are planted 6 by 10 ft.

In the West, species planted are commonly Douglas fir, ponderosa pine, white pine, and, at higher elevations, noble fir.

In the Central states, the species commonly planted are red pine, jack pine, white pine, and, in the southerly portions, loblolly and shortleaf pines.   Scotch pine has been used to some extent but its use ordinarily is not recommended.   Hardwoods often planted are walnut, yellow poplar, and oaks.

Tree windbreaks east of the Mississippi are usually made with red pine, white pine, spruce, or southern pines within their appropriate range.   Scrub pines, cottonwood, and various shrubs are also used. In the Great Plains and in the West, the coniferous species used are red cedar (except in the vicinity of apple orchards where this species is the alternate host for a rust on apple trees), ponderosa pine, Austrian pine, and Black Hills spruce; hardwoods are black locust, cottonwood, Chinese elm, and hackberry; shrub species are lilac, Russian olive, Caragana, tamarisk, snowberry, and American plum.   Shrubs primarily useful west of the Great Plains are squawbush, chokecherry, and buffalo berry.

Cuttings of such species as cottonwood, poplar, and willow are used in stream-bank planting and sometimes in sand-dune planting; cut them from new growth about ½ in. thick at the butt and 8 to 10 in. long.

Making Mixed Plantings.   Such plantings consist of two or more species and are desirable where the growth habits of the species are similar.   If one fast-growing species is mixed with one of slower growth habits, the latter will be overtopped by the former.   For example, where red pine and white pine have been planted together, the red pine commonly overtops the white pine.   Mixtures of pine and black locust have not proved satisfactory.   Most authorities now recommend block plantings instead of an even mixture.   The block planting can take the form of six or more rows of one species alternating with an equal number of rows of another species, but square blocks or patches are also recommended. Differences in soil and slope can be taken advantage of, using the species best adapted to different soil conditions. A mixture of species always makes a safer forest because diseases and insects that attack one species rarely

FIG. 25. Mixed planting larch and black locust in alternate rows 19 years after planting on the Edward Woolman Tree Farm in Pennsylvania. Black locust has been cut for fence posts. (*Soil Conservation Service.*)

attack others. The following even mixtures of southern pine are reported to have proved satisfactory: shortleaf and loblolly, loblolly and slash pine, shortleaf and white pine, shortleaf and Virginia pine, or shortleaf and pitch pine. It is rarely advisable to plant a mixture of hardwood and pine except where the pine is planted as a nurse crop. In a great many coniferous plantations and in natural young coniferous stands, it is to be expected that as the soil is improved by the coniferous forest litter, hardwood growth gradually will appear, resulting in a conifer-hardwood mixture. This is a logical ecological development, and where harwodods originally occupied the site, it is usually to be encouraged.

Finding Sources of Planting Stock and Tree Seed.   One of the important considerations in any planting is the source of seed from

FIG. 26. Mixed planting of red oak and red pine on Edward Woolman Tree Farm in Pennsylvania.   Red pine is outgrowing the oak.   (*Soil Conservation Service.*)

which the planting stock has been produced.   Utilize a source of seed from a climatic zone similar to that in which the trees are to be planted.   Preferably the stock should be produced from locally grown seed.   Ordinarily you will have to depend on the nurseries from which the planting stock is obtained to secure their seed from the proper sources, but it is well to ask about this before purchasing stock.   Sometimes planting stock can be obtained locally from wild seedlings. However, unless they are taken up and handled very carefully without removing the soil around the roots, the survival of this class of stock will be less than from nursery-grown stock.

A satisfactory source of stock available to farmers is the state nursery usually operated by the state forester. In many parts of the country, lumber and pulpwood companies produce tree-planting stock and offer it to farmers free or at very reasonable prices. Soil conservation

FIG. 27. Mixed planting of yellow poplar and white pine, alternate four-rows, on the Edward Woolman Tree Farm in Pennsylvania. Both species are growing well; the poplar is slightly taller. (*Soil Conservation Service.*)

districts in some cases maintain their own nurseries and sell planting stock to cooperating farmers at cost. In other cases they buy stock from commercial nurseries in wholesale lots and resell to farmers at cheaper prices than they would otherwise have to pay. Another method for obtaining satisfactory planting stock where especially sturdy plants are needed is to buy seedling stock (1—0 or 2—0) and plant it in transplant rows, cultivating for one or two years before transferring to the final location.

Inspect carefully trees received from nurseries before they are accepted. Open a few bundles and examine particularly for dry roots or mold, either of which is an indication of injury in transit or in handling. If the planting stock looks doubtful, it is better not to accept it than to take a chance on planting trees that are already dead or seriously injured.

FIG. 28. Mixed planting of yellow poplar and Norway spruce, alternate rows on the Edward Woolman Tree Farm in Pennsylvania. Poplar is outgrowing the spruce but the spruce will probably survive because of its greater tolerance. (*Soil Conservation Service.*)

Transplanting Conifer Seedlings to Transplant Rows. The purpose is to promote root growth and a balance between root and top growth. One or two years in the transplant row produces a sturdier, stronger plant, able to survive under more difficult conditions than can be expected of seedlings. As already indicated, this practice is commonly confined to the northern and western conifers, such as white and red pine, spruce, balsam fir, hemlock, ponderosa pine, and Douglas fir. Transplanting is done in early spring or late fall while the plants are dormant. Great care must be exercised to prevent any drying out of the roots during the transplanting. Cool, cloudy days with little or no wind are best for transplanting.

Usually seedling stock is obtained from state or commercial nurseries. Seedlings may, however, be grown from seed in a nursery on the farm. Growing plants from seed is a highly technical job, and unless

FIG. 29. Block planting of Monterey pine with eucalyptus (blue gum) at the right in California after 12 years growth: pine 45 ft. and blue gum 75 ft. tall. Block planting is necessary where growth rates of species vary widely. (*Soil Conservation Service.*)

you wish to grow seedlings as a farm enterprise with a view to selling plants to supplement farm income, do not undertake it. If you wish to grow seedling stock as a commercial undertaking, you can obtain full instructions from textbooks or from publications of the state and the U.S. Department of Agriculture. Growing transplants from seedlings is, however, a relatively simple operation and entirely within the field in which a farmer is equipped by experience.

Most pines make satisfactory transplant stock in one year, but an additional year gives them greater size and increased vigor. Spruces and firs normally require two years in the transplant row to attain the required size and vigor. When the transplants reach a height of about 6 in. with bushy tops and well-developed root systems, they are ready for field planting.

The steps commonly followed in transplanting are:

Prepare the Ground as for a Garden. Choose a light soil, if possible one that is reasonably free from weeds and one that has had a green manure crop plowed under the year before. Lay out the beds. These may be 6 by 21 ft. or 4 by 32 ft. With seedlings planted in rows 6 in. apart and the trees 3 in. apart in the rows, each of these beds will hold 1,000 seedlings. Sometimes seedlings are planted only 2 in. apart in the rows, in which case a bed containing 1,000 seedlings would be 4 by 21 ft. Unless space is limited, set plants 3 in. apart in the rows to ensure plenty of room. For hand cultivation, rows 6 in. apart are satisfactory; for machine cultivation, they may be separated any desired distance. The following instructions are for beds 4 by 32 ft.; rows 4 ft. long, 6 in. apart; plants set 3 in. apart in the rows.

Set the Seedlings. Use a board 4 ft. long, 6 in. wide, and about ¾ in. thick. Cut 16 small notches 3 in. apart along one side of the board suitable conveniently to hold the seedlings. Lay the board flat on the ground across one end of the bed, the smooth edge marking the first row. With a spade dig a trench deep enough to take the roots of the seedlings and with a vertical edge along the smooth side of the board.

Next, reverse the board so that the base of the notches are over the vertical side of the trench. Put one seedling in each notch so that each seedling will be set at the same depth it grew in the seed bed. Throw in the loose soil against the roots, fill trench, and tamp firmly. Tip planting board forward on notched edge, freeing it carefully from the planted seedlings.

Now with the notched edge of the board next to the first planted row, repeat the operation for the second row, and so on until the bed is filled. Water the beds thoroughly at the end of each day's transplanting.

Care for the Transplant Rows. Keep beds free from weeds. Water in dry weather, or if no water is available, use shallow cultivation or mulch with leaves or sawdust. In severe winter climates, unless continuously protected by snow, use mulch of leaves or straw.

Do not use commercial fertilizer in the transplant bed.

8. Preparing the Ground

This subject has already been partly covered in the preceding pages. On poor sites, a mulch of coniferous brush, straw, or similar material is most useful and is the best insurance against failure. Over extensive areas, however, the use of mulch becomes very expensive. The plowing of furrows is a common practice where it is necessary to get rid of the competition of vegetation in order to aid in establishing the planted trees. On slopes, plow furrows that follow the contour and make the plowing some time before the trees are to be planted. For spring planting, make the furrows in the fall in order to allow the overturned soil to settle. The plants will have a better chance if set in the overturned furrows rather than in the bottom of the furrows. Where it is impossible to plow furrows and where vegetative competition is severe, site preparation often consists of "scalping" a square or a circle in which the tree is to be planted. By the use of a mattock, the vegetation is removed to mineral soil for a space approximately 18 to 24 in. square, and the tree is planted in the center of the cleared area. As previously mentioned, scalping is not advisable for fall-planted trees. For windbreak and shelter-belt plantings and for fence posts, plow and harrow the ground thoroughly. For windbreak planting in heavy soil, the use of a subsoiler facilitates the planting and helps the planted trees to get a start.

9. Taking Care of Trees before Planting

If trees received from a nursery are to be used within a period of about 10 days after their receipt, they can remain in the bundles. Keep the bundles moist, however, by frequent watering. If they are to be held longer than 10 days, remove the trees from the container and place in a heel-in bed (Fig. 30). The heel-in bed is a slanting trench dug sufficiently deep to hold the roots. Loosen the bundles, thoroughly moisten, and place them on one side of the trench; then pack the dirt firmly about the roots, leaving the tops exposed. Select a heel-in bed site preferably in light, well-drained soil and in a place protected naturally from direct sun. If necessary, prepare an improvised shelter such as brush supported on poles. Nursery stock is ordinarily properly pruned before shipment from the nursery. If it is not, it is best to cut off with a sharp knife long roots of either conifers or hardwoods; this facilitates planting.

10. Placing Trees in the Ground

Machine planting and the planting of nuts have already been described. The principles of tree planting with hand tools are the same whether the tools are the mattock, the spade, or the planting bar.

Fig. 30. A heel-in bed for holding nursery stock (North Dakota). (*Soil Conservation Service.*)

They are illustrated in Fig. 31*a*. The planting bar, or iron, Fig. 31*b*, is a good substitute for the mattock in loose sandy soil. The spade is chiefly adapted to planting hardwoods where a deep hole is required.

The essentials of planting in the field are:

1. Keep the roots moist.
2. Avoid skinning or breaking the roots.
3. Get the roots straight and well spread in the slit or hole.
4. Keep leaves and other trash out of the hole.
5. Set the tree in the ground the same depth that it grew in the seed bed.
6. Tamp the earth firmly about the roots.

Probably the most important of these specifications is to set the tree the same depth that it grew in the nursery. Trees planted too deep or too shallow may live but will be very slow in getting started and will often remain stunted for a long period.

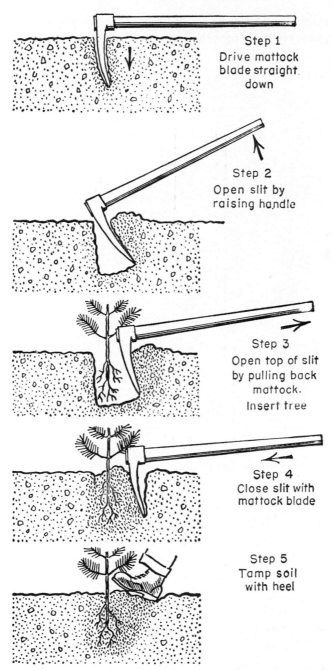

Step 1
Drive mattock
blade straight
down

Step 2
Open slit by
raising handle

Step 3
Open top of slit
by pulling back
mattock.
Insert tree

Step 4
Close slit with
mattock blade

Step 5
Tamp soil
with heel

FIG. 31a. Steps in the mattock-slit method of planting. (*Farmers' Bulletin* 1994, 1948.)

The organization of crews is not very difficult on most farm plantings. If furrows have not been plowed to indicate the rows, it is necessary to use poles with white or colored flags in order to keep the rows straight. Three or more flags are required to mark one row

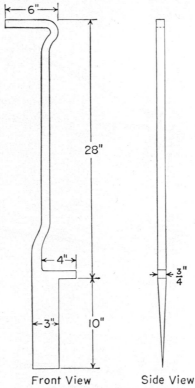

Front View   Side View

Fig. 31*b*. Planting bar or iron.

across a field, depending upon the length.   Place flags at intervals of 100 or 200 ft., depending upon the topography.   Where two or more men are planting, mark only one row with flags.   The other men follow the lead man at the proper interval decided upon for the row spacing.   As soon as a flag has served its purpose on the first row, move it over to where it will serve when the planting lines are reversed. This is better explained by the diagram shown in Fig. 32.

Foreman places flags on row 1 before planting begins.   Man 1 follows flags, planting trees every 6 ft.   Each man (2, 3, and 4) follows at 6-ft. distances, planting trees the same distance apart.   Foreman moves flags as the planters pass them from row 1 to row 5.   Row 5 is then ready as a guide to the crew for the return trip. When the direction of planting changes, row 1 man then becomes row 5 man, row 2 man becomes row 6 man, and so forth.

Sometimes two men are employed as a planting unit, one to dig the hole and the other to plant the tree, but for most farm plantings a one-man unit is sufficient. He will carry the trees, dig the hole and plant the trees, and thus the entire responsibility for the work is

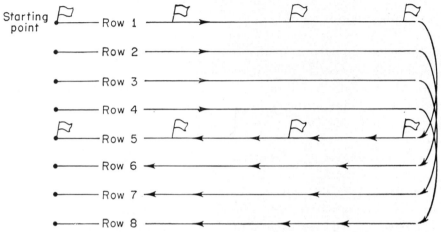

FIG. 32. Flags to mark planting rows 6 by 6 spacing: rows 6 ft. apart and trees 6 ft. apart in rows. A four-man crew and a foreman are used.

on one man.   Trees are carried from the heel-in beds to the planting site by any convenient method so long as the roots are kept moist. The planters carry the trees in pails, baskets, or trays with the roots in water or covered with moist moss, straw, or burlap.   Make frequent inspection of planted trees.   Test first for depth of tree in the ground; second for firmness by gently pulling the plant to see that the earth is properly tamped about it; and third to see that the surface of the ground around the tree is left as intended—mulch of leaves, trash, or loose dirt, or as little disturbance as possible to ground cover.

11. Taking Care of Planted Trees

Protect all plantations from fire and grazing.   This is particularly true in hardwood plantations.   A little grazing in coniferous plantations reduces the fire hazard and theoretically can be employed for this reason.   Cattle, especially, seldom browse coniferous trees, and therefore very light and infrequent grazing theoretically is not serious.

However, grazing animals trample the soil and are generally not considered of sufficient benefit to justify the risk of injury. It is safer to exclude all grazing animals. This is a matter that each plantation owner must decide for himself, but the results of even light grazing should be watched carefully. Cultivate plantations of fence posts, shelter belts, and windbreaks for the first three or four years. Exceptions are shelter belts in the Plains country planted in light sand; they cannot be cultivated because of the unstable soil. Otherwise cultivation is the rule.

In the first year after the planting, make a survival check to determine what proportion of the trees planted are still living. If any replanting is needed, make it the following year and in no case later than the second year following the original planting. The percentage of the trees living at the end of one year considered to be satisfactory depends upon the purpose of the planting. If the purpose is erosion control, where a great deal of volunteer vegetation can be expected, a survival as low as 50 percent may be satisfactory. For shelter belts, fence posts, and Christmas trees, a survival of at least 90 percent is essential. This is particularly true for shelter belts where small breaks in the tree barrier do a good deal of damage. For plantations where wood crops are desired, a survival of at least 70 percent of the trees is usually considered essential. Any less survival than as indicated above calls for replanting.

Sometimes in the South, so-called "prescribed" burning is used in longleaf-pine plantations since burning is useful in controlling the brown-spot leaf disease. This, however, is a very local and exceptional practice and should not be used without the advice of local foresters (Fig. 157).

In general it will be seen from the preceding discussion that reforestation work is a decidedly local and often a difficult problem. Discussion of general principles is helpful, but it is always advisable, where possible, to get the advice of farm foresters or other local experts before undertaking any extensive planting work.

SUPPLEMENTARY ACTIVITIES

Gathering and Storing Nuts

1. Collect nuts in the fall or early winter as they fall from the trees of hickory, walnut, oak, pecan. Keep each species separate; remove the outer coverings.

2. Examine and test the nuts for soundness. Walnut is usually 90 percent or better good seed; throw out the dry, lightweight nuts. Hickory nuts have a lower percentage of perfect seed; throw out those with wormholes and those of light weight and very dark color. Acorns are often badly weeviled; test by placing them in a tub of water and discard those that float.

3. Choose one or more boxes of sizes suitable to hold the quantities of nuts you have gathered; it is best, but not essential, to store nuts of each species in separate boxes. Get a quantity of clean sand.

4. For each nut box, put in a layer of moist sand about 2 in. deep; then a layer of nuts about the same depth, alternating sand and nuts until all nuts are in the box.

5. Select a well-drained spot out of doors. Dig a hole suitable to hold each box of nuts almost as deep as the box. Set each box in a hole and cover with soil around the box and with a thick layer of leaves on top. Weight the leaves with rock or boards. Leave until planting time next spring.

Planting Cuttings

1. Gather 24 cuttings from twigs of willow or cottonwood trees, about $\frac{1}{2}$ in. in diameter and 12 in. long. Cut them in the spring just before growth starts.

2. Plant 12 of them along a creek or riverbank, where it is eroded. Use a sharp stick to make a hole for each cutting. Push each cutting into the hole about two-thirds of its length, and firm the soil with your heel.

3. Check up in August or September and report how many grew.

4. Plant the other 12 in a sandy place (or a box of sand). Keep them moist until roots sprout. Keep the tops covered with leaves.

5. When rooted, plant these cuttings in the same location as the first 12. Be careful to keep the roots moist in handling.

6. Check up on these also in August or September. How many of these grew?

3. Weeding and Releasing Young Trees

LOGICALLY the next step after getting the forest started is its care. Forestry begins with the forest. After the new trees are established, steps must be taken to ensure their growth at a normal rate. A forest has been born. What to do with it to make it grow and prosper in its early life is the subject matter of this chapter. The first step, other than protection, is to weed out what is not wanted and to give the good trees room to grow. The problem is similar to that encountered in the growing of cotton, corn, or carrots. It is a weeding operation. Usually it must be done without getting a cash return from the material that is removed. In a forest weeding, this is not always true because sometimes very small products, such as tomato stakes and bean poles, can be utilized or sold. It is always well to inquire about the local market for any material likely to be cut in weeding operations. By and large, however, a weeding either in the field, in the garden, or in the forest is an investment of labor for future returns. Farmers do that for other crops, and it is equally important for the forest crop.

Weeding has a greater and, when properly applied, a more beneficial effect on the make-up of a stand than any other silvicultural operation. A few dollars wisely spent in improving a stand in its youth, when the least effort produces the greatest improvement, will result in a greatly increased net income from the final crop. In some cases, a single weeding may be the means of converting a stand, which would naturally produce only wood worth but a few dollars per acre, to one of saw timber worth several hundred dollars per acre.[1]

The advantages which farmers have in this type of work as opposed to other forest owners have already been mentioned. Weeding operations are sometimes called "cleaning," but it is the same

[1] A. C. Cline, "Forest Weeding with Special Reference to Young Natural Stands in Central New England," Massachusetts Forestry Association, Boston, 1929.

process. The problems will be discussed in this chapter under the following activity headings:

1. Weeding Young Hardwoods
2. Weeding Young Hardwood—Conifer Mixtures
3. Releasing the Better Trees in Older Stands
4. Poisoning Inferior Trees and Weed Species

1. Weeding Young Hardwoods

Essentially even-aged stands of young natural hardwoods must be weeded in order to prevent stagnation in the growth of the stand and particularly to prevent the best trees from being overtopped and killed. Cutover lands grow up to a mixture of brush, sprouts, seedlings, shrubs, and vines. Sprouts appear on live stumps in clumps much too thick for profitable growth, and the whole mass of vegetation, unless weeded, is likely to produce a low percentage of good tree species. The better trees are covered up by the growth of inferior trees or brush such as hazel, rhododendron, spice bush, dogwood, or, in the West, by such species as salal, Ceanothus, or salmonberry. Plantations on brushland soon encounter similar conditions. Experience indicates that in natural young growth without weeding, the forest manager can expect 20 to 30 percent of the final stand to be desirable species. If weeded carefully, as high as 80 percent of the final stand will be composed of good species.

Selecting the Time to Start. The time to start is when the young stands are 5 to 15 years old, or as soon as the better species have reached an age when they can be readily recognized and, especially, when they are ready to start rapid height growth. This can be determined by observing trees of similar age located in favorable spots. It is, of course, essential to recognize the foliage, bud characteristics, and branching arrangement of the trees to be favored. For example, oaks, basswood, elm, beech, birch, and gums have alternate branching. Maple, ash, and dogwood have opposite buds and branches. Young specimens can be compared with the leaves and branches of older trees that are known, or they can be identified from pictures and descriptions in the many books referred to in Appendix I, Bibliography, page 335. It is an advantage to be able to recognize the different trees in their young stages in both winter and summer, but it is certainly essential to recognize them in full leaf.

One indication of the time to begin weeding young stands is when they reach the stage where some trees begin to show "dominance," in other words, when they begin to push ahead of the others. This means the period of rapid height growth is at hand. It is time to free the trees that you want to grow and to discourage or eliminate undesirable competitors. It is time to choose the "crop" trees and help them to attain a place of dominance in the stand.

Selecting the Method of Weeding. Weeding is not a wholesale cutting of everything except the trees selected for future growth; use the crop-tree method. Choose the best species and the best individual trees at selected intervals, and remove only the growth immediately surrounding these trees. This means that only a small percentage of the actual weed growth is removed. Leave all vegetation not directly interfering with the growth of the selected trees to protect the soil and to act as trainers to shade the lower part of the stems and to keep the crop trees from spreading out instead of growing straight up. For a first weeding operation, select crop trees as nearly as possible at intervals of 6 to 15 ft. Go through the young forest in strips spaced about 15 ft. apart and attempt to pick out a desirable crop tree about every 6 ft. along each line. Actually the choice may have to be at distances anywhere from 10 to 15 ft. Usually, preliminary marking of trees to be favored is not necessary. As the weeder proceeds, he picks out the best trees he can find, then cuts the weed trees and brush interfering with their growth. Usually this is within a space of about 2 to 3 ft. from each selected tree.

If the selected trees, when released, are not easily seen, attach a white rag or paper to an occasional one in order to keep the proper distance between lines. In the case of stump sprouts, retain one that has its origin close to the base rather than one from the top of the stump (Figs. 33 to 36). If possible, choose sprouts not over 2 in. in diameter from stumps less than 12 in. in diameter, and, of course, where there is a choice, choose seedlings in preference to sprouts. Crop trees preferably should be nearly the same height as the surrounding vegetation in order to be sure that they have not been injured by suppression. If selected crop trees are already well above the general level, there is danger that they may develop into "wolf" trees (Fig. 33). However, suppressed tolerant trees such as maple, beech, basswood, hemlock, or spruce will stand considerable suppression and yet grow well when the overhead shade is removed. Attempt to keep crop trees properly spaced even if occasionally it becomes necessary to choose inferior species.

Providing Suitable Tools.   These are the machete, brush hook, and, for some purposes, a hand pruner or a small pole ax.   The choice

Fig. 33. A wolf tree.   A large oak in a Mississippi woods to be removed because it occupies too much room.   (*Soil Conservation Service.*)

of tools depends upon the weeder's preference and upon the size of the growth to be removed.   Experience indicates that the machete is one of the most generally useful tools for this type of work.   Where much of the vegetation to be removed is over 1 in. in diameter, such tools as the brush hook, or an ax will be better than the machete.

Determining the Degree of Release.   This is a question not fully determined.   General experience seems to be that a relatively light cutting, if it can be repeated as needed every 3 to 5 years until the crop trees are safely in the lead, is better than a more severe cutting.   One specification is to cut, in a space of 2 ft. surrounding the crop tree, all

FIG. 34. A group of redwood sprouts, California.   Originally there were five but two have been removed and one is marked for removal.   (*Soil Conservation Service.*)

FIG. 35. A eucalyptus-sprout forest, California.   (*Soil Conservation Service.*)

growth that reaches to one-third or more the height of the crop tree and, in a space of 4 ft., all vegetation taller than the crop tree. Complete or partial severance of the stems of vegetation to be removed and, also, cutting or breaking the stems at any convenient height are satis-

Fig. 36. A close-up of the sprouts shown in Fig. 35.   Two of the best specimens should be retained.   (*Soil Conservation Service.*)

factory. Oak and soft maple sprouts may be an exception. Experience in New England indicates that it is best to sever them completely from the stump.

The following rules for release cuttings in Southern Appalachian hardwoods have application to this type wherever it occurs.

1. Free and dominant trees require no release.
2. If the growth rate of the weed trees is greater than that of the crops trees, release cutting should be heavier than where the growth rates of weed and crop trees are approximately the same.

3. If the weed trees are taller than the crop trees, release should be heavier than where they are approximately the same heights.

4. A second weeding 3 to 5 years after the first one will improve the composition and produce better crop trees.

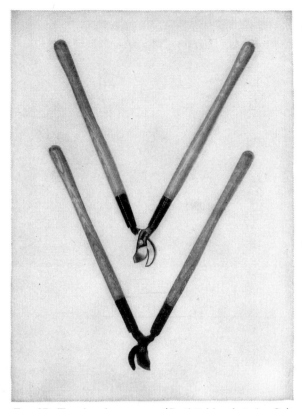

Fig. 37. Two-hand pruners.   (*Bartlett Manufacturing Co.*)

5. If the crop trees are vigorous in appearance, this is an indication that overtopping has not been of long duration.   One weeding will probably be sufficient.

6. Yellow poplar is susceptible to frost injury, especially so unless very vigorous.   Release of this species should not be attempted on poor sites or in known frost pockets or, in any case, unless the yellow poplar is still sturdy and vigorous.

7. White oak and sugar maple respond well to release cutting and weeding.

Choosing the Season to Cut.   This is more or less a matter of being able to recognize the crop trees to leave.   Most work in the forest can be done to best advantage in the winter when the leaves are off, but in hardwood young growth the presence of the leaves is often necessary to ensure recognition of the desirable trees. Cutting in the fall will probably result in the least sprouting of the cut stumps. Weeding will usually be done in the early fall while the leaves are still present or in the spring as soon as they are sufficiently advanced to ensure recognition of the best trees.

Estimating the Costs. Such work may vary considerably in cost, depending upon the amount of growth and the stage of development. In New England from 4 to 12 man-hours per acre were used in this type of work in pine and hardwood. When the growth is not too large, averaging 4 in. and under in diameter, one man should be able to weed an acre a day. One or two man-days per acre were employed in weeding and release work in Southern Appalachian hardwoods. On the best sites, where growth response is most rapid, repeat the weeding more often than on poorer sites. Sometimes one weeding is sufficient, but sometimes two or three are required at intervals of 3 to 5 years. Early weeding results in a marked stimulation in the diameter growth of crop trees, but the chief result is the increased percentage of good trees in the stand. The opportunity to cut merchantable material also comes at an earlier age than in unweeded stands.

2. Weeding Young Hardwood Conifer Mixtures

Problems similar to those already discussed for pure hardwood stands are encountered in this mixture. It is easier, however, to pick out the crop trees because in such mixtures the conifers are the preferred species. If they are favored, the hardwoods will be able to take care of themselves. Under such conditions, it is seldom wise to attempt complete conversion from hardwoods to conifers. This would prove to be very expensive, and besides a minor percentage of hardwoods in the stand is helpful in maintaining soil moisture and in adding organic matter to the soil. The problem of growing conifers in hardwood mixtures is encountered in most regions of the United States but particularly in the Lake states, in the woods of New England, New York, and Pennsylvania, and in the South. It is also encountered on the West Coast where hardwood shrubs, alders, and willows often overtop conifer reproduction. In the New England spruce-fir-hardwood forests, conifers are often cut and the hardwoods left or cut very lightly. On the cutover areas, conifer reproduction is soon badly overtopped by the hardwoods. While the conifers are preferred, a great many of the hardwoods will produce valuable wood products. A partial transformation from hardwoods to conifers in this type is satisfactory. The same thing is true in parts of the Lake states where spruce and white pine are growing under the shade of aspen and paper birch.

Another method of weeding hardwood-conifer mixtures is first to locate natural groupings where the young growth is chiefly either soft-wood or hardwood. If this can be done, weed in the softwood groups to put the conifers in the lead; in the hardwood groups favor the hard-wood growth because it is already in the ascendancy.

In the South there are large areas which can be transformed from worthless hardwoods to pine by cutting or poisoning the hardwood overstory, thus releasing the pine young growth.

Selecting the Time. The best time for weeding such stands is usually from 3 to 8 years after cutting the previous stand or at any time when the conifer reproduction is well established. Experience indicates that weeding can be delayed with such species as spruce, fir, and white pine until the young trees begin to show signs of decreased terminal growth. When the overtopping trees begin to injure the conifers, it is time to start weeding. As long as the conifers remain vigorous and thrifty as shown by deep green needles and height growth of 6 in. or more a year, there is probably little need for weeding operations. When they begin to show signs of failing vigor through lessening length and fading color of the needles, thinning of the foliage, and slowing down of the terminal growth, then it is time to free the conifer young growth of overhead shade.

If the weed trees are dense and the conifers are weak and spindling, a partial weeding at first is desirable to prevent damage from sudden exposure. In localities where white-pine weevil damage is serious, a partial release of white-pine trees decreases weevil damage. Weevil damage is greater in full sunlight than where the pines grow in partial shade.

The same problems are encountered whether the conifer young growth is natural or obtained by planting. Weeding and release operations have been found to be necessary after planting pine under a worthless overstory of oaks in the South and under gray birch and other hardwoods in New England.

Selecting Methods. The methods to be followed and the tools applicable are very similar to those already described. Sometimes one weeding is sufficient, but often two or three may be advisable at intervals of 3 to 5 years. As mentioned in connection with pure hardwoods, a greater number of weedings are needed on good than on poor sites, but of course the response and hence the resulting values are greater on good than on poor sites. In the North and West, the season for weeding is usually late fall or early winter before the snow comes. In the South most any time is satisfactory, but preferably during the dormant period for hardwoods and brush.

Estimating Costs. This type of weeding varies greatly and averages have little value. In the case of northern hardwoods and spruce, weeding operations are reported to have cost from 2 to 8 man-hours in labor per acre for the area actually weeded. The best record of costs for this type of work is from New England. It is given in Table 5.

TABLE 5. COSTS OF WEEDING OPERATIONS IN NEW ENGLAND

Cases	Number of weedings needed	Man-hours per acre*
1. Mixed hardwood following old-field pine............	1–3	12–24
2. Mixed hardwood following saw log hardwood.......	2–3	20–30
3. Conifer-hardwood mixture following old-field pine....	1–3	12–30
4. Releasing pine from gray birch..................	1–	8 24
5. Conifer plantations on brushy fields and pastures.....	1–2	10–20
6. Conifer plantations on cutover land (heavy soil)......	2–3	20–30
7. Same as 6 (light soil)...........................	1–2	10–20
8. Conifer plantations on scrub-oak land.............	1–	4–10

* Cost of supervision not included.

3. Releasing the Better Trees in Older Stands

This type of work is also known as "liberation cutting." It is needed on stands that have advanced too far for strictly weeding operations. The majority of the trees are from 2 to 10 in. d.b.h., and often there are wolf trees of large size scattered through the woods (Fig. 33). Many good trees, either hardwoods or conifers, are overtopped by less desirable hardwoods, shrubs, or wolf trees. This type of release cutting sometimes approaches a weeding on the one hand and a thinning or an improvement cutting on the other.

The procedure in conducting release work in this type of woods is much the same as for weeding. It is best to go through the stand in parallel strips from 15 to 30 ft. apart, and pick out the trees to be released before any cutting is attempted. The selected trees should

Fig. 38. Girdling a cull beech in West Virginia. (*Soil Conservation Service.*)

be labeled with colored cloth, paper, or some similar means. Then follow with an ax, cutting the hardwoods or brush that interferes with the growth of the selected crop trees. At the same time the wolf trees should be girdled or poisoned (Figs. 38 and 39).

Comparing Results of Release Work. On a typical upland pine-hardwood mixture at Crossett Experimental Forest, Arkansas, low-grade hardwoods from 1 to 20 in. d.b.h. and averaging about 4 in. were overtopping 1,200 pine seedlings per acre, most of them less than 7 ft. high. Three degrees of treatment were used: (1) hardwoods 6 in. d.b.h. and over were removed; (2) hardwoods 2 in. d.b.h. and

Fig. 39. Growth of pine seedlings in an Arkansas woods after girdling of hardwoods. (*Soil Conservation Service.*)

over were removed; (3) hardwoods over 5 ft. high were removed. Ten years later the pines were thinned for pulpwood. Results were as shown in Table 6.

TABLE 6. RESULTS OF RELEASE CUTTING
(Figures on basis of one acre)

Item	Treatment		
	1	2	3
Hardwoods removed (number).....................	15	136	431
Removal costs in 1939 (converted to 1949 rates)......	$0.53	$1.84	$2.43
Volume cut in thinning 1949 (cords)................	0.19	1.51	1.62
Stumpage value of thinnings, $2 per cord............	0.38	3.02	3.24
Returns from thinning less treatment costs...........	−0.15	1.18	0.81

NOTE: These results were obtained on a stumpage basis. The labor returns from harvesting pulpwood are not included in the figures.

In another example from the Crossett Experimental Forest, all hardwoods overtopping a natural stand of pine seedlings were cut. An adjacent and similar area was left untouched. Seven years later the released pine trees contained 1½ cords of pulpwood per acre; the untouched forest $\frac{1}{10}$ cord per acre.   The cost of the release work (1,948 pieces) was $1.49 per acre.   The stumpage value of the pulp-wood produced more than offset the cost of release.

In Louisiana, the Resettlement Administration of the Second World War purchased some timberland that later was administered by the Soil Conservation Service.   On typical areas of pine-hardwood land, the worthless hardwoods were overtopping and killing the young pines. It was estimated that out of every 50 acres about 36 acres were completely dominated by these worthless hardwoods.   In other words, on only 14 acres, or 28 percent of large areas, did the pines have any chance to survive in competition with hardwoods.   To determine what could be done, 50 acres were treated; 22,739 hardwood trees of all sizes, or 455 per acre, were cut.   The cost, with labor at $6.00 per 8-hr. day, was $4.96 per acre.   This is much cheaper than reforestation of open land (Fig. 39).

In the Lake states an example of a stand in need of this type of release cutting has been recorded by the Lake States Experiment Station.   Aspen and paper birch averaging 13 ft. tall with 3,600 stems per acre overtopped 2,500 spruce averaging 6 ft. tall.   The remedy was obviously to remove a portion of the aspen and paper birch in order to allow the more valuable spruce to survive and grow vigorously.

Girdling.   On trees 6 in. d.b.h. and larger this is cheaper than cutting them.   If they contain no usable or salable wood, this practice is commonly followed.   Experience shows that girdled trees die slowly and gradually cast off their limbs and, when they finally fall, do minimum damage to the young growth.   Sprouting is not stopped by the girdling, but this is equally true of cutting.   The most satisfactory way to girdle trees is to make, with the ax, a complete ring of hacks or chips around the tree trunk at a depth of at least $\frac{1}{2}$ in. into the sapwood.   Some trees, for example, the gums and elms, are very hard to kill by girdling and require a depth of cut of about 2 in. into the sapwood.   Often a system of double hacking or chip girdling is used; two rings of ax cuts are made with downward strokes of the ax, the second from 2 to 6 in. above the first, resulting in the removal of bark and wood between the two rings.

Naturally costs for this type of work vary widely.   Following are records from two operations.   The time required is about as follows: for 6-in. trees, 0.8 min.; for 10-in. trees, 1.2 min.; 14-in., 1.6 min.;

18-in., 2 min.   An average figure runs from 1.25 to 5 man-hours per acre.

In a southern operation, the costs are reported in Table 7, where labor and supervision together totaled approximately $0.85 per hour.

TABLE 7. COST OF GIRDLING TREES

SIZE OF TREE, IN.	COSTS PER TREE
10	$0.038
12	0.047
14	0.055
16	0.064
18	0.074

Girdled trees die in varying periods from a few months to as long as 3 to 5 years.

Results of a girdling operation in a sixty-year-old hardwood stand in New Hampshire, overtopping spruce young growth, are as follows. The girdling was carried out by the U.S. Forest Service in 1905. Three plots of ½ acre each were established.   In plot 1, two successive cutting and girdling operations removed 65 percent of the hardwood trees.   In plot 2, 90 percent of the overhead hardwood was removed. Plot 3 was left undisturbed.   The costs of the operation in 1905 were $2 and $2.60 per acre in plots 1 and 2, respectively.   In 1935, 30 years later, the plots were examined.   On the plot where 65 percent of the overhead was removed, nearly half of the spruce was large enough to make merchantable pulpwood, amounting to 4.9 cords per acre.   On the plot where 90 percent of the overhead was removed, two-thirds of the spruce was merchantable as pulpwood, amounting to 11.4 cords per acre.   On the plot that was not touched, there was no merchantable spruce pulpwood.   The examiners drew these conclusions: first, red spruce in New England released by girdling and cutting operations from overhead shade produced merchantable pulpwood several times as fast as similar stands untouched; second, wherever a satisfactory conifer understory is present, girdling of the overhead hardwoods will convert a mixed spruce-hardwood forest to one almost entirely coniferous.

Release, by girdling or poisoning of hardwoods, of planted pine trees in heavy scrub oak stands in Louisiana resulted in a marked increase in survival and growth of the pine.   Loblolly and slash pines were interplanted under the oak stand.   Immediate release operations resulted, two years after planting, in a survival for loblolly of

86 percent and a height growth of 2.3 ft.   The slash pine showed 46 percent survival and an average height growth of 1.7 ft.   Where the release was delayed one or more years, the results were very unsatisfactory; if no release followed the planting, the survival and growth of the pine was about half of the above figures.

FIG. 40. Cutting grapevines growing on maple trees in a West Virginia woods.   (*Soil Conservation Service.*)

Removing Vines.   Sometimes vines are a problem, and steps must be taken to remove them.   For grapes it is usually a question of systematic work with an ax to cut off the vines close to the ground. Sometimes this has to be repeated, but usually one thorough cleaning of a wooded area will keep the grape nuisance to a minimum for a great many years.   Honeysuckle often comes into stands from the edges, especially where the stand is open.   The Japanese honeysuckle is most troublesome.   It can be killed by spraying with a 0.2 percent solution of 2, 4-D, a poisonous spray. Apply the spray on a hot day when four hours of sunshine afterward is reasonably assured. Cut vines which climb into trees and cannot be reached with the spray. Thoroughly wet all foliage. A back-pack pump or a pressure sprayer is satisfactory. A 90 percent kill can be expected. This spray will also kill other types of vegetation, and therefore if there is valuable reproduction present, it is a choice of killing that along with the honeysuckle or releasing the reproduction by more tedious and expensive methods. Probably spraying the honeysuckle and planting the area afterward is most satisfactory. The toxic effects of the spray disappear after two or three months. *Kudzu* plantations often are troublesome along the edges of timber. This vine can be kept from growing into the timber if the edge of the kudzu planting next to the woods is worked several times each growing season, using a drag, a spring-tooth harrow, or a plow.

4. Poisoning Inferior Trees and Weed Species

In recent years numerous experiments have been carried out using various poisons to remove weed species as an alternative to the use of an ax, a saw, a bulldozer, or other mechanical methods. The difficulty with all mechanical methods is the sprouting from stumps or roots that follows the first operation. Sometimes the trees released can get ahead of the resulting sprouts, but often the area must be gone over one or more times later to get rid of the sprout growth. Poisoning has been found, in many instances, to be cheaper and more effective than mechanical methods because the poison kills both tops and roots of plants. Methods of poisoning are still in the experimental stage, but research has progressed far enough so that some fairly reliable methods and specifications for poison mixtures can be given.

The poisons found most satisfactory are sodium arsenite, ammonium sulfamate (the latter, in the form of crystals containing 80 percent of this poison, is sold under the trade name "Ammate"), and 2,4-D. The third, 2,4-D, is used as a spray mostly in the eradication of brush and vines as already mentioned. Sodium arsenite has proved to be quite successful, but it has the serious objection that it is highly poisonous to both man and beast. Therefore, its use is very limited. Ammate, on the other hand, is not poisonous to either man or animals and seems to be quite effective in killing weed trees and brush.

The method of application is either to spray the foliage or the cut stumps of brush and small trees with Ammate or to apply poison crystals to the cut stumps. Standing trees are poisoned by the application of Ammate crystals into the sapwood by means of either

Fig. 41. Valuable young loblolly pines making fast growth after worthless overtopping hardwoods were poisoned (Louisiana). (*U.S. Forest Service.*)

"cups" or "frills." These terms will be explained later. The conditions where poisoning seems to be applicable are:

1. Where young growth of weed species is already established and it is necessary to clear the way for the planting of better species. Removal of the cover by mechanical means, followed by heavy sprouting, sometimes creates conditions as bad or worse than the original situation. If desirable young growth is already established but overtopped, the poison can be

applied to the stumps of the material cut, thus preventing most of the sprouting. If the established young growth is thrifty and well advanced, 5 ft. or more in height, release by cutting is often sufficient since usually it is well able to keep ahead of the sprouts. Poisoning under such conditions is, of course, not advisable.

2. Where wolf trees are present that must be killed either to release young growth or as a preliminary step to tree planting. In this case the question is whether poisoning or girdling is cheaper, taking into consideration the problem of sprouts after girdling. Usually it has been found that poisoning is cheaper and more satisfactory.

3. Where heavy brush is to be cleared along roads or trails. Here spraying with 2,4-D or Ammate is effective. However, a thorough job is expensive, but it is justified where the spraying can be confined to small areas.

Fig. 42. Base of a large blackjack oak tree with cups 6 in. apart. Ammate being applied to one cup (Louisiana). (*U.S. Forest Service.*)

The "cups" referred to previously are notches cut into the bark of trees usually near the base. The cup is made by means of two ax cuts, one about 2 in. above the other, with the chip between the cuts removed. Place crystals of Ammate in the cups. This method is effective but also somewhat more expensive than the use of "frills" or

single-hack girdles.   These are a ring of overlapping ax hacks around
the tree at a convenient chopping height.   Into the frills are placed
Ammate crystals or a solution of Ammate.   The Southern Forest
Experiment Station in 1946 and 1947 indicated the following results.
Ammate was applied to blackjack oak in low cups.   The result was an

FIG. 43. Pouring Ammate solution into a frill.   This method is cheaper than cupping and
works better on trees more than about 12 in. in diameter.   Frills, however, allow more
sprouting than do low cups.   A red dye is added to the Ammate solution to assist in
readily spotting treated and untreated trees (Louisiana).   (*U.S. Forest Service.*)

almost complete kill of the tops with very little sprouting. There was
no practical difference in the results where the poison was applied at
any particular season of the year.   Poisoning of blackjack oak in frills
was also tried.   Spring and summer treatments using 2 lb. of Ammate
crystals dissolved per gallon of water was not quite as satisfactory but
much cheaper.   Table 8 gives the costs of poisoning and girdling.

TABLE 8. COMPARATIVE COSTS OF POISONING AND GIRDLING WORTHLESS TREES
(Costs in cents per tree)

Size of tree, in. d.b.h.	Method of treatment		
	Frills, 2 lb. Ammate per gal. of water	Low cups, Ammate crystals	Girdling only
6	2	2.7	2.2
8	2.5	3.8	3.0
10	3.1	4.9	3.8
12	3.8	5.9	4.6
14	4.6	6.9	5.5

Why Use Ammate?* Landowners in the upland regions of the South are finding Ammate an effective and economical way of getting rid of blackjack oak and other undesirable hardwoods that may be crowding valuable trees out of the forest . . . reducing the grass in woodland pasture, or otherwise getting in the way.

Ammate (trade name for 80 percent ammonium sulfamate), when properly used, kills trees faster than girdling, and treated trees sprout less than those that are girdled or chopped down. Stands of sprouts can be killed by spraying with a strong water solution of Ammate. Ammate is poisonous only to plants. This gives it a big advantage over sodium arsenite, which is an effective tree killer but a deadly poison to animals and humans.

The southern Forest Experiment Station started tests with Ammate as a poison for blackjack oak in October, 1944. Since then, Ammate has been tried in different forms, quantities, and seasons, and compared with sodium arsenite, 2,4-D, diesel fuel, and other poisons. Most blackjack oaks were killed when Ammate was applied in the strengths and by the methods recommended. Trees treated with Ammate sprouted less than those poisoned with sodium arsenite. 2,4-D and its salts reacted more slowly and were more variable in effect than Ammate. Ammate spray proved effective on stands of sprouts and brush.

On the basis of these tests, Ammate is recommended as the most effective of the chemicals studied thus far for killing blackjack oak and many other upland hardwood species. However, sodium arsenite works better than Ammate on bitter pecan (water hickory) and other bottom-land hardwoods.

Ammate On Trees Over 3 In. in Diameter. Table 9 summarizes the two methods of applying Ammate that are most often used on trees over 3 in.

* These detailed instructions covering the use of Ammate are taken from the publication of the U.S. Forest Service "How to Control Southern Upland Hardwoods with Ammate" by Fred A. Peevy, Southern Forest Experiment Station, New Orleans, La.

d.b.h. (4½ ft. above the ground): (1) placing Ammate crystals in cups (notches) in the tree trunk, and (2) pouring Ammate solution into a frill chopped into the trunk.

For best results, cups should be as near the ground as possible—on the main

TABLE 9. TWO METHODS OF KILLING TREES WITH AMMATE

AMMATE CRYSTALS IN CUPS	AMMATE SOLUTION IN FRILLS
Where	
Recommended where complete kill with least sprouting is necessary, as in clearing land for pasture and in timber-stand improvement for longleaf pine in the grass stage.	Suggested where moderate sprouting is permissible, as in timber-stand improvement to release desirable trees at least 1 to 2 ft. high. Better than the cup method for trees over 12 in. d.b.h.
How	
Put 1 level tablespoonful of Ammate crystals into each freshly cut notch or cup. Cups at the base of the tree should be 6 in. apart from edge to edge. Two are enough for trees up to 6 in. d.b.h.; an extra cup is needed for every 2-in. increase in tree diameter. If the cups are 2 or 3 ft. above ground, they should be only 4 in. apart.	Mix not less than 2 lb. (19.3 percent solution) and preferably 4 lb. (32.4 percent solution) of Ammate crystals in each gallon of water. Ammate solution is almost colorless. To help tell treated frills from untreated ones, many users mix in enough red dye to stain the wood in the frill. Pour solution into freshly cut frill, saturating the frill without wasting solution.
Species	
Blackjack oak, sweet gum, black gum, elm, ash, bay, willow, red oak, post oak, willow oak, persimmon, and small hickory. Use a double dose for large hickory, beech, and white oak.	Blackjack oak, red oak, post oak, and willow oak. Unsatisfactory with sweet gum and hickory. Experience is lacking with other species.
When	
Winter best, but effective during any season.	Winter, spring, and summer.
Equipment	
Ax, container for Ammate crystals, tablespoon, and Ammate.	Ax, gallon oil can with small spout or tube for pouring solution into the frills, container for mixing, dye, Ammate, and water.
Crew	
A three-man crew, two to make cups and one to apply the poison, is efficient.	A four-man crew is efficient, with three men making frills and one applying Ammate.
Cost	
Chemical. At 18 cents per pound, Ammate for treating a tree 10 in. in diameter with five cups costs 2.8 cents, or 0.56 cent per cup.	*Chemical.* At 18 cents a pound for Ammate, a gallon of 32.4 percent solution costs 58 cents. A tree 10 in. d.b.h. can be treated for about 1.5 cents, or 0.15 cent for each inch in diameter. One gallon will treat 40 trees averaging 10 in. d.b.h.
Labor. At 60 cents an hour for labor, the cost of cupping and applying Ammate to a tree 10 in. in diameter is 2 cents, or 0.4 cent per cup.	*Labor.* At 60 cents per hour, the labor cost is 1.5 cents for frilling and applying the chemical to a 10-in. tree, or 0.15 cent for each inch in diameter.

roots if these show. Cups may also be made 2 or 3 ft. up the trunk, but then the tree top dies more slowly than with low cups, and sprouting is greater.

For trees more than about 12 in. d.b.h., the frill method is more effective than the cup method (Fig. 43). With cups, the chemical must do the whole job of killing, and the dosage may be too small to be completely effective.

Fig. 44. A tablespoon of Ammate crystals placed on the top of the stump of small trees immediately after felling, will prevent serious sprouting (Louisiana). (*U.S. Forest Service.*)

But a good frill will itself kill the tree crown in time, and Ammate solution hastens the death—and also reduces sprouting.

To keep down sprouting, the poisoned trees should be left standing for at least a year. Ammate solution is absorbed by the tree almost immediately, and crystals within 24 or 36 hr., but the poison works for 12 months or more.

A way of clearing land is to cut the trees off close to the ground and immediately apply Ammate crystals to the outer sapwood of the stump top to prevent sprouting.

Ammate on Small Trees. Trees too small to cup or frill should be cut down close to the ground, leaving a **V**-shaped stump (Fig. 44). One tablespoonful of Ammate crystals should be applied immediately to each freshly cut stump. Sprouting should not be serious, especially if treatment is in summer, fall or winter.

Ammate on Sprouts and Brush. Sprouts and brush are harder and more expensive to kill than larger trees. They can be controlled by spraying the green leaves thoroughly with a 32.4 percent solution of Ammate (4 lb. of crystals per gallon of water), preferably in late spring. The kill is better if the stems as well as the leaves are sprayed. Any good pressure spray gun can be used. The common 3-gallon type is convenient for small patches of sprouts. Let the sprouts stand for a year after spraying.

Where to Buy Ammate.   Ammate crystals can be purchased at large seed stores, farm supply stores, drug companies, and through agricultural cooperatives. The costs of poisoning given in Table 9 are based on a price of 18 cents per lb. In lots of 350 lb. or more, the cost is usually less than this, but in small amounts it is more.

Precautions in Using Ammate.   Ammate is very corrosive. The spray gun should be cleaned promptly and thoroughly after each use. Rinse it first with clean water to which lime has been added, then oil the metal parts with lightweight lubricating oil. Other metal equipment should also be rinsed thoroughly. Prolonged handling of Ammate may irritate the skin. Workmen should avoid wearing wet gloves and clothes which have been dipped in Ammate solution or on which Ammate crystals have been spilled.

Ammate is likely to injure or kill any vegetation it touches. Do not spill or spray it on desirable plants.

Before much time or money is spent in applying Ammate to trees other than those listed or in areas other than the southern pine-hardwood uplands, the dosage and methods of application should be tested on at least 10 trees. If the trees are poisoned in fall or winter, an examination in the middle of the following summer should tell if the poison will work. If the poison is applied in spring or summer, results cannot be judged accurately until midsummer a year later.

SUPPLEMENTARY ACTIVITIES

Girdling Wolf Trees

1. Locate five wolf trees in a farmer's woods; name the species.
2. Get the farmer's consent; take an ax and girdle two of them.
3. Get some Ammate and poison the other three; use frills on two and cups on one.
4. Make a record something like this:

Species	D.b.h., in.	Kind of treatment	Date treated	Date when completely dead

5. If any of the trees failed to die within 3 years, try to find the reason. Was the work improperly done? Perhaps one or more trees were species hard to kill, or perhaps you did not cut far enough into the sapwood.

Weeding Young Hardwoods and Conifers

1. Locate a hardwood forest cut clean 5 to 15 years ago. (Inquire of the county agent or a local sawmill man.)

2. Get permission of the owner to do some weeding on $\frac{1}{2}$ acre (8 by 10 rods). Mark the boundary clearly.

3. Proceed as directed in the text.

4. How many trees of different species did you free of competition?

5. Visit the plot once a year for at least 3 years and note growth of crop trees. Write a brief report of your success or failure.

Poisoning Vines or Brush

1. Locate a spot where Japanese honeysuckle, poison ivy, or worthless brush is taking over an area that might be growing good trees.

2. Get the farmer's permission to poison about $\frac{1}{4}$ acre (5 by 8 rods). Mark the boundaries.

3. Use 2,4-D or Ammate in a spray pump, according to the manufacturer's directions.

4. Return in about a month and repeat the treatment, if necessary.

5. Keep track of the costs of labor and materials.

6. If you can, get the farmer to buy and plant trees on the poisoned area the following spring. Advise about the kinds to get, where to get them, how many, and the technique of planting. Perhaps you will be willing to help plant them.

7. Visit the area once a year for 2 to 3 years and see what happens. Write a brief report of your experience.

4. Thinning Tree Crops

FORESTS GROW as aggregations of trees covering acres or forties or square miles of land surface. The individual trees that make up the forest are mere incidents in the forest canopy. The value of the forest is determined by the sum of the values found in all of its trees. The highest values are obtained where all trees are of good form, of good species, and distributed so as to stock the ground fully.

FIG. 45. Forests grow as aggregations of trees. A coniferous forest—chiefly spruce—in the mountains of Colorado. (*Soil Conservation Service.*)

In an uneven-aged forest, this means that there are a great many more young than old trees, but each tree theoretically occupies space according to its size and its growth requirements. In an even-aged forest, it means that there is less diversity in tree sizes and greater uniformity in space requirements of individual trees.

While, from the standpoint of the whole forest, the individual tree is a mere incident, from the standpoint of the forest grower, it is all important. The forest, at any given stage in its development, is the end product. The individual trees are the raw material out of which forests are made. The species, the form, the health, and the spacing of individual trees are the facts of forest life which determine the character of the forest. With these factors, the forest grower deals when he plants, tends, and harvests his forest.

The proper spacing of forest trees at different stages in their life is accomplished by thinning. Spacing affects directly the health, the form, and to a limited extent, the species of trees in the forest. The growth rate and the value of wood products are profoundly affected by adjusting the growing space allowed each tree. Hence thinning

FIG. 46. Forests grow as aggregations of trees. Hardwood forest in Ohio. (*Soil Conservation Service.*)

is one of the vital steps in producing a forest. After establishment of young trees and early weeding, thinning takes over the job of development of young stands by controlling the space available to individual trees.

Some *benefits* from *thinning* are:

1. Better trees when they reach a size decided to be suitable as the final crop. If this is 20- to 24-in. d.b.h. saw-log trees, thinnings in young

stands will result in straighter, smoother stems with less rot than if no thinning is made.

2. In mixed stands the percentage of better species is raised.

3. The rate of growth is increased, and hence the time required to grow crop trees to maturity is decreased.

4. The growth is concentrated on a relatively few stems instead of being scattered among many smaller ones.

5. Thinnings increase the total yield of wood products. Studies indicate that the intermediate cuttings from thinnings will amount in volume to as much as or more than the final yield. If not removed and utilized, this wood growth is lost.

Here are some examples:

A well-stocked forty- to fifty-year-old second-growth northern hardwood stand grew after thinning 1.4 to 1.8 cords per acre per year. Before thinning it grew 1.0 to 1.2 cords.

Another stand of northern hardwoods grew 1.02 cords per acre per year unthinned, and after 38 percent of the volume had been removed, it grew 1.73 cords per acre per year.

Stands of young jack pine in the Lake states are reported with a wood volume of 36 cords per acre, including 15 cords in inferior trees merchantable as pulpwood. If the latter are not cut, the wood volume will be lost and the retention of the inferior trees will retard the growth of the main stand. A stand of red pine is reported in similar condition, 42 cords total, 12 cords in inferior trees.

Further discussion of the problems of thinning will be presented in this chapter under the following activity headings:

1. Becoming Familiar with Timber Growth and Principles of Thinning
2. Deciding When to Start Thinning
3. Gauging the Amount to Cut
4. Making the Thinning
5. Protecting the Edges of the Stand
6. Observing Thinning Operations of the Past
7. Applying Thinning Principles to All Cutting Operations

1. Becoming Familiar with Timber Growth and Principles of Thinning

Observing Tree Growth. Our common forest trees grow in diameter by adding rings of wood on the outside of the trunks. Growth is from the cambium layer of live cells between the bark and the sapwood.   Both the bark and the wood are built by division of new cells in the cambium.   The bark stretches, cracks, and sloughs off as the tree grows; the woody stem increases in thickness with every year's growth as long as the tree lives.   Height growth comes from the

Fig. 47. Old growth of White oak in Indiana.   Note long clean stem.   (*Courtesy S. B. Detwiler.*)

expansion of the terminal buds into shoots.   Expansion of the crowns comes from the growth of buds on the top end of each of the many branches.   Most conifers have straight central stems; broadleaf trees are inclined to have spreading crowns.

The *growth habits* of forest trees are affected by their environment. Closely grown trees usually will grow straight with single stems and narrow crowns.   The lower branches die and drop off, leaving clean stems (boles) (Fig. 47).   The rate of growth in both height and diameter is influenced by the soil conditions (site) and by the amount of light that reaches the crowns.   Moisture and light are the two critical factors that determine how fast forest trees grow.

Moisture for growth is obtained from the soil; so are minerals and such things as nitrogen, phosphorus, potassium, lime, sulfur, boron, and others.   Air in the soil is essential to maintain the living organisms that make the nutritive elements available in forms that trees can use. In a forest soil, the retention of moisture is determined largely by the physical condition of the soil—the presence or absence of organic matter in the top layer and the nature of the subsoil.   If the latter allows free penetration of tree roots, holds moisture but is not wet, and if, in addition, organic matter is allowed to accumulate on the forest floor, moisture for tree growth will be adequate.   Of course, sufficient precipitation to support forest growth is assumed.   Where these moisture conditions prevail, there will also be present adequate nutritive elements in the soil.   The term "site" as used by foresters is partly a measure of soil moisture as influenced by top-layer and sublayer soil conditions.   A good site has plenty of moisture but is not saturated.   Too much or too little moisture in the soil makes a poor site.   Soil fertility in a forest is closely related to soil moisture.

Light, or the energy from the sun, is the motive power that enables all plants with green leaves to manufacture food.   Water from the roots and carbon dioxide from the air are united to form food compounds (starches and sugars) by a complicated process known as photosynthesis.   All life is dependent on this leaf factory.   Forest trees manufacture their own food and convert it into the woody structure of stem, bark, roots, branches, and crown.   The amount of sunlight reaching the crowns of forest trees and the abundance of moisture from the roots determine how much food forest trees manufacture and hence how fast they grow.   The size of the crowns of individual trees, in turn, determines whether the total growth potential of the forest is used in producing a great number or a relatively few stems per unit of area.

Nature's method of starting a forest on cutover or burned land, when abundant seed is available or where roots and stumps are left to sprout, is to carpet the soil with woody growth of shrubs and trees.   A veritable jungle results.   The young trees grow and, when not overcome by the shrubs, form thick stands.   Thousands of young trees fight for existence.   Where there is good soil moisture (on good sites), some trees quickly assume the ascendancy.   They grow ahead of

others less fortunate. Their tops reach up where they get the sunlight. They become dominant. Others, literally thousands, are
suppressed, covered up, overtopped, and eventually die. Between
the dominant and the suppressed are trees classified by foresters as
codominant and intermediate. These struggle on but grow slowly.
Some are fortunate and are able to push into the dominant class, but
the majority eventually are pushed into the suppressed class and die

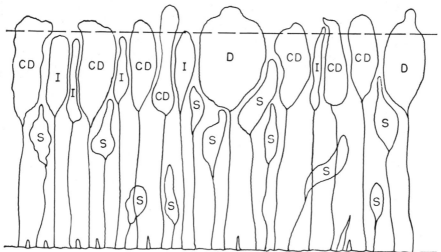

Fig. 48. Crown classes of forest trees: *D*, dominant; *CD*, codominant; *I*, intermediate; and
S, suppressed.

for lack of moisture and sunlight. The struggle goes on among the
dominants. As they grow in size and their crowns spread, they compete with one another and assume new positions of dominant, codominant, intermediate, and suppressed. This intense struggle goes on for
20 to 40 years. Partial victory has come to the 300 to 400 trees
remaining, spaced 10 to 12 ft. apart, but the struggle goes on. It is
less intensive now, but the same classification persists.

Figure 48 shows crown classes. The poorer the site, the more
difficulty the young trees have in arranging themselves into these
crown classes. Few trees are able to become dominant. Often complete stagnation seems to prevail for long periods. Planted trees
escape much of the early struggle, but as soon as their crowns meet,
the same process begins.

The competition results in surviving trees with straight single stems,
clear of lower limbs for one-third to two-thirds of their total height.

The lower limbs have been shaded until they have died and dropped off.   Clean, smooth boles are now present, ready to produce clear lumber as diameter growth continues.   Planted stands, because the trees do not grow so close together in early youth, sometimes fail to produce clear stems.

Tolerance is a useful term in talking about the light requirements. While all trees, to grow, must have sunlight on their crowns, the different tree species may vary considerably in their ability to endure shade, or, to put it another way, in their ability to function with differing intensities of light.   Hemlock and beech, for example, will live and grow slowly under partial shade of other trees.   Aspen, walnut, locust, yellow poplar, and most pines must have full overhead light or they soon die.   Other tree species are in between these extremes. Shade-enduring species are known as tolerants, those requiring full light are intolerants, and those in between are known as intermediates. Table 10 indicates the degree of tolerance of some of our common forest trees of the United States.

Tolerance is, of course, a relative term.   Some species are inclined to be more tolerant on good sites than on poor ones.   Young trees are more tolerant than older ones.   Good soil moisture apparently enables a tree to live under partial shade where it would die with less abundant moisture.   Intolerant trees grow best in even-aged stands. They produce clean boles much more readily than tolerant trees.   It will be advisable for the forest manager to make his own tolerance table for species with which he has to deal.   This can be done by observation or with the help of a local forester or the state forester.

The requirements of trees for moisture and light and their reactions to abundant or short supplies of one or both on different sites are the things to keep constantly in mind in all forest operations.   Moisture and light are now to be considered in their relation to the problems of thinning young stands to assist Nature to produce good trees, with clean boles, in the shortest time.   Thinning will ease the struggle of young dense stands and bring it to a climax in a shorter period than if Nature is left to her own slow processes.   These two forces will occupy a prominent place in this text in the discussion of all steps to be taken in developing farm woodlands.   Just now we are concerned with the step known as "thinning."

Cautions.   The purpose of thinning operations is to give the best trees and the best available species the growing space that they need

TABLE 10. SCALES OF TOLERANCE*

VERY TOLERANT		TOLERANT	
West	*East*	*West*	*East*
Yew	Southern white cedar	Port Orford cedar	White spruce
Engelmann's spruce	Balsam fir	Incense cedar	Red spruce
Alpine fir	Frazer fir	Blue spruce	Northern white cedar
White fir	Hemlock	Redwood	Beech
Red cedar			Sugar maple
Hemlock			Silver maple
Sitka spruce			Red maple
			Black gum
			White elm
			Cork elm
			Basswood
			Sycamore

INTERMEDIATE	
West	*East*
Douglas fir	Loblolly pine
Big-cone spruce	Scrub pine
Amabolis fir	Pitch pine
Grand fir	White pine
Noble fir	Chestnut
Yellow cypress	Cherry birch
Big tree	Yellow birch
Western white pine	Black walnut
	Umbrella tree
	Cucumber tree

INTOLERANT		VERY INTOLERANT	
West	*East*	*West*	*East*
Red fir	Jack pine	Alpine larch	Longleaf pine
Ponderosa pine	Red pine	Western larch	Shortleaf pine
Jeffrey pine	Scarlet oak	White-bark pine	Bald cypress
Sugar pine	White oak	Knob-cone pine	Tamarack
Bristle-cone pine	Chestnut oak	Foxtail pine	Black locust
	Mockernut hickory	Coulter pine	Willow
	Shagbark hickory	Limber pine	Cottonwood
	Butternut	Single-leaf pine	Large-tooth aspen
	Tulip	Pinon pine	
	Black cherry	Digger pine	
	White ash	Lodgepole pine	

* Adapted from *Foundations of Silviculture upon an Ecological Basis*, 2d ed., by James W. Toumey and Clarence F. Korstian; published by John Wiley & Sons, Inc., 1947.

for rapid growth. The removal of competing trees reduces the struggle for available moisture and light. Growth is concentrated on a relatively few stems instead of many. That will make marketable trees and more valuable products in much less time than if Nature is left to her own devices.

Thinning operations must be conducted cautiously, especially at first. Results must be watched and studied. Too much cutting will expose the selected trees to the risk of damage by wind, snow, and ice; to the risk of sunscald where thin-barked trees are suddenly exposed; to the risk of failure to produce clean boles (most likely with tolerant

Fig. 49. Thinning in twelve-year-old planted slash pine in Louisiana. (*Soil Conservation Service.*)

Products cut and values per acre at the farm were:

5.6 cords pulpwood @$6.20	=	$34.72
670 fence posts @ 0.11½	=	77.05
		$111.77

species); and to the risk of incomplete utilization of the productive power of the soil. On the other hand, too light a cutting may have little or no effect in stimulating the growth of the selected trees. A heavy thinning may prove to be just right in a stand on a good site, while the same degree of cutting on a poor site will prove to be injurious (Fig. 49).

The farmer or forest manager, keeping in mind general rules and principles for thinning operations, will learn how to thin by actually thinning his dense stands. That is one reason why he should be cautious and start on a small scale and watch results. The same advice is good for an experienced forester operating in a new territory. At best, thinning of timber stands is not an exact science. There is a great deal that foresters do not know about exactly how to conduct a thinning operation in a particular stand. The most experienced forester will have to do some guessing in planning the operation. One thing foresters do know. It is better to thin than not to thin even if mistakes are made. Usually the mistakes are not disastrous but

FIG. 50. Planted white pine in Vermont before thinning and pruning. (*Soil Conservation Service.*)

only disappointing. Nature goes right ahead filling gaps and covering up errors. The end result of thinning operations, where conscientiously carried out, is a better stand, faster growth, greater profit (Figs. 50 and 51).

General Rules for Thinning

1. Decide on the approximate spacing desired between selected trees (explained later).
2. Use the crop-tree method of selecting trees to be left. This means the best trees and the best species available at the approximate spacing decided upon. This usually means dominant and codominant trees.
3. Thin heavier on good than on poor sites; heavier with intolerant than with tolerant species.
4. The first thinning in any stand should be lighter than later ones. Be especially cautious in "stagnated" stands on poor sites.

5. Watch the edges of the stand, especially on windward sides. Keep a dense barrier to stop winds. This may mean heavy cutting or none at all, as explained later.

The *spacing requirements of forest trees* must be known or guessed at in order to conduct thinning operations. Numerous studies of forest stands have been made to determine in fully stocked even-aged stands

Fig. 51. Same stand as in Fig. 50 after thinning and after 250 trees per acre were pruned. (*Soil Conservation Service.*)

the number of trees and their average diameters at breast height to be found at different ages and on different sites. The examination of fully stocked stands has been for the purpose of learning the maximum number of trees that an acre of ground would support under a given set of conditions—age, species, site. It takes longer to grow trees to a specified diameter on poor than on good sites. The rate of growth also is influenced by the inherent growth qualities of the species of trees and by the *spacing of the trees* in the stand.

What the farmer wants to know when he starts to thin a dense stand of young trees in his woodland is how much space should be given each tree that he selects for further growth. In other words, how far apart should his good trees stand when he gets through thinning? It is evident that there is a minimum space that trees in crowded stands will tolerate and still stay alive, and a proper spacing that will allow them to grow and develop at the fastest rate of which the site is capable. In the latter case, the spacing may be so great that the trees fail to make clean boles. Also, the number of trees may easily be so few on a given area of land that maximum wood production is not attained. Fortunately, out of the welter of discussion among foresters about this question, have come some simple rules easy to apply. A forester in Texas has given us the answers.[1] He has applied the rules for a number of years in southern-pine and hardwood forests. Other foresters have tested the rules and found them applicable with slight modification to most of our forest types.

Spacing Rules

For most types in the eastern United States, on all sites, for all species, and for all ages, the dominant and codominant trees 6 in. and over d.b.h. will tolerate a spacing expressed by the formula $D + 4$. D is the diameter in inches at breast height, and 4 is a constant. For example, dominant and codominant trees 10 in. d.b.h. will tolerate a spacing of $10 + 4 = 14$ ft. between trees in the same height class. This is equivalent to saying that the minimum spacing for 10-in. trees is 14×14 or 196 sq. ft. of ground space. When they are spaced as closely as this, the stand needs thinning. The rule for thinning is to enlarge the space for each tree so that they stand $D + 6$ ft. apart, or, in the case just cited, 16 ft. apart, equivalent to 256 sq. ft. for each tree.

Figure 52 is a diagram of crowns of trees to show $D + 6$ spacing of dominant and codominant trees.

$D + 6$, then, for trees 6 in. and up breast high is the spacing goal to be aimed at. In the case of trees of different sizes, which is almost always the situation, the diameters at breast height of two trees to be left are averaged and the constant added. For example, two trees 6 and 10 in. d.b.h. should be spaced $(6 + 10/2) + 6 = 14$ ft. Two trees 8 and 12 in. should be spaced $(8 + 12/2) + 6 = 16$ ft. Remember, this applies to dominant and codominant trees; the others may or may not be removed, as will be explained later. It also applies on any site, to any species, and to any age. The scientific basis for this simple rule is not given here, but it is well supported by careful studies in many types of stands both hardwoods and conifers. The years required for the selected trees, after thinning by the $D + 6$ rule, to

[1] H. C. Mitchell, Regional Forester, Soil Conservation Service, Fort Worth, Texas.

enlarge their crowns and increase their diameters to the point where the spacing is once more reduced to $D + 4$ is the proper period between thinnings.   This is called the "cutting cycle."   For example, in a stand where the average diameter of trees left after thinning was 10 in., the trees are spaced on the average 16 ft. apart.   When the

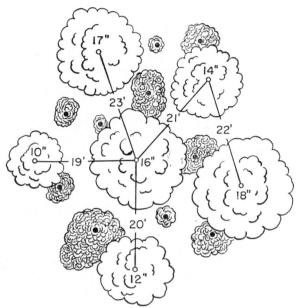

FIG. 52. Bird's eye view of tree crowns in a forest to show applications of spacing rule. (*Soil Conservation Service.*)

same trees grow to 12 in., they are spaced $D + 4$ (instead of $D + 6$) ft. apart, and it is time for another thinning (Fig. 53).

Since it is not possible actually to achieve the exact spacing theoretically desirable, the forest manager comes as close to it as possible.   He tries to reach average spacing in the forest in each small group of adjacent trees.   Also he will try to save the best individual trees and the best species for further growth even at some sacrifice of the theoretically desirable spacing.   Sometimes one tree may be entirely free of neighbors in one direction and be crowded on the opposite side. For example, if the spacing aimed at is 16 ft., an individual tree may have 20 ft. free of competition on one side and two trees as close as 12 ft. on the other.   The second thinning, of course, means a reselection of crop trees since a lesser number will be selected than was done the first time. The spacing per tree must be greater because the trees are larger.

The same spacing rule for thinning $(D + 6)$ is used for each site, good or poor, and for every species. Since growth response is better on good sites and with some species than under less favorable conditions, it follows that the elapsed time between thinnings (the cutting

FIG. 53. Second growth loblolly pine in Louisiana marked for thinning to D plus 6 spacing. (*Soil Conservation Service.*)

cycle) will vary by several years. This can be adjusted by cutting more conservatively under poor conditions as compared to good growing conditions, or an average period for the cutting cycle can be taken and followed. For example $D + 6$ cutting in southern pine is often assumed, under average site conditions found on farm woodlands, to require a 5-year cutting cycle. If farmers follow such a cutting cycle, they will find much less cutting is required to reach $D + 6$ spacing in making the second thinning on poor sites than on good ones. In other words, the general rule to cut more conservatively on poor than on good sites will be automatically taken care of.

Spacing Rules for the Western United States. The principles remain the same, but the constant in the formula is reduced. Research on the matter of a spacing formula to guide thinning operations is not complete.   Therefore, farm-woodland owners in the West would do well to check with local foresters about the spacing rule applicable to their woodlands.   These seem to be the spacing requirements in some Western forest types for trees *after thinning:*

Types	Spacing
True ponderosa pine type........................	$D + 4$
Mixed conifers of Northwest (white pine, larch, Douglas fir, ponderosa pine)........................	$D + 3$
West Coast Douglas fir and redwood..............	$D + 2$
For sapling stands anywhere under 6 in., unless otherwise advised by local forestry authorities, try	$D + 4$ in the East* $D + 2$ in the West

* $D + 6$ is theoretically correct even for sapling stands, but on account of usual crowded stands, lack of expression of dominance, and danger of wind or snow damage, first thinnings should be on a very conservative basis.

Two kinds of thinnings are usually recognized by foresters.   They are useful in describing operations.   *Thinnings from the top* (or above) mean

Fig. 54. Monterey-pine plantation in California thinned to D plus 4 spacing; pruned to 8-ft. height.   (*Soil Conservation Service.*)

cutting more or less of the dominant and codominant trees. *Thinnings from below* mean cutting more or less of the intermediate and suppressed trees.

2. Deciding When to Start Thinning

One important reason for starting a thinning operation is that some of the trees have reached a size from which usable or salable products can be produced. This is the economic reason for thinning. Merchantable pulpwood or mine timber can be produced from trees 5 to 12 in. d.b.h. In some localities conversion wood is used for fiberboard and insulating material. Trees down to 4 in. d.b.h. will qualify for this product. Most of the hardwoods, such as ash, maple, basswood, beech, birch, cherry, elm, gum, poplar, oak, hickory, sycamore, and most of the conifers, especially spruce, balsam, hemlock, Douglas fir, and pine are accepted as pulpwood. Not all are salable in a particular local market, so inquiry must be made before starting cutting operations about species, sizes, and specifications acceptable to local mills. If the thinning operation will produce only trees 5 to 7 in. d.b.h., the pulpwood produced will be small in average size. Be sure that it will be accepted.

Posts can be made from trees 4 to 6 in. d.b.h. Acceptable fuel can be made from most species. Small material will often make satisfactory garden stakes for tomatoes and beans or posts for electric fences.

From the standpoint of the rapid development of a dense young forest, a stand that has grown to the point where usable or salable products can be cut has waited too long for cultural treatment. Thinning should start, if the most rapid growth is to be obtained, at a much earlier stage. If the stand is not too dense, less than 2,000 trees per acre, or about 4- to 5-ft. spacing between trees, an early thinning before merchantable products can be cut often is not needed.

The best guide in deciding when to start thinning in any stand is the *condition of the trees*. It is time to start thinning:

1. When the crowns of adjacent dominant and codominant trees touch or interlace.
2. When the live crowns of the best trees are less than 40 percent of their total height.
3. In mixed stands, when the best species are being injured by crowding.
4. In any stand that has stagnated because of overdense stocking.

Fig. 55. Eight-year-old Monterey-pine plantations in California before thinning. (*Soil Conservation Service.*)

Fig. 56. Same stand as that in Fig. 55 after thinning and pruning. (*Soil Conservation Service.*)

Tolerance and growth energy are rough guides for both weeding and thinning. The greater the tolerance of the species and the greater the vigor of the best trees in the stand, the greater will be the response to early thinning. This is especially true of hardwoods. On good

FIG. 57. Twenty-year-old red-pine plantation in New York after thinning. Products cut were sold to a hunt club for jump ways, posts, and rails. (*Soil Conservation Service.*)

sites and with tolerant species such as maple, beech, basswood, hemlock, and spruce, good growth response has been obtained from early thinnings. A local tolerance table should be used rather than one made on a regional basis (Figs. 55 and 56).

Plantations usually require thinning at a somewhat later stage than natural reproduction. This is because fewer trees make up the stand, and the struggle for light and moisture does not become intense in the early stages. Natural reproduction often requires thinning at the age of 5 to 10 years, while plantations normally will grow for 15 to 25 years before thinning is required (Figs. 50, 51, and 57).

3. Gauging the Amount to Cut

If the trees to be removed are too small to be usable or salable, the least amount of labor will, of course, be spent consistent with the purpose of the thinning.   If the area in need of thinning is large, more than 4 to 5 acres, try several methods on small portions—plots of ¼ acre each—and watch results for three or more years before undertaking large-scale operations.   Always seek local forestry advice before starting thinning operations.   Study the stand to determine whether all or only part of it requires thinning and whether or not heavy thinning is needed on some portions and light thinning on others.

Remember that there must be enough cutting to free the crowns of the selected trees; otherwise the work will accomplish nothing.   At the same time, enough understory must be left to aid in cleaning the boles of crop trees.

The question of how many years before you plan to make a second cut brings up the question of how much to cut now.   Suppose you tentatively plan an interval of 5 years.   Look at the rate of growth of side branches on good trees already exposed to light.   If they grow 6 in. in 1 year, in 5 years they would expand 2½ ft.   Therefore a clearance of 5 ft. between crowns of crop trees would be sufficient. That growth means a very good site.   Crop trees could be spaced a distance of 5 ft. plus the average width of present crowns.   A poor site might require only half that much clearance to allow for 5 years' growth.   This is another way to test the vigor of the growth of your trees.

So the *amount to cut* depends on conditions in the stand.   Light cuts repeated at intervals of 3 to 5 years are generally considered to be safer than heavy cuts at longer intervals.   For one thing, light cuts avoid the danger of heavy damage by ice and snow which sometimes occurs if trees previously crowded are suddenly exposed.   Light cuts give the trees a chance to adjust themselves gradually to the new conditions.   For another thing, light cuts can always be followed by heavier ones if the trees do not respond.   The results will speak for themselves.

If the thinning is one where products for use or sale can be produced, the situation is quite different.   If products cut in thinnings "from below" are merchantable, these can be added to those "from above" to make the total cut, provided this does not open the stand too much. The suppressed and intermediate trees, or part of them, may be needed as "trainers" to clean the boles of crop trees. In any case a good rule is not to cut more than 30 percent of the total volume of the stand at one time.

A rough way to find out what this would amount to is to lay out a few square-rod plots and count the trees in each d.b.h. class. For example, suppose the average of 4 plots showed three 4-in. trees, two 6-in. trees, one-quarter 8-in. trees, total $5\frac{1}{4}$. This would indicate $5\frac{1}{4} \times 160$ or 840 trees per acre. Volumes compare roughly as the square of the diameters. Relative volumes would then be:

$$
\begin{aligned}
&\text{4-in. trees, } 3 \times 16 = 48\text{, or } 35 \text{ percent of the volume} \\
&\text{6-in. trees, } 2 \times 36 = 72\text{, or } 53 \text{ percent of the volume} \\
&\text{8-in. trees, } \tfrac{1}{4} \times 64 = 16\text{, or } 12 \text{ percent of the volume} \\
&\phantom{\text{8-in. trees, }} \text{Total} = 136\text{, or } 100 \text{ percent of the volume}
\end{aligned}
$$

If 30 percent of the total volume is to be a. guide, most of the cut would likely have to come from the 4- and 6-in. trees because, presumably, the 8-in. trees would be the most desirable to reserve for crop trees. Of course there probably would be individual exceptions. Approximately one-half of the 6-in. trees, plus a few of lower diameters, would add up to the limitation of 30 percent of the volume.

Actually, this would be tested by sample marking, using the D-plus rule as a guide. If the trees marked for cutting under this system failed to add up to 30 percent of the volume of the stand, then abide by the sample marking. The D-plus rule is a safer guide than any volume limitation.

In any case, you now know approximately how many trees and of what sizes the thinning will produce. Suppose the result is one-half of the 6-in. trees or a total of 160 trees to be cut. The volume tables in the appendix indicate that it takes from 17 to 24 trees of this size to make a cord of pulpwood, depending upon the type of timber. If the stand is southern pine, the pulpwood cut would be $\frac{160}{20}$, or 8 cords per acre. If it is Douglas fir 60 ft. tall, the result would be about the same. Spruce would amount to 6 or 7 cords. The total merchantable stand (6- and 8-in. trees) would be about 20 cords (basis, southern pine). The proposed cutting would therefore be $\frac{8}{20}$ or 40 percent of the merchantable stand.

If only 6- and 8-in. trees are salable, the 4-in. trees could be left except where they interfere with the growth of crop trees. The forest manager now knows about how to cut his stand and about what volume he can cut. He is in a position to seek a market and negotiate a sales contract.   Naturally he would not want to guarantee delivery of 8 cords of pulpwood for each acre cut because his estimate, on the above basis, may prove to be a little wide of the mark.   It could be 30 percent or more high or low, depending on how carefully he selected his sample plots and how representative they proved to be.

A word about the spacing rule.   Any spacing rule should be applied only as a guide.   The condition of the crop tree selected—its species, its form, its vigor—is all important.   If the rule says 13-ft. spacing, pick the best tree as near that distance from other crop trees as possible, but vary the distance in order to leave good trees.   Silviculture is a matter of individual tree selection, and the success of forestry depends upon the sum of the growth of those selected trees.   A spacing rule is a useful mechanical guide, but it does not think; the thinking must be done by the forest manager.

In any case, the farmer or forest manager must decide how and how much to cut.   Seek forestry advice if it is available, but no forester can tell exactly how much to cut or exactly how to do it.   Forestry research has not progressed that far.   One thing is sure.   If a stand is too thick (and that is easy to determine), any cutting carefully planned and carried out will do more good than harm.   Mistakes are likely to be on the conservative side, but whether the cutting proves to be too heavy or too light, the error can be corrected in later thinnings.   Nature has a wonderful way, through growth, of covering up and mending false steps in cultural operations.

4. Making the Thinning

The appropriate spacing of crop trees has already been decided. Also, it has been decided whether or not the cutting is to be primarily from above or from below.   In either case, the first job is to select the crop trees to be left and put labels on them that can be seen clearly from one direction.   Labels can be white or colored paint, white or colored paper, or chalk.   Paint can be applied with a brush or a paint gun (Fig. 75).   Pieces of paper (preferably cardboard) can be fastened with tacks or small nails, or a common desk paper fastener, using staples, is suitable.

Go through the forest in parallel strips about as far apart as the spacing distance between crop trees.   Two men, or a man and a boy, are best for this job, one to select the trees and keep directions and the other to label the trees.   Where salable products are to be removed from "below" but some of the dominant trees are needed to raise the quality of the products, this fact will affect the selection of crop trees. Some sacrifice of trees desirable to leave, in order to help pay for the thinning, may be advisable. How far to go in sacrificing the best crop trees in order to make the thinning pay its way must be decided by the forest manager. It is his forest; therefore, the decision must be his. The important point is that he should recognize the sacrifice even though he feels that it is necessary. In that case he will substitute codominant or even intermediate trees for some of the dominants in the selection of crop trees. In other words, he makes the best selections he can under the limitations he has imposed upon himself.

Cutting may begin after the crop trees are clearly labeled so that the workmen cannot mistake them. Sometimes it may be advisable to follow the selection of crop trees by marking each tree to be cut into the salable products. This will avoid cutting trees not usable. If this is done, the trees for cutting should be marked with an ax blaze at breast height, usually on two sides.

After the merchantable trees are cut and the products removed, an inspection of results should be made by the forest manager. If the crop trees have been sufficiently freed of adjacent tree growth so that he is satisfied, then the thinning operation is over. There may be some wolf trees to girdle or poison and perhaps some slash to lop and scatter, but the main job is finished.

Where no utilization of the trees to be cut can be made or where such utilization is insufficient to free the crowns of the crop trees, this crown-freeing job must be done. The forest manager must handle this himself or leave it to a trained subordinate. Only two or three workmen can be supervised by one trained man because the trees *not* to cut are as important as those to cut. Each selected crop tree becomes the center of a separate operation. Only enough trees are removed to free the crown as planned. All others are left unless there is a use for the products. Dead trees may be removed, but this is not essential. Diseased trees should be cut except where there are so many that their removal would open up the stand too much. In that case, it is better to leave most of them for later cutting.

The *disposal* of *cut trees* having no useful products is another question for the farmer or forest manager to decide. Usually because of the fire risk and sometimes because of the danger of attracting bark

beetles, it is better to drag the trees out of the woods.   A good way of
using small stuff is by converting it into chips with a portable chipper.
Chips are useful as bedding for livestock, as organic matter for cultivated fields and pastures, and as mulch.   More about this in Chap.
7.   If not usable for any purpose, perhaps forcing the cut trees to lie
flat on the ground will be sufficient.

Tools used for thinning work may be machetes for slashing and
hacking small stuff, or double-bit or pole axes.   In some cases brush
hooks are suitable.   Experiments have been conducted using various
types of power equipment which either drags material not wanted out
by the roots or cuts it off with knifelike blades or with saws.   Such
equipment is still very much in the experimental stage.   Such
machinery is chiefly useful only on noncommercial thinnings or
weedings.   Many farmers may be able to reduce costs of some types
of thinning operations by adaptations of farm or road machinery.

5. Protecting the Edges of the Stand

This subject will be mentioned many times in the pages of this book.
The supply of soil moisture is one of the things the forest manager can
influence.   One way is to keep drying winds from full access to the
interior of the forest.   This can be done by blocking the edges of the
forest by means of heavy vegetation.   The very first cultural measures
should be conducted with a view to control of soil moisture.   On the
edges of the stand, especially on the windward sides, cutting should
cease, or its character should be changed, to encourage the growth
of a dense wind barrier of trees and shrubs.

Thinning operations open the overhead canopy and permit the
sun's warmth and drying effect to reach the forest floor.   Subsequent
vigorous growth of the crop trees soon closes the crown cover.   The
sun's energy is then used by the leafy structure of the trees to manufacture food for tree growth, concentrated on the selected trees instead
of being divided among many.   The sun no longer reaches the forest
floor to sap it of moisture by evaporation.   If the wind cannot enter
from the sides, the forest manager has done all that he can to conserve the soil moisture that his trees require for good growth.   The
wind is a most effective drying agent.   To keep it out of the growing
forest is an important part of forest management.   Here are some of
the measures available to the forest manager.   The objective of
thinning operations is twofold: first, shade the boles of crop trees so
that lower side branches will die and drop off, thus producing clean

stems; and, second, clear away growth from the upper crowns to give them a chance to expand. The opposite procedure is required at the edges to stop the wind. Develop trees with luxurious limb growth from top to bottom, supplemented by shrubs in the understory.

In *young dense stands* this means selecting trees with full foliage and freeing them from competing trees so that they will continue to present a hedgelike wind barrier. Favor the tolerant species and conifers as opposed to hardwoods. The wind barrier should be from 1 to 2 rods wide on the windward edges and half that width on other sides. Leave all shrubs unless they compete with full-foliage conifers.

In *older stands*, where a dense border has not been grown naturally, it is often difficult by cutting, to induce the needed thick growth. One method, in hardwoods, is to cut trees and let the stumps sprout, later selecting those sprouts most suitable for the purpose. Sometimes it is worth while to plant one or two rows of conifers just outside the limits of present growth, spaced 8 by 8 ft. or 10 by 10 ft. Another method, especially on the border between the forest and cultivated land, is to plant a rod-wide strip to shrubs. If shrubs are selected for their fruits and blossoms, the border will have particular value in providing wildlife food and in adding decorative effects to the woodland scene. Where possible, cultivation of such a planted border will speed its growth. Shrubs and evergreen trees can be planted at the edge of the forest to supplement the growth of established shrubs and stump sprouts (Fig. 20).

Whatever method is used, the end result should be a thick tree-and-shrub border to act as an effective wind barrier. Such a border is desirable at the edge of all woodlands and especially those subject to severe winds or those on soils naturally deficient in soil moisture. So far, in the United States, the dense border is a very much neglected forestry practice. It is one that is essential to intensive forestry. That is the kind of forestry with which this book is concerned and the kind that farmers particularly are in a position to practice. Dense borders to woodlands conserve soil moisture and help forest trees grow; they also encourage wild birds and animals; both are worthwhile farm objectives.

6. Observing Thinning Operations of the Past

A few records of thinning operations, methods, and costs follow:

Thinning Red Pine in Minnesota. A natural stand twenty-three years old, 2,800 to 5,600 trees per acre averaging 1 to 2 in.

d.b.h., was thinned in 1927 using 6-, 8-, and 10-ft. spacing of crop trees.   After the 1927 thinning, there were 1,254 trees per acre, 6- by 6-ft. spacing.   Seventeen years later, in 1944, there were 837 trees per acre, 7- by 7-ft. spacing.   Wider spacings produced larger trees, but the trees were limby.   The 6- by 6-ft. spacing (about $D + 4$) gave the best all-around results.   The next thinning can wait until a light pulpwood cutting can be made.

Fig. 58. Fifty-year-old Douglas-fir stand from which a light thinning has been made. Part of the cut trees have been made into fuel wood.   (*Soil Conservation Service.*)

Plantations of red pine will produce pulpwood in 30 years.   Natural stands (unless thinned at early ages) require 35 to 40 years.   A red-pine plantation spaced 8 by 8 ft. at 30 years of age on the Superior National Forest is reported in thrifty condition, but *does not need thinning*.

Thinning Dense Jack-pine Seedling Stands in the Lake States. In stands five years old with 10,000 and more stems about 1 in. d.b.h. per acre, thinnings were tried using 4-, 6-, 8-ft. spacing.   The latter proved to be entirely too wide.   Work was done with 2¼-lb. axes and cost: 4- by 4-ft. spacing, 4.22 man-days per acre; 6- by 6-ft. spacing, 4.75 man-days per acre.   The best time for work is September to April—there is less insect damage.

Thinning Douglas Fir on the West Coast. Thinnings and how to conduct them are reported to be more or less experimental. Therefore no thinning is recommended except where usable products can be obtained. This may be at any age. For example, in second-growth stands, Christmas trees can be obtained from stands five to fifteen years old; fuel, car stakes, pulpwood from stands twenty to twenty-five years and older; poles, ties, car decking from stands thirty to forty years and older; piling and saw logs from stands forty-five to fifty years and older.

Thinning Loblolly Pine in Even-aged Stands. On old fields very dense stands develop, and unless thinned, serious stagnation of growth results. Typical stands are shown in Table 11.

TABLE 11. TYPICAL OLD-FIELD STANDS OF LOBLOLLY PINE

Age, years	Average No. of trees per acre	Range in d.b.h., in.	Average d.b.h., in.
10	2,200	0–6	2
20	800	2–11	6
30	420	3–16	8
40	280	3–20	10
50	205	4–23	12
60	160	4–25	13

Recommendations for thinning, based on experiments of the Southern Forest Experiment Station, where both saw timber and pulpwood are desirable products and wood removed in thinnings is usable or salable, are as follows:

1. Wait until most of the dominant trees are clear or have dead branches for about 17 ft. (1-log length), or prune the crop trees to 17-ft. height after thinning.
2. Thin on crop-tree basis. Remove only trees directly interfering with the selected crop trees.
3. Thinnings have the most marked beneficial effect on the growth rate of remaining trees when made very early in the life of the stand. First thinnings should begin when dominant trees are about 3 to 6 in. d.b.h. (about 10 to 15 years).
4. First thinnings can be postponed until dominant trees are 6 to 9 in. d.b.h. (about 15 to 25 years) if there is a use for wood cut at this age and not at the earlier age.

5. Thinnings that remove trees competing directly with crop trees increase the growth of the crop trees if made heavy enough and often enough. Thinnings that remove only the poorest, smallest trees seem unlikely to be of benefit to the crop trees. They should not be cut unless usable or salable.

6. Thinnings give far greater beneficial results on good than on poor sites. Thin experimentally, if at all, on poor sites and watch results.

Thinning Young Second-growth Hardwoods, Wisconsin. An eleven-year-old stand with 2,810 trees per acre, 0.6 in. and over d.b.h., dominant trees 2 in. d.b.h., 21 ft. tall, on a good site contained the following species: sugar maple, 67 percent; elm, 15 percent; white ash, 5 percent; ironwood, 5 percent; basswood, cherry, and others, 8 percent.

Thinnings were on basis of selected crop trees, leaving 320 to 400 per acre about 11 by 11 ft. Two methods of cutting were to (1) remove everything for 2½ ft. from crop tree; (2) remove eveything for 5 ft. from crop tree. Scattered wolf trees were girdled.

The 5-ft. clearance gave the best growth response. Maple and elm showed best growth, basswood a poor third. Ash and black cherry showed a very poor response. The 2½-ft. clearance showed no increased growth rate but a much better stand, with a higher percentage of ash.

Costs: girdling, 3.2 man-hours per acre; thinning, 2½ ft., 10 man-hours per acre; 5 ft., 24.8 man-hours per acre.

Thinnings in Cedar Swamps. A forty-five-year-old stand on a relatively well-drained site with over 7,500 trees, 1 to 7 in. d.b.h. per acre, was thinned in 1935 to 4- by 5-ft. spacing, leaving 2,140 trees per acre. This is approximately $D + 4$ spacing after thinning. Products removed were 590 poles 2 to 3 in. d.b.h. plus many trees suitable for fencing. Forty-three percent of the volume was removed.

In 8 years' growth, the volume was 85 percent of that on the unthinned stand. After 8 years, the thinned plot contained 320 trees 5 to 8 in. d.b.h. The unthinned contained only 80 trees of this size.

On a wet swamp, thinning did no good. No cost data is available, but the statement has been made that thinnings as above can be made at a small profit.

Thinning in Thirteen-year-old Shortleaf Pine Plantation, Illinois. The original stand contained 1,126 trees per acre, on a good site, with 850 dominant and codominant trees per acre, averaging about 4½ in. d.b.h., 25 to 30 ft. tall. It was thinned in 1948—about 25 percent of the volume was cut, or 207 trees per acre. The thinning was on a crop-tree basis; 200 dominant and codominant trees were cut, leaving 650, spaced about 8 by 8 ft. or about $D + 4$. Products removed were 3.7 cords or 240 fence posts 7 ft. by 3 in. and larger, worth $12 stumpage.

Good growth response resulted from the thinning, but crop trees will have to be pruned to make clear butt logs.

TABLE 12. THINNING YOUNG SLASH PINE

(1)		(2)	(3)	(4)
Approx. size of average dominant and codominant trees		Recommendation: Thin if—	Trees per acre to leave	Average spacing after thinning, ft.
D.b.h., in.	Total height, ft.			
Under 2½	Under 15	(1) Over 5,000 trees per acre, or (2) Less than 40% of total ht. in crowns of dominant and codominant trees	600 to 800	7½ to 8½ $D + 5$ to $D + 7$
2¼ to 4	15 to 30	(1) Over 1,500 trees per acre (2) Less than 40% crown, etc.	400 to 800	7½ to 10½ $D + 4$ to $D + 6$
4½ to 5½	30 to 40	(1) Commercially feasible to leave stand in col. (3) (2) Less than 33% crown, etc.	300 to 600	8½ to 12 $D + 4$ to $D + 6$
6 to 8	40 to 50	(1) Usable volume of products can be removed (2) And stand col. (3) can be left	200 to 400	10½ to 15 $D + 4$ to $D + 7$

AUTHOR'S NOTE: From these data it appears that $D + 6$ spacing as an average would not be far wrong.

Thinning in the Southern Appalachian Forests. One thinning in young hardwood, when dominant and codominant trees are 5 to

Fig. 59. Thinning and improvement cutting in hardwood forest in Michigan. Split white-oak posts were part of the products. (*Soil Conservation Service.*)

Fig. 60. Young stand of ponderosa pine in Montana thinned for corral poles and fuel. (*Soil Conservation Service.*)

8 in. d.b.h., is usually sufficient. (NOTE: This does not include possible earlier weedings.)

In yellow poplar, dominance is asserted early and thinning is rarely advisable until stands pass twenty years. After this age, thinnings can advantageously be made to increase crown space for the best trees.

Spacing recommended for mixed hardwood indicates thinning to $D + 6$ would be correct; for yellow poplar the trees will stand closer spacing, $D + 4$ or $D + 5$.

7. Applying Thinning Principles to All Cutting Operations

So far the discussion of thinning has been treated as a distinct operation to be undertaken or not as the forest manager wishes. That is partly true, of course, because young stands are often entirely separate and distinct from other parts of the woodland. However, except where clear cutting is employed, the principles of spacing requirements of forest trees must be applied in all types of cutting operations. What is referred to later as improvement cutting (Chap. 6) is actually in large part the problem of choosing the right trees properly spaced for the best growth. Clumps or patches of timber will be found that require thinning; spacing of the trees to leave, based on moisture and light requirements, must be studied and spacing rules applied. All cultural operations as well as harvest cuttings must consider the individual needs of each tree in the stand. In fact, all silviculture is a problem of spacing individual trees in the forest. The end result sought is the mass of trees that make up the stand, but the approach is the requirements for moisture and light of each separate tree. Limitations on the amount to cut in order to build up or to maintain the growing stock, and thus produce a sustained yield, often call a halt on thinning as well as other types of cutting. This will be explained in Chap. 6, but such limitations do not affect the application of the spacing principles. They only spread the cutting over a period of years to adjust it to the labor load of the farm or to the growth of wood volume produced annually by the forest (Fig. 60).

SUPPLEMENTARY ACTIVITIES

Getting Acquainted with Trees, Crown Classes

1. Pick any woods with complete cover. Walk through it in straight lines and tally, on a strip 2 rods wide (16½ ft.), each side of your line.

Tabulate the information on a form like this:

	Number of dominants	Number of codominants	Number of intermediates	Number of suppressed
Actual tally..............				
Number per average acre....				

2. Use an assistant.   Either measure the linear distance or determine it by pacing.

3. Figure the acres or fractions of acres in your strip.   Multiply your linear distance in rods by 2.   Divide this by 160; the result is the acres in your line on which you counted crown classes.   Record the number of trees in each crown class for an average acre in the last line of the above table.

Testing the D-plus Rule for Spacing Trees to Leave in Thinning Stands

Pick a pole stand (trees 6 to 14 in. d.b.h.).

1. Lay out a $\frac{1}{5}$-acre circular plot (52.7 ft. radius; see Chap. 6).

2. Choose a tree for the center; measure with a tape 2 radii from center tree to circumference.   Mark the two points on the circumference by flags on trees or any other means.

3. Measure only dominant and codominant trees within the plot.   Use a diameter tape, caliper, cruiser's stick, or an ordinary linen tape; measure the circumference and divide by 3; result is approximate d.b.h.   That will do for this study.   Use a record something like this:

D.b.h., in.	Number of trees, dominants and codominants only	Number of trees to leave after thinning, D-plus spacing rule*
6		
7		
8		
9		
10		
11		
12		
13		
14		
Totals......		

* Use $D + 6$ in eastern United States and whatever spacing rule is appropriate if you live in the West.

4. Record in col. (2) all trees of each d.b.h., dominants and codominants. Record in col. (3) all that should be left, according to the spacing rule.   Mark

the trees listed in col. (3) with paper fastened with a desk stapling machine (or designate by any convenient method).

5. If all unlabeled trees were cut, do you think the marked trees would have a better chance to grow?

6. On the basis of this $\frac{1}{5}$-acre sample, how many trees could be cut in a thinning per acre?

7. What would be about their average size in inches d.b.h.?

8. What could they be used for on the farm?

9. Would they make salable products? If so, what products? What would they be worth in the pile where a truck could get them?

5. Pruning Tree Crops

PRUNING IS THE OPERATION of removing the limbs, living or dead, along the lower trunk of living forest trees, in order to aid Nature in producing clear, knot-free lumber from this part of the tree stems. In the original forest, Nature produced trees with clear stems for lengths of three to sometimes as many eight or ten 16-ft. logs. The process required a very long time and very large trees. The big trees in the forests of the Pacific Coast have long clear boles, and they reach sizes of 48 in. d.b.h. and upward. The inner portion of the big clear logs, however, may be full of knots, producing only low-grade lumber. The same thing was true of the famous white pine trees of the original forests of the Northeast and the lake states. The clear boles of the virgin forest were produced by natural pruning (Figs. 47 and 62).

In the managed forests of today, few owners can afford to wait for Nature unaided to produce the clear stems and the big trees of the original forest. Besides, Nature's method is a very wasteful one. Tremendous quantities of wood were lost through the death and decay of competing trees in the process of bringing the relatively few crop trees to maturity. Management, according to the principles of forestry, attempts to aid Nature in arriving at a comparable result in a much shorter time and without the loss of wood volume through the intervening years until the crop trees mature. The ways of aiding Nature are through the cultural operations—weeding, thinning, pruning. The latter is the means of producing clear boles on trees 12 to 24 in. d.b.h. at the time of harvest. By removing the limbs from the lower trunk of crop trees when they are young—usually less than 8 in.—one or sometimes two logs of knot-free lumber are produced. The quality of the wood product is therefore raised. The forest manager is rewarded by a higher average price of his product (Fig. 61).

Pruning is a present investment for the sake of increased future profits. There are few cultural operations in the practice of forestry

132

that offer greater rewards. Usually only trees destined to make large poles or saw logs are pruned, but there is much to be said in favor of pruning trees to be cut for such products as pulpwood or mine timbers.

The theory of pruning is very simple. Saw logs are commonly

FIG. 61. White-pine plantation, Superior National Forest, Minnesota. Pruned at seventeen and twenty years of age. (*U.S. Forest Service.*)

graded 1, 2, and 3. Number 1 grade contains the high-grade clear logs with a thick layer of knot-free wood. Numbers 2 and 3 are the lower grades. Grade 1 logs are worth about four times as much as grade 2 logs and from six to twenty times the price of grade 3 logs. Values per acre of $100 greater from pruned stands over unpruned stands are predicted.

From 25 to 50 percent of the total board-foot volume of trees is found in the butt logs. In a specific example, the values would work out to be as follows:

Assumption: Grade 1 logs worth $50.00, other logs worth $12.50.

Butt log 25 percent of total value of each M ft. b.m.:

$$25 \text{ percent of } \$50 \quad = \$12.50$$
$$75 \text{ percent of } \$12.50 = \$ \ 9.37$$
$$\text{Total value} = \$21.87 \text{ per M ft. b.m.}$$

Increased value due to pruning $9.37 or $21.87/$12.50 = 1.73.

FIG. 62. Clear No. 1 logs in the lower portion of these hardwood trees produced by natural pruning (Indiana). (*Soil Conservation Service.*)

If the butt log represents 50 percent of the total value, the average value would become $31.25 per M ft. b.m., and the increased value because of pruning $18.75 or 2.5 times unpruned value. A case is cited from New England where white pine trees were pruned to a height of 17 ft. and harvested 30 years later. The value of the pruned logs was $45.10 as compared to $29.90 for unpruned logs. The relation was 1.5 to 1.0.

Weeding and thinning speed up the growth of crop trees. They are given more sun and moisture—more room to grow—and consequently the process of natural pruning is slowed down or stopped. Limbs persist that must be removed to improve quality. Any forest owner who can invest the labor in pruning will be rewarded by greater profit at harvest time. However, pruning must be done at the right stage in stand development, with the right species, and with the right tools. These details affect costs and final returns. They will be discussed in the following pages under these headings:

1. Choosing Tools and Methods
2. Pruning Coniferous Stands
3. Pruning Hardwood Stands
4. Protecting Forest Edges
5. Comparing the Results of Experimental Pruning of Different Species

1. Choosing Tools and Methods

Since the objective of pruning is to produce a clean, smooth bole, remove limbs carefully so as to permit rapid healing of the wounds. The growth of the trees in diameter results in covering the limb scars with wood and bark. The closer to the trunk the limb is severed and the smoother the scar, the more rapidly will the healing process be. Hence a saw is the safest tool to use; a sharp ax is good in the hands of a skillful axman but dangerous with all others; a heavy club does a fairly satisfactory job in removing dead limbs, and it results in low costs.

Do not reduce the length of the live crowns of the trees being pruned too much. Otherwise the rate of tree growth will suffer. The general rule is never, at one pruning, remove limbs a distance of more than two-thirds the total height of the trees or more than one-half the live crowns. The elapsed time between prunings usually should be from 5 to 10 years. Two stages in pruning operations in the same stand are recommended as follows: (1) When crop trees are 3 to 5 in. d.b.h. and 20 to 25 ft. tall, remove not to exceed one-third the live crowns or a distance of 6 to 8 ft. from the ground. (2) When crop trees are 6 to 10 in. d.b.h. and 35 to 40 ft. in height, remove limbs a distance of 17 ft. along the trunk. This will clear a 16-ft. butt log.

Most pruning is confined to the butt log, but sometimes two log lengths are pruned. A third stage is then introduced. If the crop trees have already reached the 6- to 10-in. size without pruning, the first stage has passed and pruning is conducted on the basis of the second stage.   Be careful, however, not to remove more than one-half the live crowns.   If this does not produce the 17-ft. lengths of clean bole, then follow with another pruning about 10 years later. The foregoing are general rules to be modified somewhat as applied to some species as discussed later.

Deciding on How Many Trees to Prune.   Only crop trees are eligible for pruning, that is, trees that are prospects for producing saw logs.   In the first stage, obviously, it is difficult to choose the exact trees that you think will make final crop trees.   Many things can happen to the prospects, and so it is best to be very liberal in the choice of crop trees; for another reason, too, it is wise to prune a large number of trees.   Removing limbs up to 6 or 8 ft. is a cheap operation because all work can be done from the ground.   The pruning makes access to the thick stand easy.   It removes part of the fire hazard and reduces the cost of later thinnings—part of the swamping is already accomplished.   Where pulpwood is marketed as an inter-mediate crop, the clean butt logs enhance the value of the pulpwood. In the second and third stage, pruning must be conducted from a ladder or by means of pole saws, and so the number of trees pruned is more restricted.   In the larger sizes, also, it is easier to pick final crop trees.

The numbers to be pruned will probably work out about as follows:

Stage 1.   Small trees, thick stands.   Prune a minimum of 200 to 250 trees, spaced 12 to 15 ft. apart.

Stage 2.   Larger trees, up to 10 in.   Prune a maximum of 100 trees, spaced about 20 ft. apart.

Stage 3.   Same trees as stage 2, but grown to 12 or 14 in.   Prune a maximum of 75 trees, spacing about 24 ft. apart.

Pruning Only on Better Sites.   The success of the pruning operation depends a good deal on the growth response of the trees.   As already pointed out, it is essential to have the pruning wounds quickly heal.   If they do not, insect and fungus diseases may effect entrance through the wounds.   The operation then may be more harmful than helpful.   Therefore choose only thrifty, vigorous trees to prune.   This means that pruning should be confined to the better sites, those that grow trees relatively fast.   We are sure that it pays good dividends in thrifty young stands. It is doubtful that pruning will pay where growing conditions are poor. If doubtful about how your stand will respond, try pruning on a small scale and watch results. If the wounds heal quickly and completely in a few years, it is safe to prune on a larger scale.

Developing Technique. Cut all limbs as nearly as possible flush with the trunk. Painting wounds is not necessary for conifers; it is often advisable for hardwoods. Remove both dead and live branches; the scars made in removing the latter usually heal more rapidly than scars made in removing dead limbs.

Limit the size of limbs to be removed to a 'maximum of 2 in. at the base. Choose trees with this in mind. If an occasional limb larger than 2 in. is unavoidable, make two cuts, the first one several inches from the trunk and the second flush with the trunk. This will avoid injury to the cambium when the limb falls.

Prune only when the growth is dormant. Injury to the growing tissues is less likely when trees are dormant than if pruned during the active season of growth.

Selecting Tools. For first-stage pruning, when the operator can reach all limbs from the ground, the curved pruning saw is suitable.

Fig. 63. A curved pruning saw. Blade 1½ in. wide at handle, 14 in. long, 7 points, and reversed teeth. (*Henry Diston & Sons.*)

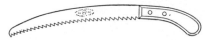

It can be obtained in any desired length (Fig. 63). For the second-stage pruning, the operator must use either a handsaw from a ladder or a pole pruning saw with a 7-ft. or longer pole (Fig. 64). For pruning higher than one 16-ft. log, considerable care and ingenuity are required. Normally, it is not advisable to prune more than the butt log because of the cost, but this is something for each forest manager to decide. If he is trying to grow trees to a 24-in. d.b.h. size or larger on a good site and a good species like white pine, southern pine, sugar pine, Douglas fir, or the better hardwoods, it may be a good gamble. It will certainly raise the quality of the product. It is a question of labor investment against the increased returns at harvest time.

High pruning must be done from a ladder, with a combination of ladder and pole saw, or by climbing the tree and pruning limbs on the way down.   In the latter case the limbs must be stout enough safely to hold the operator (Figs. 65 and 66).

For low pruning from the ground, heavy shears with long handles (Fig. 37, page 82) are sometimes used for small limbs.   Their use is reported to accomplish the task more rapidly than can be done with a saw.

Using the Hebo Pruning Club.   This tool is a club consisting of a mattock, hazel hoe, grub hoe, or pick handle shod on the end with a piece of ⅛-in. thick steel.   The lengths of the ferrule and of the

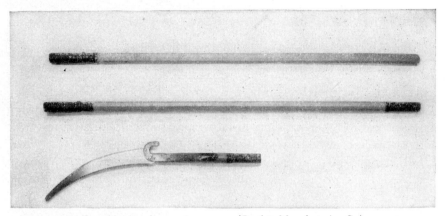

FIG. 64. A pole pruning saw.   (*Bartlett Manufacturing Co.*)

handle vary, depending on the pruning method by which the tool is to be employed.   When the tool is used in two hands, as it is in pruning from the ground, the ferrule is 8 in. long and the handle 33 in. long.   When the club is to be used in one hand by a climber, the handle is 17 to 19 in. long and the ferrule 5 in. long.   The total weight of the long club is about 3½ lb. and of the short one about 2¼ lb.

The limbs are severed by a blow at or near the branch collar.   One blow is ordinarily sufficient to break off a branch up to 1 in. in diameter, but two or three blows are usually needed to break off larger branches. The tool is known to work efficiently on branches as large as 2 in. in diameter.   Generally an underhand blow aimed at the underside of the limb, followed by a blow from above, is sufficient to break off one of these larger branches.

The club has been used mostly in the Douglas fir region.   Under some conditions, it has been used very successfully, and men prefer it to saws or axes.   Under other conditions, it has been difficult to get

Fig. 65. *A.* Pruning southern pine with a handsaw from a ladder. (*U.S. Forest Service.*) *B.* A 10-ft. ladder and a handsaw are used in pruning loblolly pine up to 17 ft. (*Photo by Dr. C. F. Korstian.*) *C.* Same operation as *B* with a 10-ft. pole pruning saw. The lower stem is pruned from the ground as high as a man can reach. A 10-ft. ladder or 10-ft. pole is used to complete the work up to 17 ft. Duke University Forest favors handsaws and ladders because the limbs can be cut closer to the stem. (*Photo by Dr. C. F. Korstian.*) *D.* Pruning loblolly pine to a height of two 16-ft. logs (34 ft.). A 20-ft. ladder is being used. (*Photo by K. L. Carvell.*)

the men to use the club.   There may be some question about the rapidity of healing of wounds from limbs broken off as compared to those removed with a saw.

Enough has been said about methods and tools to indicate that no

FIG. 66. Pruning twenty-seven year-old Douglas fir from the ground with a 14-ft. pole saw. (*U.S. Forest Service.*)

single tool or method has proved to be the one and only prescription. A great deal depends upon conditions and upon the preference of the pruners.   Farmers have a well-deserved reputation for plenty of ingenuity in making tools and devising methods.   The results of pruning operations in improving the quality of the product are so promising that pruning should be systematically carried on as part of the development program of the woods.

Following Step-by-step Procedures.   The first step in a pruning operation is the careful selection of trees to be pruned.   This is a job of first importance to be done by or carefully supervised by the forest manager. The pruning operation often accompanies or follows a thinning. Go through the forest in strips and label the selected trees. If trees are to be pruned to varying heights, attach a card to each tree giving the heights from the ground to which the pruning is to be limited. Slash resulting from the pruning operation is usually left where it falls except to pull limbs away from the base of the pruned tree. If the fire hazard is high, drag the brush away from sources of danger, such as roads or trails, or pile and burn it.

Estimating Costs. Not much can be said about costs of pruning because averages are difficult to obtain. Costs vary with species, the skill of the operators, and the heights to which the trees are pruned. Usually pruning to one log length (17 ft.) costs at the rate of 30 to 60 trees per man-day. First-stage pruning is approximately one-third that of 17-ft. pruning. Pruning the second log obviously costs much more than first-log pruning.

2. Pruning Coniferous Stands

Most of the pruning done so far in American forests has been in coniferous stands. This is partly because conifers do not prune naturally as well as most hardwoods and partly because most plantations are of coniferous species. Planted trees are given preference in pruning over natural stands by most forest owners. Certainly plantations, because of relatively wide spacing, require prompt attention to pruning needs to produce clear boles. Another reason, of course, is that plantations are thinned to stimulate growth, and this decreases natural pruning. There are, however, many opportunities to improve the quality of the product by pruning in natural stands of coniferous growth (Fig. 67).

Thinning increases volume production on fewer stems, but it does not necessarily produce quality wood. Therefore thinning and pruning go hand in hand to produce the highest woods income (Figs. 50 and 51).

Plantations of tolerant or intermediate species, such as white pine, spruce, red pine and Douglas fir, are especially in need of pruning if satisfactory profits are anticipated. With the intolerant trees like southern pines, lodgepole pine, or any of the scrub pines, pruning is not so urgent because, in close stands, the lower limbs die and some of them drop off. However, only by pruning can clean boles be produced.   Many natural stands of the intolerant species grow up in old fields under conditions where wide spacing permits side branches to persist. Pruning in such stands as a development measure becomes imperative (Fig. 65A).

Fig. 67. Plantation of southern pine in Ohio pruned at twenty-five years of age.   (*Soil Conservation Service.*)

3. Pruning Hardwood Stands

In pruning hardwoods, there is not nearly so much experience to draw on as there is in pruning conifers.   The vigor of the tree pruned is more important in hardwoods than in conifers.   Therefore only young, small, vigorous trees on the best sites should be pruned, at least until the forest manager knows from his own experience what can be accomplished.   Nevertheless, quality is important in hardwoods no less than in conifers, and so although be cautious, do not hesitate to try hardwood pruning under favorable conditions.

Pruning of some hardwoods causes "epicormic sprouts," commonly called water sprouts, to form.   Sometimes these persist for a few years and then die, causing no serious damage.   White oak is particularly subject to persistent water sprouts.   This species should be pruned in the first stage before the trees reach 5 in. d.b.h.   Water sprouts on maple and elm are reported in some instances to drop off and disappear in about 8 years after pruning.   White ash and basswood show very little tendency to form water sprouts.   Besides the water sprouts, pruning of hardwoods introduces the danger of the entrance of disease and disfiguring stains through the branch wounds.   They are much more subject to infection from wounds than are conifers.

Fig. 68. Young hardwood stand in Wisconsin after thinning and pruning.   The pruned trees are 1 to 3 in. d.b.h.   (*U.S. Forest Service.*)

Quick healing is therefore highly important.   Painting the wounds would help to minimize this risk, but, of course, it would also add to the costs.   What experience we have indicates that hardwood pruning should be confined to removal of limbs that make a maximum wound $1\frac{1}{2}$ in. in width.   The vertical length of the wound is not so important since the healing process chiefly is from the growing tissues at the sides of the wounds.   If occasional larger wounds are necessary, cover them with a paint having an asphalt base.

Late winter just before the growing season has proved to be the best time for pruning hardwoods.   Wounds made at this season are more likely to be promptly covered by new wood growth.   Experience also indicates that it is safer to prune while the side branches are alive.   Wounds made by removal of live branches heal faster than those from dead ones.   Where dead limbs are encountered, cut through the live callus at the base.   This will speed the healing process (Fig. 68).

Open-grown stands of walnut, basswood, red oak, and possibly others can be pruned successfully.   White ash should not be pruned except when small and when growing in thick stands.

Where a handsaw can be easily manipulated either from the ground or from a ladder, this tool is to be preferred.   In very thick stands,

FIG. 69. A sixteen-year-old plantation of Chinese chestnut on the George Washington National Forest in Amherst County, Virginia.   The seeds from which these trees origi-nated reached Tientsin, China, by camel caravan from beyond the Great Wall in Northern China.   (*Bureau of Plant Industry, Soils, and Agricultural Engineering*.)

however, a ladder is difficult to manage, and so for second-stage prun-ing in such stands, a pole saw does better work.   An ax is never a suitable tool to use in pruning hardwoods.

4. Protecting Forest Edges

At the risk of overemphasis and unnecessary repetition, you are again reminded of the very essential practice of closed borders. Vigor of the trees pruned, you will remember, is essential to success. Maintenance of soil moisture is accomplished by control of the over-head canopy and by thick borders that keep out drying winds. Hence, do not prune or thin trees within one rod of the edge of the stands; encourage the growth of shrubs, and, if necessary, plant a shrub and evergreen border.   These precautions are helpful for both hardwoods and conifers, but they are particularly essential in the case of hardwood stands.

5. Comparing Results of Experimental Pruning of Different Species

What has been said in the preceding pages of this chapter constitutes the general pruning guides. In this section, what research workers have reported about pruning in specific stands and under specified conditions will be presented briefly.

With Southern Pines. Natural pruning in well-stocked stands is reported to be complete in about the following periods: longleaf and slash pines, 6 years after limbs die; loblolly pine, 8 years after limbs die; shortleaf pine, 12 years after limbs die.

Pruning speeds up this process, and it is essential where stands are not well stocked. Pruning is usually confined to trees 3 to 8 in. d.b.h., but occasionally trees up to 10 or 12 in. are pruned. Limit pruning to limbs not over $2\frac{1}{2}$ in. in diameter; confine any operation to two-thirds of total tree height and one-third of live crown. Remove cut limbs from the base of trees.

Time for pruning: any season except when extreme drought prevails; the winter season is preferred.

First stage: up to 8 ft. when trees are 3 to 6 in. d.b.h.

Second stage: 5 years later, up to 17 ft.

Number to Prune. Examples: A stand 3 to 6 in., 280 out of 920 per acre, or 7 out of every 23. Another stand 6 to 10 in., 160 out of 400 per acre, or 4 out of 10.

Costs. Example in Mississippi: An open-grown limby stand; 1,200 trees 3 to 8 in. d.b.h. were pruned to 17 ft. Pruning was done by a three-man crew as follows: (1) hand work from ground up to 7 ft.; (2) short pole saw 7 to 12 ft.; (3) long pole saw 12 to 17 ft. Labor, including time walking between trees, rest periods, and so forth, was for 4-in. trees, 3 min.; 6-in. trees, $4\frac{1}{2}$ min.; 8-in. trees, $6\frac{3}{4}$ min. Disposal of cut limbs would add 25 percent to this time.

With Eastern White Pine. Planted stands do not clear without pruning. Limbs die but persist long enough to prevent formation of clear lumber when trees reach 16 to 18 in. d.b.h. Pruning white pine costs more than similar work with most other species, but it is worth while.

Example: Planted stand 6 by 6 ft. pruned to 17 ft. in 1935 when twenty years old; average size, 5 in. d.b.h. Costs were on the basis of 40 trees pruned per man-day. Handling brush would add one-third more.

With Red Pine in Minnesota. This species prunes naturally much better than white pine. Lower limbs die as soon as crowns close, and many drop off by age twenty-five or thirty years. Nevertheless, pruning is necessary to produce clear lumber within a reasonable time. The more open the stand the greater the need and, of course, the greater the cost of pruning. Select only dominant, fast-growing trees of good form for pruning, and not to exceed 100 per acre. The best prospects for paying dividends are offered by the best sites. Pruning wounds heal in 5 to 6 years.

Start pruning in the dormant season when trees are not over 3 to 4 in. d.b.h. and branches are under 1 in. in diameter.

In the first operation, prune to one-half the height of the tree, removing about one-third of the live crown. Subsequent operations should clear the bole to a 17-ft. height, using a pole saw.

With Douglas Fir in the West. If the first 16-ft. log on crop trees is pruned before the tree is 6 in. d.b.h., at least 25 percent of the net volume harvested at age one hundred will be clear of knots. Prune when the branches are mostly 1 to 1½ in. and not over 2 in. Prune when there is an expectation of at least 12 in. additional diameter growth before harvest.

Prune only on better sites trees 4 to 12 in. d.b.h. in stands twenty to forty years old. Pruning is not recommended in younger stands or in any stands on poor sites. Pruning in thick stands must be accompanied by thinning. Prune plantations as well as poorly stocked natural stands. The latter will mean larger limbs to be removed, but the operation is worth while. Prune not more than 100 vigorous trees per acre.

Use the Hebo pruning club on dead limbs. On whiplike limbs and on green ones over 1 in. in diameter, use a pruning saw. For the first 6 to 8 ft. prune from the ground with a club or handsaw or both. In open stands on the balance up to 17 ft., use a pruning saw on a 14-ft. pole. In dense stands use a 7-ft. pole saw to 11 ft., a 14-ft. pole saw for the balance of one log length.

A four-man crew is suggested for most Douglas fir stands: man 1 to select trees and prune to 7 ft., man 2 to prune with a 7-ft. pole saw to 11 ft., man 3 and man 4 to prune the balance with 14-ft. pole saws. Use curved saws, well mounted, of stiff, high-quality steel, 5 to 8 points per inch, cut on draw stroke. Pruned limbs should be scattered on ground. This kind of pruning has cost at the rate of about 4 trees per man-hour or 32 per 8-hr. day.

With Hardwoods. Pruning, in spite of advantages, is of questionable value among most hardwoods. The following conditions seem to justify pruning.

1. High-value species such as white oak and black walnut on good sites. (White oak in open stands should not be pruned because of water sprouts.)
2. In species such as scarlet oak where pruning makes a tremendous difference in the value of the first log.

Most hardwood pruning wounds require about 10 years to heal. Pruning hardwoods should usually be confined to trees between 3 and 4 in. d.b.h. Late winter or early spring is recommended as the best time to prune. Select not more than 50 to 60 trees per acre. White oak and sugar maple produce water sprouts after pruning. Maple sprouts tend to remain small and soon die; white oak sprouts tend to persist. A ladder and a handsaw are best for hardwoods. Stages for small trees: (1) lower 8 ft., (2) balance of one log length 10 years later.

With Pines. Trees preferably should be 3 to 5 in. d.b.h. Pruning before trees reach 25-ft. height requires two operations for 17-ft. clearance. White pine will stand removal of one-third the live crown. With the yellow pines minimum live crown must be one-third the total tree height.

Handsaws and ladders are the best tools. Labor costs vary with species, tools, size of limbs, and so forth. Twelve acres of shortleaf pine were pruned on a crop-tree basis in 1948 on Bent Creek in North Carolina. Trees averaging 6 in. d.b.h. were pruned with pole saws to 17 ft. at the rate of about $8\frac{1}{2}$ trees per man-hour.

White pine pruned to 9-ft. height required about 10 min. labor.

With Open-grown Longleaf Pine. Pruning should be restricted to trees at least 18 ft. high. Open-grown trees should be pruned to 40 to 50 percent of their total height. It is better for a farmer or other seller of logs or stumpage to prune all of the length for one 16-ft. log in one operation than in two. This necessitates postponing pruning until trees are about 35 ft. tall.

Labor for pruning one 16-ft. log in one operation, including moving and idle time, is recorded as 4.4 min. per tree or at the rate of more than 100 trees per man-day (8 hr.).

With Ponderosa Pine in the Southwest.   Crop trees should be pruned to maximum of 9 in. d.b.h. (rarely, larger trees with small limbs to 11 in. d.b.h.).   The height of pruning should be 17 ft., or half the total height.   This may necessitate two operations.   The tools are: ax, handsaw, and a pole saw with a 12-ft. handle.   Use an ax to a height of 4 ft.; a hand saw to 7 ft.; a pole saw 7 to 17 ft.   The labor required will be 3 min. for a pine tree in dense stand to 17 ft., 10 min. for an open-grown tree.   The butt log commonly contains 40 to 50 percent of the total merchantable value of tree.   Estimates are that pruning will double the value at harvest time.

With Western White and Ponderosa Pine.   Experiments show that not more than one-third of the live crown can be removed in pruning without substantially lowering the growth rates, in both diameter and height.

A pruned butt log of white pine having a 4-in. knotty core and harvested at 21 in. d.b.h. will yield lumber worth $48.56 *more* per M ft. b.m. than an identical unpruned log.   The same comparison for Ponderosa pine shows the increase in net profit from pruning to be $53.72 *more* per M ft. b.m.

SUPPLEMENTARY ACTIVITIES

Bud Pruning of Pines

Russian foresters developed a method of pruning buds instead of branches. The method is in the experimental stage in the United States; therefore, it cannot be recommended as a general practice.   It is, however, recommended for trial by students and farmers on a small scale.

Bud pruning consists of removing all lateral buds on young pine trees as they develop so that only one branchless leader is produced, usually to the height of one 16 ft. log or one 12 ft. log.   It is best adapted to species that produce only one branch whorl per year, such as white or red pine.   With species, such as the southern pines, that produce laterals several times in a season, the pruning of shoots as well as debudding will be necessary unless the trees are bud pruned promptly each time the lateral buds develop.

1. *Start* with young trees at least 3 ft. tall and not over 5 ft. tall.   Leave the lower two or three whorls of branches to grow and supply nourishment to the tree.   Above these lower-branch whorls, allow no side buds to develop.   As soon as the buds form (after height growth has terminated in

June or July), pinch off (with the fingers or a clipper) all lateral buds sur-rounding the terminal bud. Be careful to avoid damage to the one terminal bud left. Ordinarily this debudding is done once a year. By the time the second debudding is done, there may be branchlets which have grown from unsuspected buds. These should be removed with clippers. With southern pines, if bud pruning is limited to once a year, all the lateral growth of the previous season should be removed with clippers.

2. Repeat this process until the desired length of clear stem is obtained. Thereafter the bud-pruned trees are allowed to develop their crowns nor-mally until the trees reach a size suitable for harvest. After the crowns are developed, the lower-branch whorls may be removed if desired. Until the trees are about 10 ft. tall, they can be bud pruned by bending the tree until the pruner can reach the buds. After that a stepladder will be needed to reach the top.

At least 5 and preferably 10 or more trees well distributed through a plantation or a natural stand should be selected. It is easily possible, with only one terminal bud per tree, that something will happen to destroy that bud. The experiment would then be a failure. Hence the suggestion that 5 to 10 or more be selected. Adjacent trees that interfere with the develop-ment of the pruned trees should be removed.

3. The lower limbs left on each bud-pruned tree develop rapidly into elongated branches, while the main stem grows without any side branches as long as bud pruning continues. The result is a rather bizarre appearance not unlike an inverted umbrella.

The principal *advantages* claimed for bud pruning are: (1) it produces com-pletely knot-free boles; (2) less time than for branch pruning is required to grow clear logs; and (3) the danger of fungus infection is reduced because branch scars are absent.

The *disadvantages* may be: (1) it is very risky since leaders are likely to be damaged by insects, animals, or weather; (2) the few whorls of branches left at the base of the tree tend to grow vigorously to produce a "candelabra" effect; and (3) costs may excel those of the conventional branch pruning, but this has not yet been determined.

Pruning Coniferous Trees

1. Locate a patch of young coniferous trees. Name the species in the stand.

2. Describe the stand. Include extent (area), average size, and range in sizes (d.b.h. and heights). Are they limby; in other words, do they need pruning?

3. Lay out three square-rod plots (16 ½ by 16 ½ ft.) in different parts of the stand. Mark the boundaries plainly. Decide how many trees should

be pruned on the average per square-rod plot. Multiply this figure by 160 to get an estimate of how many should be pruned per acre.

4. On the plots, select and mark (by cardboard fastened to the bark) the trees to be pruned. On the cards for each tree, write the height in feet from the ground to which each tree is to be pruned. Remember the general rule—prune to not more than two-thirds the total height or one-half the live crown.

5. With the owner's permission, get a handsaw (and a ladder if needed) and prune the selected trees.

6. Cutting the Wood Crop

UP TO THIS POINT, this text has concerned itself with cultural operations designed to develop the young forest stand. These operations are called establishment or starting the forest, weeding, thinning, and pruning, discussed in Chaps. 2 to 5. Most of them involve more or less cutting of wood products. The primary purpose of cultural operations, however, is not the removal of wood products for immediate use or sale but to prepare the stand for the cutting of products at a later date—the production of products that will return worth-while revenue to the forest owner. In this chapter will be discussed the silvicultural and other problems connected with cuttings primarily designed to remove material for immediate use or sale, to produce a forest revenue. The development process continues because in any forest at any stage of development, cultural operations must accompany the harvest of wood crops. The harvest of today is the result of the growth of many previous years. The harvest of tomorrow is the result of operations of today and of yesterday.

The well-tended forest is the personification of conservation. The successful forest grower conserves his soil and wildlife resources, his growing stock of young trees, and his "crop" trees. The latter he cuts gradually. He tends his growing stock carefully to produce the harvests of the future. Tomorrow's harvest is always present. The forest manager removes today's harvest and adds the revenue to his annual income. He conserves tomorrow's harvest until tomorrow. That is conservation. If the farmer will practice the conservation lessons of the forest on his open field and pastures, there will be no more run-down or worn-out farms.

The method of cutting the wood crop to produce an immediate revenue constitutes the mainspring of practical forestry. Two classifications are usually used to distinguish basic differences in objectives of cutting. These are improvement cutting and harvest cutting. In practice they seldom are separate so far as location and timing are concerned. Both types of operation commonly are conducted on the

151

same area at the same time.   In fact, both improvement and harvest cutting may also include one or more strictly cultural operations discussed in Chaps. 3 to 5.   So far as the cutting operation itself is concerned, there is little need for, or advantage in, thus classifying woods operations.

The value of such classifications is in the planning of the woods operations and particularly in the preliminary preparations, such as selecting the trees to cut, girdle, or poison.   Giving names to the different kinds of cutting emphasizes the reasons which prompt the forest manager to choose a particular tree for removal.   Silviculture is a matter not of acres but of square rods, not of forests but of individual trees.   There must be a reason for the selection of each tree to stand or to go.   The man who makes the selection must have clearly in mind the purpose that is to be served by the removal or retention of each particular tree.   Names, classifications, designations of one kind or another help in discussion of the problems involved and therefore in learning applied silviculture.   The logger, the wood-cutter, is not concerned with such theoretical matters.   They involve silvicultural and management principles that affect the long-time development and the sustained productiveness of the forest.   Also they involve compromises between silviculture and economics in order to make some profits now at the sacrifice of profits in the future.

Clearly these are problems of management rather than of logging. Hence, most of this chapter is devoted to such matters and only a minor part to the mechanics of cutting and processing products. Cutting the wood crop is discussed under the following headings:

1. Improving the Forest by Cutting
2. Harvesting the Mature Trees
3. Making Use of Management Aids
4. Applying Recognized Silvicultural Systems of Cutting
5. Estimating Timber by Sample Plots
6. Processing Wood Products

1. Improving the Forest by Cutting

The forest soil and its management deserve first consideration in all cutting operations.   Upon soil productiveness depends the growth of the forest.   Let's see what it is and what to do about it. The quality of any soil is related to its physical structure, chemical content, and biological activity.   Soils cleared of forest growth and used for production of ordinary farm crops must be carefully managed (1) to prevent actual loss of topsoil through erosion and (2) to maintain and to replace organic and nutrient matter destroyed by erosion, exposure, and intensive use. Conditions of use tend to destroy the biological organisms found in undisturbed forest and prairie soils. Hence plant foods and soil amendments are needed. Organic matter must be added in the form of green manure crops, barnyard manure, sawdust, wood chips, and various kinds of mulch.

These measures to a degree counteract destructive forces inherent in the growth of annual crops. They improve the physical structure of the soil; encourage the growth of soil organisms capable of reducing organic matter to chemical bases suitable for plant growth; they provide plant food ready for use; they add air to the soil and create a physical structure favorable to the retention and conservation of soil moisture. On crop and pasture land, these measures must be repeated year after year. The farmer has a constant battle to maintain a productive soil, and a major campaign must be waged to rebuild a soil lost through erosion or misuse.

Managing the Forest Soil. Forest soils require management, but in a different way from agricultural soils. They do not require the addition of fertilizers or soil amendments or organic matter. They do not require cultivation. Sometimes these measures are used for a brief period on soils newly planted to trees, but once the forest is established, they are no longer needed. Perhaps later research will find that fertilization of young forests will be profitable under some conditions. There is, however, no present indication that it would result in any measurable increased growth.

The physical structure of the forest soil is dependent upon the reaction of the forest community upon the mineral and rock base upon which the forest grows. This reaction in turn depends upon the nature of the mineral soil and many other factors, such as climate and local topography. Essentially the soil consists of a top layer (A_1 and A_2 horizon) and the subsoil (B_1 and B_2 horizon). The former, in a forest soil, is a mixture of organic and mineral matter, plus the colloidal form to which organic matter is reduced by biological processes; the latter is largely mineral matter. Of course, there is the parent rock beneath the subsoil sometimes considered to be part of the soil (Fig. 70). If the subsoil is deep, loose, easily penetrated by plant roots, and of a consistency that permits it to retain moisture but is not wet, the soil (combination of topsoil and subsoil) is good.   If other conditions are favorable, this would make the best site for tree growth.   If the subsoil is stiff, resistant, or hard, or if it is shallow or waterlogged (swamp), the site is poor.

FIG. 70. A look at the soil, known as Muskingum loam, under a stand of white oak (Ohio). Numbers 1 and 2 represent the approximate base of the layers of topsoil (A_1 and A_2); the numbers 3 and 4, the base of layers of subsoil (B_1 and B_2).   The parent rock begins at a depth of about 40 in.   It consists of sandstone and shale.   The A horizon is classified as loam and the B as clay.   Note that roots are abundant through the A and B_1 horizons as far down as number 3 and are much less frequent below that depth.   (*Courtesy Dr. R. N. Gaiser, Central States Forest Experiment Station, U.S. Forest Service.*)

These are necessarily generalized statements.   Soils are very complex in both physical and chemical structure.   Some pines will grow well on land underlain by plastic clay subsoils, for example, loblolly and longleaf pines in parts of the southeastern coastal plain.   For purposes of this brief study of forest soils, such examples may be considered as the exceptions that prove the rule.

As a matter of fact, good and poor forest sites are difficult to define in terms of the soil itself. Topography, climate, and tree species are factors that react on the soil and determine the real quality of the land for forest growth. In general, however, we know that the structure of the subsoil is one very important factor in determining whether or not a particular piece of land is good forest land.

These are the factors and conditions upon which the forest community acts to produce good, medium, or poor forest growth. Nature has adapted tree species to climates, topography, and soils so that the best results in tree growth are achieved under a given set of conditions. These adaptations we recognize as forest types.

Root penetration, expansion and contraction with changes in temperature and moisture content, and the activities of worms, insects, and animals tend to make a forest soil porous. The forest is a builder and a preserver of soil porosity. The penetration of roots and their eventual decay leave the soil interpenetrated with tubelike cavities, hence in good condition to absorb and hold moisture.

The key to the processes of forest-soil building and maintenance is the litter that accumulates on the forest floor. A dense forest each year deposits on the forest floor 1½ to 3 tons of leaves, twigs, and branches. This is the forest litter. The total accumulation of litter and humus seldom amounts to more than three or four times the annual deposition. The exceptions are the spruce forests of the North and the coniferous forests at high altitudes. These forests accumulate litter deposits often one foot or more in depth. Such large deposits are due to the low temperatures which prevail in the forest floor, and this condition is reflected in the slow growth of the forest. In the central hardwood forest, the litter deposit is seldom more than one inch in depth. More than three years is required for the complete disintegration of any one year's litter.

The litter serves as an absorbent, acts as mulch or insulation against rapid evaporation of moisture, prevents compaction of surface soil by impact of rain, decomposes and furnishes plant food, and serves as a medium for microbiological activities (Figs. 71 and 72). The litter is incorporated into the soil through the action of large populations of animals, fungi, and bacteria. Under favorable conditions of moisture and temperature, the transformation is rapid; under unfavorable conditions, such as cold northern climates or in swamps, it is very slow. The litter is first converted into humus and then

FIG. 71. A shelter belt in Nebraska grazed for two years by sheep.   Compare the litter with that in Fig. 72.   (*Soil Conservation Service.*)

FIG. 72. The litter in an ungrazed shelter belt adjacent to that shown in Fig. 71.   (*Soil Conservation Service.*)

reduced to a colloidal form and becomes a part of the soil. The primary attack on the litter is by wood-rotting fungi, termites, ants, larvae of large insects, earthworms, millipedes, and mites. The secondary attack is by other organisms that feed on these, their offal, what is left of the litter, and on each other. The total animal population of soil and litter together probably approaches 10,000 per sq.

FIG. 73. The soil under a well-tended forest becomes a self-serving, self-renewing food table at which feeds the forest community. (*Soil Conservation Service.*)

ft. The litter and humus are rich in plant nutrients because nitrogen and its important bases are all conserved in the process of changing litter to the colloidal organic matter of the soil (Fig. 73).

Thus the soil under a well-tended forest becomes a self-serving, self-renewing food table at which feed the forest community of trees and shrubs and the myriads of minute animals, insects, and fungi in the forest floor. Indirectly, the forest floor is the source of life to larger animals, birds, and insects that live in the forest.

The influence of the forest on the soil is inseparably connected with the forest litter. The production and retention of adequate quantities of forest litter are dependent upon good silvicultural practices. The decomposition of the litter is dependent, as already indicated, upon favorable conditions of temperature and moisture. Both of these factors can be influenced, to a degree, by manipulation of the over-head canopy and the control of winds that sap moisture from the soil. Opening the forest canopy to permit the direct rays of the sun to reach the forest floor will warm the soil and hasten the process of disintegration of the litter. It will, at the same time, reduce the amount of the annual litter deposit. This may be helpful where the litter accumulation is abnormally large, but where the amount of litter is below normal, such action may be harmful. Safe limits for cutting possibly may be indicated by the effect on the forest floor. Very likely they have been exceeded when the litter is consumed more rapidly than it is deposited.

The ways of cutting the wood crop so as to retain the delicate balance between litter accumulation and soil building are still a subject only slightly understood. It is a subject worth careful study by every forest manager. Conditions vary widely between different forest stands, but an observant and interested forest grower will soon learn to watch the condition of the litter and be guided in gauging the extent of cutting by its effect on the forest floor. The things already emphasized are important in this respect—keeping out the wind by closed borders, keeping out grazing animals that destroy the effective action of litter and humus, keeping out fire that destroys the litter and humus and the organisms that live and work in the forest floor. An understanding of the working relations in the forest community is the key to good silviculture. The success of the program for development of the farm woodland depends upon maintaining the balance in the forest community. The litter that supplies the nutrients for tree growth and creates conditions favorable to the retention of moisture is the barometer of healthy conditions in the forest. The forest grower must learn to read it, interpret it, and to use the information as a guide in his forest operations.

Making Improvement Cuttings. This name includes a variety of different kinds of cutting but always some form of selective cutting as contrasted with clear cutting. Selective cutting means removal of single trees or small groups of trees with as little disturbance to the forest canopy as possible. The Society of American Foresters defines improvement cutting as "a cutting made in a stand past the sapling stage for the purpose of improving its composition and character by removing trees of less desirable species, form, and condition in the main crown canopy" (Fig. 74).

The type of cutting called "improvement cutting," obviously a catchall name, includes a great variety of cutting operations such as liberation cuttings; thinnings; removal, girdling, or poisoning of wolf trees; and the harvesting of some mature trees. The main purpose,

FIG. 74. An improvement cutting has been completed in this hardwood forest in Pennsylvania. Note the good trees left for succeeding cuts. The man stands among 4-ft. poplar seedlings. (*Soil Conservation Service.*)

as the definition states, is to improve the "composition and character" of the stand. The forest manager plans the cutting so that a net revenue will be returned. That means an immediate compromise between desirable silvicultural practices and a type of cutting that will produce enough usable or salable products to make the operation pay its way or yield a satisfactory net profit. The time has come when the forest is expected to begin to yield revenue. At the same time, the main objective is to build up a growing stock that will be able to yield better and more profitable harvests in the future. In planning an improvement cutting, the least amount of harvest cutting is included that is absolutely necessary to make the operation profitable.

Improvement cuttings are most commonly applicable to stands not previously managed with any thought of continuous sustained production. The farmer may have sold stumpage in the past and allowed the buyer to help himself to the best trees, leaving the worst. Or he may have cut products himself without consciously trying to build up the growing stock. In a mixed stand of conifers and hardwoods, the merchantable saw-log trees of pine or spruce or fir or hemlock have been cut and the hardwoods left, or both hardwoods and conifers of the best species and the larger sizes have been removed. In pure hardwoods, the same system of cutting has reduced the stand to inferior species and relatively small sizes of the better species. In pure or nearly pure conifer stands, past cutting has left only small sizes and the rough or crooked or defective trees of larger sizes.

In addition to these destructive methods of cutting, fire or grazing damage may have prevented the establishment of any worth-while young growth. There may, therefore, be two principal defects in stand structures: (1) no adequate foundation of young trees, and (2) a shortage of good trees and good species approaching harvest sizes—trees that will make poles, piling, or saw logs. Possibly also the forest floor is hard, compact, and incapable of taking and retaining moisture. All or part of these conditions very commonly are found in woodlands when the first steps in a development program are planned (Fig. 5).

Taking Preliminary Steps. Planning the improvement cutting involves sizing up conditions in the particular woodland. Walk through the woods and note

1. **Soil Condition.** Is it as good as the site and forest type permit? Soil in a hardwood stand should be loose and crumbly. The annual litter deposit should be undisturbed, the soil underneath moist. Pine stands commonly occupy drier sites. The soil is not as moist as under hardwoods, but the litter should be present and functioning. Compare soil condition in your woods with that in the best woods of similar type that you can find. Decide what, if anything, is wrong with past treatment of your soil and what can be done about it. Is there fire or grazing damage? Is the forest canopy too open? Does the wind blow through unhindered and sap up the moisture from the soil?

2. **Young Growth.** Is it present wherever there is sufficient light? Is it mostly good species or the "weed" species? What about sizes? Is the general average of young trees 6 to 8 in. d.b.h. (diameter breast high) and none smaller? Is the situation unsatisfactory? If so, what can you do about it? Will protection and careful cutting provide an adequate foundation of young trees for the future forest, or do you want to under-plant now?

3. **Stand Conditions.** Is the stand even aged? This usually means a fairly narrow range of size classes. Is it uneven aged? If the latter is true, what is the range of size classes from 6 or 8 in. d.b.h. to harvest size? A well balanced all-aged stand probably should have the following relationships:

Trees 6 to 12 in. d.b.h. inclusive	Should include 70 to 75 percent of the total trees 6 in. d.b.h. and larger.
Trees over 12 in. d.b.h.	Should include 25 to 30 percent of the total trees 6 in. d.b.h. and larger.

For example, if the total of trees 6 in. and larger on an average acre is 135, between 95 and 100 should be 6 to 12 in. and 35 to 40 larger than 12 in. This is only a rough guide, but more than 30 percent of the total in trees above 12 in. may indicate too large a proportion of larger sizes. Compare these relationships using Tables 17 and 18, pages 199 and 200.

The degree of stocking is also important. Does the stand represent full stocking or something less—perhaps one-half or two-thirds? Are the size classes all represented, or is there a distinct shortage in some size classes? An inspection should indicate the species that are predominant in the different size classes. If all trees in the large-size classes are the inferior species, for example, beech, elm, hickory, or scrub pine, the stand will be difficult to cut at a profit. The proportion of defective and crooked trees and downright culls is also an important factor.

The foregoing inspection will give the new forest manager an impression of what his forest is like and, in general, the critical points that need attention in his development program. Part of his findings will be things to be taken care of partly through careful management over future years, for example, poor soil condition, lack of sufficient young growth of desirable species, or lack of closed borders to the woodlands. The things to be considered immediately are the type of cutting that will yield some profit and how much additional non-profit cutting can be done. In most woods, it is out of the question to attempt complete renovation in the first cutting cycle. The complete job must be spread over two or more cutting cycles. This is desirable, too, for a very important reason—the forest manager will learn a great deal about how his forest responds to constructive cutting by watching results of his first efforts.

Therefore, the forest manager's general conclusion is likely to be to start cutting on a conservative basis that will gradually improve his growing stock. But he needs to know more precisely just what kinds and what volume of products he can cut that are usable or salable. Also there is the question of the size of the job. If this forest manager is a farmer, he is starting on a program of growing wood as a farm crop. The important thing is to get an annual income from his woods. That is even more important than a rapid transformation of a poor woods into a good one. Remember, too, that almost any cutting, except removal of crop trees, carried out according to the principles of improvement cuttings, will benefit the stand and tend to put it in condition for larger future production. The volume of cutting, then, is partly a question of markets and partly one of how much the farmer wants to undertake as an annual project.

Deciding on the Amount to Cut. This problem can be approached from several angles. First, approximately how much time each year can the farmer spare for work in the woods? To make a success of his woodland enterprise, he must devote his own time or that of a trusted employee to the supervision of the job. In other words, he must become the *forest manager* or delegate the job to someone who is interested and willing to assume the responsibility. It may be the tenant farmer, the farm manager, or the farmer's son. There is another alternative, where the woodland is large and the values high, that is, turning over the management to an agent, preferably a consulting forester, who will undertake the job on the basis of a satisfactory fee—a percentage of gross revenue or an annual fee based on the estimated time required.

The employment of an agent is likely to be the exceptional case, but where one is employed, the question of the annual amount of wood to cut is still a very pertinent question. It is if the undertaking is to be tied in to farm management, in other words, if wood is to be grown as a farm crop. Whatever the arrangement is about the forest manager, the question remains how much farm labor can be employed in cutting the wood products. The best arrangement is likely to be where *all* or *nearly all* the labor is obtained from the regular farm employees at a time when they can best be spared from other farm work. On most farms, this will be the winter season. Regular farm laborers may not be experienced in woods work, but they can learn, and once the system is established, it gives assurance of longer continuous employment and creates an added incentive for annual cutting of wood products.

So, on whatever basis the job of forest manager is decided, the days or weeks each year to be devoted to labor in the woods must be arrived at and translated into total man-days. Roughly, that indicates how many acres can be worked annually on the basis of ½ to 1 man-day per acre per year (Chap. 1). For example, a 40-acre woods should require from 20 to 40 man-days of labor each year, depending upon stand and market conditions and intensity of management. If the farmer plans to use the labor of two men for six days, or 12 man-days, his cutting probably would be very light. With twice this amount of labor, he could do a very good job. If three times this amount of labor, or 36 man-days, is available, it may prove to be too much in relation to the size of his woods. He may later buy additional woods or plant additional acres. Time will tell.

Second, what products will be cut with the man-days available? To answer that question requires some knowledge of local markets, an estimate of farm needs for certain products, and a tally of trees and products to be cut. The latter can be obtained by actually marking all or part of the timber selected for cutting. Probably the best plan would be to select about ⅕ of the total woods area for the first year's cutting. Then lay out some sample plots of known area, mark the trees to be cut, and tally the products to be made from the trees. The products can be reduced to an acre basis and, multiplied by the acres to be cut, will indicate the total products available for the first year's cut. The methods applicable to this type of timber estimating will be explained later on in this chapter.

The results of the sample marking may indicate something like the following amounts to be cut from 8 to 10 acres: 20 cords of fuel, 10 cords pulpwood, 300 posts, 3,000 ft. b.m. (feet board measure) log scale of saw logs. This may require as much as 30 man-days of labor plus labor for a day or two with a team to bunch the products, especially the saw logs. If this is more labor than is available, reduce the area to be cut. Or it may represent more products than can be sold or used. This also would call for a reduction of the area to be cut. Of course, another alternative would be to change the marking so as to cut fewer products. In any case, the forest manager has the basis for his first year's cut. He is making a start on a development program for his woods.

Marking Trees to Cut. For this type of woods operation, always mark each tree to be cut rather than attempt to control the cutting by designating sizes of trees to be cut. Mark trees by blazing at breast height on two sides so that they can be easily seen by the cutters. If the felling is to be done by contract, an additional blaze is often placed below stump height and stamped with a special hammer that leaves initials or any symbol desired. Stump blazing and stamping, of course, are done as a means of checking to ensure that no unmarked trees are felled. Usually it is unnecessary in small operations. The character and intensity of the marking will have been decided by the sample plots already mentioned. In marking the cutting area, go through the area in parallel strips about a chain wide with one assistant. The forest manager selects the trees to be cut and an assistant does the marking. The forest manager examines the trees approximately on each square rod, watches the crowns, the form, signs of defect, the species, the young growth, the spacing, and the products that the trees will make. On the basis of these factors, he decides upon trees to leave and to cut.

Marking trees with paint or whitewash, rather than by blazing with an ax, is preferred by many forest managers. Painting spots with a brush or a paint gun is quicker, the spots are often easier to see and to erase in case of error, and they do not injure the tree. A blaze may allow the entrance of insects or fungi. Whitewash is satisfactory, but of course, the marks are good for only a short period. White, red, yellow, or blue have been found to be good paint colors. Work the paint into the crevices of the bark so that it will not wash off or be lost if the outer bark peels. If used in a paint gun, thin the paint with an equal volume of kerosene (Fig. 75).

You are the forest manager; you will always keep in mind the chief purpose of the cutting, which is to develop your growing stock—to improve the stocking of well-formed young trees of the desired species, to remove objectionable growth, and, if necessary, to open up the stand where reproduction is needed. Of course, you will keep in mind your purpose to secure enough usable or salable products to make the operation profitable. On almost every square rod, you will have to make compromises between these two objectives. Remember that you rarely can achieve both objectives in the first operation. This is only the first cutting cycle. There will be others at three or five years, or perhaps at longer intervals. At each cutting cycle, you will have less difficulty in arriving at a satisfactory compromise than you did at the preceding one.

Except where conditions clearly indicate the advisability of creating openings to stimulate the growth of desirable young growth, strive to maintain the forest canopy or to increase its density where it is too

Fig. 75. Marking trees for cutting with a paint gun. This is a young pine stand in Louisiana. (*Soil Conservation Service*.)

thin. In this way you will build your growing stock to utilize fully the productive power of the soil. Future yields of forest products, by this means, will be increased.

Following Marking Rules. For an improvement cutting, marking rules usually include these:

1. Remove or girdle or poison wolf trees (Fig. 33).
2. Remove defective, abnormal, or diseased trees (Fig. 7).
3. Remove inferior species.
    Often the objective of rules (2) and (3) cannot be accomplished in the first cutting without opening the canopy too much.
4. Thin dense clumps of sapling and pole timber.
5. Remove dead trees only if they can be made into usable or salable products.

6. Leave all small or medium-sized thrifty trees unless they are too closely spaced (Chap. 4).

7. Cut mature crop trees sparingly and only to the extent necessary to make the operation pay. This rule is based on the assumption that the whole stand primarily needs an improvement cutting. Parts of it may already have reached the stage of harvest cutting, in which case the rules for harvest cuttings would apply (Fig. 76).

Fig. 76. Portions of this ponderosa-pine forest are ready for a harvest cut.   (*Soil Conservation Service.*)

2. Harvesting the Mature Trees

A harvest cut implies that a portion of the trees in the forest have reached the size that the forest manager has previously decided is as large as he wants to grow them. His crop trees have matured. His growing stock is at least partly developed. He is ready for the annual harvest that his growing stock is capable of producing. The annual harvest cut is often called the interest on the capital represented by the growing stock.

For a continuous cut of approximately equal annual amounts, the capital must not be depleted by overcutting. It must be maintained or gradually built up. This is the theory of sustained yield. This is the idea behind the word "harvest." Trees have grown from seedlings into saplings into poles and then into large trees—they have reached harvest size. Hundreds of specimens have died, hundreds have been removed in weeding and thinning, in the process of producing a relatively few of harvest size.

In the selection, or all-aged, forest, trees of harvest size are mixed more or less indiscriminately with all other trees of lesser size down to seedlings (Fig. 74). In even-aged forests, all or the greater part of the trees may reach harvest size at about the same time. Continuous yield in such cases must be obtained by a gradual process of developing a stair-step arrangement. In other words, in a 40-acre woods, there would be 10 acres of seedlings, 10 of saplings, 10 of poles, and 10 of harvest-size tree.

Again this is theory; in practice the age sizes usually appear in ragged patches rather than well-defined blocks. The all-aged or selection forest seldom lives up to its name. Patches of even-aged stands appear because of accidents or because intolerant trees have been favored in past management. Even-aged stands develop great differences in sizes because of crowding and some degree of tolerance of the species, for example, the second-growth Douglas fir stands in the Northwest and the Rocky Mountains. The management of such stands approaches that of the selection forest.

So when foresters talk of selection, all-aged, and even-aged forests, they may have in mind extensive areas where all sizes fairly uniformly mixed are present or where approximately one size only is present. Or they may be thinking of a relatively small area with a great many variations in size and age classes more or less in patches. In farm woodlands, the latter is more apt to represent the true picture of conditions. We need to think more of size classes than of age classes. Management has to apply to conditions actually found in the woods, but the conception of even-aged and all-aged stands must be kept in mind, because it has an important bearing on how to handle the forest.

Harvesting the mature trees becomes a problem in regulating the cut so as to maintain the desired capital stock. Prior to the time when crop trees reach harvest size, cutting is on the basis of purely cultural operations or on the basis of an improvement cutting. As already explained, in order to make an improvement operation pay, some crop trees may be cut before they have reached harvest size, and, on the other hand, good thrifty trees over harvest size may be left in order to build up the growing stock.   We therefore need to decide what is meant by "mature" trees.

Deciding When Trees Are Mature.   This is one of the first steps in management.   In essence, it is the maximum size that the forest manager is willing to grow.   The actual age to produce a given size will, of course, depend upon the forest site, the species, and upon the cultural operations already described.   In forestry terms, this size of maturity is known as the "rotation" age or size.   Most trees grow faster during the first 20 or 30 years of life than they do later.   Hence such products as fuel, posts, or pulpwood can be produced in 30 years or less from trees 6 to 10 in. d.b.h.   If the forest manager is satisfied with these products, then his trees are mature at, say, 8 in. d.b.h.   If he is satisfied with mine timbers and railroad cross ties, his trees will mature at about 12 to 13 in. d.b.h.   If he wants large poles, piling, and saw logs, maturity means 16 to 24 in. d.b.h.   If he wants high-class veneer logs, maturity for some of his trees may be as high as 30 in. d.b.h.

The lower-maturity sizes produce low-quality products and hence low prices; usually the market for low-quality products is a buyer's market; there is, normally, a surplus of these products.   Therefore, unless there are very special local conditions indicating a stable market for these products, the financial return from a forest producing such products normally is not as good as one that is managed for high-quality products.   From most woods, there is an abundance of fuel, pulpwood, mine timbers, and similar products to be obtained from cultural operations.   Forests managed to produce saw logs, poles, and piling usually pay better dividends.   These and the specialty products are in scarce supply and promise to remain in that class for an indefinite time.   Even in the best-managed forest, aimed at producing the maximum quantity of high-quality products, there will be plenty of low-grade products from cultural operations.   European experience shows that from one-third to one-half the total wood volume produced during the process of growing crop trees to saw-log size consists of the products of cultural operations.   For these reasons, most of the discussion that follows assumes that the forest manager intends to grow crop trees of saw-log size; that is, from about 18 to 24 in. d.b.h.

Deciding on the Allowable Cut.   The "allowable cut," for small woodlands, is usually calculated for a period of five years.   The annual amount is then theoretically one-fifth of the total, but considerable variation in the actual amount cut each year is permissible so long as the five-year budget is not exceeded. As far as the effect on the forest is concerned, the entire five-year budget can be removed in one year if the forest manager waits until the end of the five years before resuming the cutting. Foresters frequently recommend such procedure, but for farm woodlands it is bad practice. The reasons have already been set forth in Chap. 1. An annual cut in the woods, in the long run, will ensure a stability to the farm-woodland enterprise and a sustained interest obtainable in no other way. The farmer who wants to make his woodland contribute its share of farm income must grow wood as a farm crop. That means annual cutting, management by the farmer, and, with few exceptions, selling of processed products, not stumpage.

How is the allowable cut determined? Here are the factors involved:

1. The amount of wood volume, calculated for the next five-year period, represented by the growth of the trees in the growing stock. To this is added the volume of other trees in the stand ready to cut to make room for new growth to be added to the growing stock. If all of the trees in the forest are good thrifty growing trees, then all of them are included in the term the "growing stock." That, of course, is seldom the case, especially in the present-day forests where management is just starting. Sometimes three classifications of trees in the forest are used by foresters in calculating the allowable cut.

   a. Growing stock. The thrifty, well-formed, properly spaced, healthy trees from 12 in. d.b.h. up to harvest size. These are the growing stock. Of course, it actually includes smaller trees as well, but these normally are not included in the calculations.

   b. Stagnant stand. Other trees no longer thrifty or free from defect in the same diameter range as the growing stock. It may also include large trees beyond the harvest size. They are increasing in net volume very little, if at all. They are part of the stand but not included in the growing stock.

   c. Salvage. The rest of the stand that may be classed as pure salvage— sound dead trees; partly sound, partly dead trees; culls; and cripples— either standing or on the ground.

2. The wood volume to be obtained from cultural operations and from tops of trees cut in other classifications.

The first classification (1) would be in terms of board feet log scale; the second (2) in terms of cords, bolts, pieces—of fuel, pulpwood, mine timbers, and so forth.

The allowable cut would then be figured on the following basis, for example, on 40 acres.

  a. Growing stock. If the total growth for five years on the growing stock is, say, 20,000 ft. b.m. log scale, the annual cut would be 4,000 ft.

  b. Stagnant stand. The total volume is, say, 60,000 ft. b.m. log scale. This volume should not be removed immediately both because it would open the canopy too rapidly and also because the farmer wants a fairly evenly balanced annual cut. Suppose this volume is to be removed over a period of 15 years, or at the rate of 4,000 ft. per year.

  c. Salvage. The total volume is, say, 20,000 ft. b.m. log scale. From the silvicultural standpoint this should be cut as rapidly as possible, but it is poor stuff and might reduce the average value obtained for products offered for sale. If sold separately, it could be cut the first year, or if the market is poor, it could be held for awhile. The longer it is held the greater will be the loss in volume. It would likely be worked off at the rate of about 4,000 ft. per year.

These three items total 60,000 ft. b.m. log scale as the allowable cut for five years, or an annual cut of 12,000 ft. in saw logs or other products. Products from cultural operations and from tops of saw-log trees and culls might add 25 cords of fuel, pulpwood, and so forth, to the annual budget.

Only a forester, trained to estimate volume, calculate growth, and classify a stand properly, could be expected to arrive at the allowable cut in this manner. The example is given in order that a farmer or forest manager will understand the principles involved in the determination of the allowable cut. The example is oversimplified because it does not consider differences in growth or values due to species, types, sites, and a few other factors. Obviously, the forest manager will call upon a farm forester to assist him in arriving at his allowable cut, if one is available. If not, there are other ways of arriving at the same point by means of much simpler methods. These will now be explained.

Regulating the Cut by Application of Spacing Rule. The spacing rule explained in Chap. 4 can be used with a degree of accuracy sufficient for the first five-year period, and perhaps for a longer period. It is obvious that the allowable cut does not have to be calculated in

terms of board feet, cords, or other volume units.   It can be calculated in terms of number of trees.   The volume to cut would then be
whatever was contained in that number of trees.   This would certainly be easier to apply in the woods.   For the eastern United States,
the $D + 6$ spacing rule is applicable for determining how many trees
profitably can grow in a stand.   The application of this rule will provide whatever products are contained in the trees designated for
cutting.   The rule applies to cultural operations and to improvement
cutting.   It is the spacing for trees left to form the growing stock at
that particular stage in the development of the stand.   But, right now
in many woodlands, and sooner or later in every stand, the crop trees
reach the mature size decreed by the forest manager.   The time for
the harvest cut has come.   How many mature trees should be cut in
addition to those removed by the $D + 6$ spacing rule?   That depends
on how many years it takes to produce trees of mature size under the
conditions existing in a specific woodland and under the system of
management adopted.   In the north woods, it may have taken
Nature 150 years to grow a 20-in. sugar maple tree.   Under good
management where the trees are properly spaced, a 20-in. tree could
grow in 100 years or less.   A southern pine in a natural unmanaged
stand might require 70 years to grow to 18 in. d.b.h.; in a managed
stand only 50 years.

So the first question for the forest manager to ask, and answer, is
how many years on the average will it take *him*, under his system of
management and in his forest, to produce the mature tree that he has
decided to grow?   Probably the best way for him to get the answer is
to consult the state forester or any available local forester.   Another
way is to find freshly cut stumps of trees that have grown under reasonably favorable conditions on land similar to his and count rings of
growth.   The average number of rings per half inch along the radius
equals the years to grow one inch in diameter.   This times the diameter in inches of his mature crop tree is the figure he is looking for.   For
example, his mature crop tree is to be 20 in. d.b.h.   He estimates from
the best information available that his trees should grow at the rate of
3 in. in diameter in 10 years.   Therefore, crop trees at 9 in. d.b.h.
will be about thirty years old; at 18 in. sixty years old; at 27 in. ninety
years old.   Now refer to Table 13 for the number of trees per acre
applicable to the spacing rule in use.

TABLE 13. APPROXIMATE NUMBER OF TREES PER ACRE FOR VARIOUS SIZES AND SPACINGS

D.b.h., in.	$D + 2$	$D + 3$	$D + 4$	$D + 6$
6	680	535	436	303
9	360	303	258	194
12	222	194	170	134
15	151	134	121	99
18	109	99	90	76
20	90	82	76	65
24	65	60	56	48
27	52	48	45	40

Since in the example being considered $D + 6$ spacing was assumed, the answers are:

Size, in.	Trees per acre	Age of trees, years	Approx. no. of trees to cut per acre each year
9	194	30	$\dfrac{194}{30} = 6.46$
18	76	60	$\dfrac{76}{60} = 1.25$
20	65	67	$\dfrac{65}{67} = 1.00$
27	40	90	$\dfrac{40}{90} = 0.44$

Since the age factor is not too accurate, a conservative figure would be used of perhaps 6 trees if the crop-tree size is 9 in.; 1 tree if the crop-tree size is 18 in.; 0.4 tree if the crop-tree size is 27 in.; or 1 tree from each 2½ acres of forest.

Suppose the assumed ages are arbitrarily increased on the basis of a growth rate of 2½ in. in 10 years. This would give the following:

Size, in.	Trees per acre	Age of trees, years	Approx. no. of trees to cut per acre each year
9	194	36	$\dfrac{194}{36} = 5.40$
18	76	72	$\dfrac{76}{72} = 1.06$
20	65	80	$\dfrac{65}{80} = 0.81$
27	40	108	$\dfrac{40}{108} = 0.37$

The above calculation is included to show that the estimate of growth rate can be considerably in error without any very serious effects on the allowable cut for the first 5-year period.   For a saw-log rotation, the limit would remain at about one tree for each acre under management.   However, another factor must be mentioned.   This method of determining the harvest cut assumes full stocking.   If the woodland contains 40 acres but only three-fourths of it has a complete cover because of openings or unproductive brush-covered areas, the total number of crop trees to cut would be multiplied by 30 instead of 40. Also, in the case of existing wolf trees and culls, the gross area would be either reduced by the area so occupied, or the wolf or cull trees would have to be counted as part of the harvest cut.   The allowable cut for a saw-log rotation on a 40-acre forest would be calculated as follows:

1. The *growing* stock: 5-year cut, 200 trees; 1 year, 40 trees.
2. The *stagnant* stand: included under 1.
3. The *salvage:* Take whatever can be used or sold.

If the 40 crop trees averaged between 18 and 20 in. d.b.h. and contained 3 logs, the volume, log scale, based on Scribner decimal rule, would be about 350 ft. b.m. per tree or a total of about 70,000 ft. for the 5-year allowable cut.   The amount taken in cultural operations would be unchanged.   If the 40 acres was only three-fourths stocked, the harvest cut would be 150 trees or about 52,500 ft. for the 5-year period instead of 70,000 ft.

If $D + 4$ spacing is correct for the particular stand, it is obvious that more trees per acre can be removed as the harvest cut.   For example, calculations for a growth of 3 in. in 10 years would be:

Crop trees, d.b.h., in.	Number cut	Number cut before
9	8.50	6.46
18	1.50	1.25
20	1.14	1.00
27	0.50	0.44

From the standpoint of regulating the amount to cut so as to maintain or build up the growing stock, this system is much simpler and more easily applied than the one first explained.   While it has not been used very long and therefore a fund of knowledge based on experience has not accumulated to prove its soundness fully, it is none the less theoretically sound. Furthermore, it is an automatic system. It can be applied to any stand whether or not the crop trees have reached maturity or they have grown to larger sizes. If, for example, the system is adhered to of cutting only one tree per acre per year, representing the growth of the growing stock, the final result will be what the forest manager is aiming at. If the largest tree is chosen each time, the volume cut will correspond to the volume of that tree. If the tree is less than maturity size, the cut will be less than growth. If it is larger, the cut will be greater than the growth, but that is because crop trees have been allowed to grow beyond maturity size and consequently the growing stock has been built up beyond what it needs to be. If only a few large trees are present in the stand, the cut will temporarily be larger than can be maintained. That will be automatically adjusted because when the large sizes are exhausted, the cut must return to the volume represented by the smaller trees next in line.

Suppose the objective is crop trees about 20 in. d.b.h., but there are no trees larger than 16 in. in the stand. The forest manager can postpone collecting the interest on his capital until 16-in. trees grow to 20 in., but if he needs the revenue now he can cut one 16-in. tree per acre per year. His cut will then be about 150 ft. instead of 350 ft. b.m. His growing stock will be increasing and later on his one-crop tree will be 20 in. in size. Likewise he might want to start when his crop trees are only 9 in. Instead of taking five or six that size, he still takes only one. Eventually the one tree that he cuts will be 20 in. It is automatic if the forest manager sticks to the rule. The control is the number of crop trees per acre per year that he cuts, based on the number that can stand on an acre at maturity size, divided by the average age in years at that size. There is a more exact method of figuring the "take" of crop trees when they are below maturity size. For a 5-year allowable cut, however, the method outlined is entirely safe. Every forest manager eventually will want his allowable cut checked by a forester. Refinements in the methods, if needed, can then be introduced.

The procedure for application of crop-tree cutting is the reverse of the order first given for determining the allowable cut. In other words, all of the trees to be taken in the cultural or improvement operation and in salvage are first marked, using the $D + 6$ spacing rule (or the one applicable to the particular forest type).   Then as the last step, the calculated number of crop trees are chosen and marked. For example, in a 40-acre fully stocked woods, after all other marking is completed, the forest manager would select 40 additional trees to cut.   This system of arriving at the allowable cut is on the basis of numbers of trees.   In order intelligently to plan the work and make arrangements for the sale of surplus products, number of trees must be converted into products.   This is done by making a cruise or estimate of the volume of products contained in the trees marked for cutting.   Where there is a difference in values because of species or sizes, the estimate must be broken down to give the answers desired. The methods of doing this will be explained in a later part of this chapter.

Comparing Two Other Methods of Determining the Allowable Cut.   There are other ways of approximating the allowable cut, less desirable than the two already explained.   They can be used as a check on the two methods discussed, or as a quick judgment of possibilities in order to get an operation going.

One method is simply to guess at the growth rate using standard figures obtained by local foresters.   For example, the range in growth for upland hardwoods is usually from 100 to 300 ft. b.m. per acre per year.   For eastern white and red pine it is from 150 to 500 ft. b.m. Bottom-land hardwoods, good southern pine, and western forests of Douglas fir and white pine-hemlock often greatly exceed these figures. The forest manager might decide that his forest is probably growing at the rate of 200 ft. b.m. per acre per year.   If he cannot get any better figure and he wants to start cutting, he would be wise to use something less than that amount for the first 5-year cutting period. For 40 acres, the cut might be calculated at 40 × 150 = 6,000 ft. or 30,000 for 5 years in addition to that removed as salvage and in purely cultural operations.

Another rough check to determine how much volume to cut from the larger sizes is to estimate the volume in board feet in trees 12 in. d.b.h. and up.   Take 20 percent of this figure as the allowable cut for a 5-year period.   For example, the stand is estimated at 6,000 ft. per acre; 20 percent of this is 1,200 ft. in a period of 5 years plus the salvage and material from tops and thinnings.   The effect of this check might be to raise the estimate a little as obtained by the preceding method if the stand is obviously growing well.   For slow-growing forests, however, this last check is likely to give too large a cut.   These are rough guesses but sufficiently conservative as a basis for getting a woods operation started where the farmer is his own forest manager.   Any estimate of allowable cut should be checked before the end of the 5-year period, by a forester.   It is important, however, to get cutting operations started once the farmer has

Fig. 77.   Pine seedlings in a Louisiana forest as result of openings in the canopy.   Group selection.   (*Soil Conservation Service*.)

decided to grow wood as a farm crop.   He will learn as he goes.   Get forestry advice if it is available, but proceed with the cutting anyway, on a conservative basis.

Marking Trees for Harvest Cutting.   This is a distinct and separate operation from that for an improvement cutting or for any silvicultural cutting.   The rules for the former were given in this chapter under section 1, Improving the Forest by Cutting.   After all other marking is completed, the stand should be carefully examined again and the trees allotted for the harvest cut marked, using the number or volume of trees as the control.   Since stands vary tremendously, it is not feasible to say where and how the trees should be selected.   In some stands, they can be distributed uniformly over the entire forest or over the current year's cutting area.   In other cases, they may be bunched in one or several places to make clearings to release established young growth or to provide light to assist new seedlings to germinate and to grow (Fig. 77). Sometimes where most of the stand is mature, strip cuttings may be desirable, removing both mature and young trees within the strips. The different systems of silvicultural treatment will be further explained in this chapter under section 4, Applying Recognized Silvicultural Systems of Cutting.

3. Making Use of Management Aids

Experience in managing forests in both America and Europe has developed a few very useful aids that simplify and systematize the management job. These will be briefly described.

Following Cutting Cycles. These have been mentioned and at least partially explained in the preceding pages. The period of years between one cutting and the next on the same area is known as the cutting cycle. In the simplest case, an even-aged mature forest, over an understory of young growth, is clear cut. The years that must elapse before that young growth is ready for its first weeding or thinning is the first cutting cycle. It may be only one or two years or a longer period. The years that must elapse before another harvest cutting of mature trees may be the life span of the crop trees, but there is much cutting to do to ensure a full stand of crop trees that will grow at the maximum rate of which the site is capable. The elapsed time between cuttings, or the cutting cycle, depends upon how much is removed at each cutting and upon the growing capacity of the site. It is, therefore, obvious that the cutting cycle will vary according to the site, the forest type, the skill of the forest manager, and upon the occurrence of damage caused by storms, insects, and disease (Fig. 11).

The cutting cycle is a tool of management, but it is influenced as much by silvicultural factors as it is by the planned program of the forest manager. For example, a thinning is conducted in a pole stand using the $D + 6$ spacing rule. The appropriate cutting cycle is the time required for the crop trees in that particular stand to grow in size until the spacing becomes $D + 4$. In practice, depending upon the factors already mentioned, that may require from 4 to 10 or 12 years.

Foresters have generally recognized as desirable and have recommended a 5-year cutting cycle for the use of farmers. Very probably that is because the most common first cutting activity takes the form of an improvement cutting.   In the forest in need of such cutting, the stand commonly is understocked with desirable trees to form the growing stock, and there is a considerable volume of trees previously classed as *stagnant* and *salvage*.   It is not feasible, both for economic and for silvicultural reasons, immediately to cut so as to leave only thrifty growing desirable trees.   Even the *D*-plus rules can be applied only with approximate accuracy.   For economic reasons, it is best to concentrate the cut on a limited area rather than on the entire forest tract.   For silvicultural reasons, it is best to give the forest a chance to grow for a few years after cutting to determine the response to the operation.

For these reasons the 5-year cutting cycle has been recommended for use by farmers as one of the initial tools of management.   Perhaps some farmers will know enough about how their forests grow, based on past experience or on the advice of local foresters, to adopt initially a cutting cycle of 3 years or 7 years instead of 5 years.   Perhaps they will recognize that part of their forest is on a very good site, such as bottom-land hardwood, or they may have the best Douglas fir site or a thrifty stand of slash pine.   They tentatively might figure on a 3-year cutting cycle on such sites and a 5- or 7-year cycle on other parts of their forest tract.   In the absence of such conditions or knowledge, however, an average cutting cycle of 5 years is a good one with which to start.   Experience in management later will indicate desirable changes.   The forest manager will do well to watch the effect on his forest growth of the application of his adopted cutting cycle. This is perhaps one of the most important, and often the most neglected, means of keeping the trees that form the growing stock spaced so that they can grow at a maximum rate and still maintain full stocking.

Subdividing the Woods.   Division of the woodland into blocks or compartments is the next logical step in management.   For example, a 40-acre woods managed on a 5-year cutting cycle would be divided into 5 compartments of approximately 8 acres each, and 1 compartment would be cut each year.   If there is an obvious difference in the density or age of the forest in different portions, the compartments would be of different sizes so as to equalize the volume of products produced annually.

If the same 40-acre woodland presented two radically different site (or type) conditions justifying 3-year and 7-year cutting cycles, it might work out as shown in Table 14.

TABLE 14. PLAN OF CUTTING BY COMPARTMENTS—3- AND 7-YEAR CYCLE

Cutting by years	12 acres, 3-year cutting cycle, acres cut per year	28 acres 7-year cutting cycle, acres cut per year	Total acreage cut per year
1	4	4	8
2	4	4	8
3	4	4	8
4	4	4	8
5	4	4	8
6	4	4	8
7	4	4	8

In Table 14, 8 acres would be cut each year, and in 7 years a total of 56 acres would be worked over; 28 acres only once; 12 acres $2\frac{1}{3}$ times.

TABLE 15. PLAN OF CUTTING BY COMPARTMENTS—3- AND 5-YEAR CYCLE

Cutting by years	12 acres, 3-year cutting cycle, acres cut per year	28 acres, 5-year cutting cycle, acres cut per year	Total acreage cut per year
1	4	5.6	9.6
2	4	5.6	9.6
3	4	5.6	9.6
4	4	5.6	9.6
5	4	5.6	9.6

In Table 15, 9.6 acres would be partially cut each year or 48 acres in 5 years; 28 acres only once; 12 acres $1\frac{2}{3}$ times.

It is not always practicable to confine the annual cutting to one or two compartments as planned. Usually it can be done if the forest is reasonably uniform in type, density, and age class. Where radical differences occur, the market may be good for some species or products and poor for others. For example, the forest manager may have an opportunity to sell oak or pine piling or cedar poles. These may grow in only one place in his forest. He must, of course, get them where they grow. He may find a market for some low-grade products usually difficult to sell; he will cut them while the market exists.

The division of his forest into compartments should not interfere with a reasonable degree of flexibility in cutting to permit the forest manager to take advantage of market conditions. He may want to take all of his 5-year harvest cut in one year if the price advantages seem to be clear.   This is more likely in the case of low-grade, hard-to-sell products rather than high-grade products.   The latter can always be sold; the price is more likely to go up than down.   Nevertheless, the advantages of annual cutting in a farmer's woods are so great that some cutting should be planned for each year.   The value or the volume of the annual cuts should be approximately the same if it can be arranged, but this is not essential.

Keeping Records.   A record of products cut, the values of those used and sold, and the expenses incurred in producing them are essential to good business management.   Without records, it is often difficult to realize how much the woods do contribute to farm income. On the other hand, the records may prove that the net revenue is not sufficient to justify the time and effort required to develop a particular forest.   The records, if systematically maintained, may be an important factor in selling the farm if that should be necessary.   A good, well-managed woodland is a factor in fixing the total value of a farm, but one with records to prove an earned income over a period of years is a very decided asset.

For convenience in management, compartment boundaries usually are marked by roads, streams, ridges, blazed lines, or some combination of them.   Compartments (or blocks; the name is not important) are numbered, and records of cutting, expenses, and income are kept by years and by compartments.   If stand inventories are made, these are also kept by compartments (Fig. 85).

4. Applying Recognized Silvicultural Systems of Cutting

Forestry has been practiced in the United States, more or less, for at least 50 years and in Europe for a much longer time.   In other parts of the world, the field has been little explored.   It will be helpful to outline briefly the different silvicultural systems that have been applied to different types of forests in the United States and to point out the conditions where they have been found to be applicable to farm woodlands.

Using the Selection System.   This is sometimes called the single-tree selection system; it is the ideal method of cutting for farm wood-lands where stand conditions permit. It is defined as the removal of mature timber (of course, cultural operations proceed in addition to removal of mature trees), usually the oldest or largest trees, either as single scattered trees or in small groups, at relatively short intervals, repeated indefinitely, by means of which the continuous establishment

Fig. 78. Loblolly-shortleaf pine stand in Georgia after cutting selectively. (*Soil Conservation Service.*)

of natural reproduction in the stand is encouraged and an uneven-aged arrangement of tree sizes is maintained (Figs. 78 and 79).

This system of cutting breaks the overhead canopy as little as possible; hence it maintains the forest litter and the moisture, fertility, and organic matter of the soil. It presupposes a stand structure where all tree sizes can be maintained from seedlings to mature crop trees; it also assumes a growing stock made up of species sufficiently tolerant of shade that they will grow and thrive under such conditions. As a permanent silvicultural system, therefore, it is chiefly applicable to forests of tolerant species such as the beech-maple-hemlock-white pine forests of the north and the spruce-fir-hemlock forests wherever they occur. It is applicable also, as a beginning measure, to a large number of forest types even though the species making up the stand are characteristically intolerant. For example, it can be used in most stands of southern pine, in practically all hardwoods, and in ponderosa, lodgepole pine, and Douglas-fir stands of the West (Figs. 78 and 79).

The "beginning" measure may be continued until seedlings are needed to replace trees cut that cannot be grown without opening the canopy to admit more light. This situation leads to various modifications of the selection system attempting to retain as many as possible

Fig. 79. Second growth Douglas-fir stand in Oregon. Adapted to management under the selection system, at least for several decades. (*Soil Conservation Service.*)

of its obvious silvicultural advantages. Wherever there is a considerable variation in the sizes of trees making up the upper story of the forest canopy—in other words, the dominant, codominant, and intermediate trees—there is an opportunity to practice, for a time at least, the selection system. Removal of dominant trees makes growing space for the codominant and intermediate, which then grow into more profitable sizes before cutting. Sometimes even suppressed trees respond to more light and grow into crop trees. Sometimes the dominant trees may be left to grow to larger sizes, removing the codominant or intermediate. It depends on markets, age, and conditions of the stand. In most hardwoods, the selection system is applicable at least as a beginning measure. How long it can be continued in any forest is a problem for the forest manager to solve by watching the results of his cutting. Eventually, he must build a growing stock in which all sizes and ages of trees are represented. If he cannot achieve this result uniformly over his forest tract, he must do it by modifications of the selection system so as to produce the different sizes and ages on separate adjacent areas of his forest (Fig 80).

Using Group Selection. Although usually included in the definition of the selection system, group selection is in reality a modifica-

Fig. 80. Light improvement cutting in hemlock-hardwood type (New York). (*Soil Conservation Service.*)

tion of it. When it consists of choosing a few trees in one spot for removal, instead of only one, it is considered to be an integral part of the system. Obviously, as the groups of trees marked for cutting become larger and larger, the system is no longer intact. The forest manager, in response to the demands of his forest, has, to the extent of the size of the openings, changed from a selection system to some modification of it (Fig. 77).

Clear Cutting. Unfortunately this is sometimes necessary because of the condition of the stand. Confined to small areas of ¼ acre or less, it is a modification of the selection system often unavoidable in order to produce the stand structure wanted. For farm woodlands, it is rarely advisable to clear cut areas larger than ¼ acre at one time. The silvicultural reasons against clear cutting are many. Sun and wind dry the soil, the protective litter is soon dissipated, the biological life of the forest soil is seriously injured or destroyed. On slopes, erosion may wash away the topsoil. Weeds and brush may take over the growing space, necessitating their removal before seedlings of good trees can become established.

Clear cutting, even in small patches, wherever possible, should be limited to areas where desirable seedlings are already established. Then the forest cover is quickly reestablished and the evils of clear cutting are soon overcome. Where seedlings are not present, either their establishment by planting before or immediately after removal of the overhead canopy is advisable. Often natural reproduction can be obtained by a process of gradually, instead of suddenly, clear cutting the area. This is known as "shelterwood cutting" and will be explained in a moment.

Commercially, clear cutting often is practiced, followed by planting or by natural seeding from seed trees left for that purpose. Leave at least 10 to 12 trees per acre 12 in. d.b.h. and up with good crowns. This practice usually is confined to pure or nearly pure pine stands. Often advance growth of hardwoods and brush must be removed by burning, bulldozing, or poisoning before seedlings will grow. A modification sometimes used is *clear cutting in strips*. This practice is applicable to even-aged stands that have been previously cut selectively to the point where approximately all remaining trees are ready for the harvest cut. Clear cut a strip about the width represented by the height of the trees on the side of the forest opposite to the prevailing winds. As soon as the cutover strip has restocked with young trees and they are well established, cut a second strip. Cut strips successively in this way until the entire original stand is removed. Obviously, under this plan the rate of cutting can be held within the established "allowable cut." Farmers may find such strip cutting useful in reproducing forests of intolerant species. It has been used chiefly in softwood stands (Fig. 81).

Handling Coppice. Hardwood forests, managed on short rotations for small products, are clear cut according to any convenient pattern. Reproduction is from stump sprouts and root suckers. Such stands are known as "coppice." The system has the advantage of quickly reestablishing the forest cover with minimum disturbance to the forest soil. Coppice woods grow rapidly, and if the products are salable at satisfactory prices, the system works very well. The new forest must be weeded and thinned since too many sprouts arise from each stump.   Limit the sprouts to one from each stump, choosing one originating near the base.   Cut trees, preferably with an ax, leaving low stumps with a slanting top.   This tends to prevent rot. Low-stump sprouts grow better and are more apt to remain free from decay than those originating at the top of the stump.   The system is

Fig. 81. Clear-cutting in strips, spruce-fir type, the Frazer Experimental Forest, Colorado. (*U.S. Forest Service.*)

applicable to strips of woods maintained as shelter belts around fields where crops are grown requiring wind and frost protection.   In such cases, of course, extend the cutting over a period of years so as to maintain at all times a sufficient stand for protective purposes.   Some farmers may find the coppice system of management useful (Fig. 82).

Making a Shelterwood Cutting.   This is used as a means of securing natural reproduction where more light is required than is obtainable in the usual selective cutting.   It is therefore, in effect, a modification of the selection system.   In strips, in small groups, or in larger areas, gradually thin the overhead stand to wider and wider spacing to encourage the establishment of seedlings.   The length of time required to accomplish this largely depends upon the species and the occurrence of seed years.   As soon as a satisfactory young stand is established, remove the remaining trees. It is a safer plan than clear cutting because the soil is always protected and the young growth is not exposed to wind and frost. There is sometimes the danger of wind throw as the spacing of trees increases. This is especially true on shallow soils. The plan is worth trying where

FIG. 82. Coppice forest (Virginia).   (*Soil Conservation Service.*)

reproduction does not readily appear when the forest is being cut under the selection system (Figs. 83 and 84).

Making a Partial Cutting. This is a term that has crept into forestry literature. It may mean almost any form of cutting, short of clear cutting the entire stand. Usually it means some form of selective cutting, but it may also mean clear cutting in small patches or strip cutting. It is not a very specific term, and its meaning must be arrived at by a study of the subject matter discussed.

Disposing of the Slash. Slash disposal is not really a part of the discussion of silvicultural systems, but it is at least a corollary of them. Dry slash constitutes a fire hazard. In high-hazard areas it commonly is piled and burned at a safe time, sometimes on the entire cutover area, sometimes merely along roads and trails. Where selective cutting is followed, the slash ordinarily does not require piling and burning.   Limbs should be lopped from tops so that the slash will lie close to the ground.   Under such conditions it will soon disappear and form part of the litter of the forest soil.   This is the desirable practice for most types of cutting where the risk of fire does not preclude it. Often exposure of the mineral soil aids seedlings to start.   Disturbance

Fig. 83. Shelterwood cutting in white pine (New York).   (*College of Forestry, Syracuse, N.Y.*)

of the litter incident to logging may be sufficient, or additional effort by plow or disk may be required.   Burning the slash may also accomplish the desired result.   In case of doubt, consult the state forester.   A few piles of brush and debris scattered through the forest furnish cover for some forms of wildlife.   This may be a worth-while practice.

Following Silvicultural Systems.   A few of the principal types of forest in the United States are very briefly described to indicate the applicable silvicultural system.   Seek the advice of local foresters in

such matters.   The following discussion will be helpful in getting a
perspective picture of the whole field, but it cannot replace specific
on the ground advice.

For Northern Hardwoods.   Mixtures are of beech, birch, maple, white
ash, basswood, elm, and often more or less spruce, pine, hemlock.

FIG. 84. Shelterwood cutting in loblolly-shortleaf pine in Texas.   In 1938, 32 trees over
9.5 in. d.b.h. per acre were left.   Picture taken in 1948.   (*Southern Forest Experiment Station,
U.S. Forest Service.*)

Improvement cuttings usually are the first measures to be taken;
cut lightly.

If the stand structure is right, that is, if there is a reasonably good
distribution of size classes, the selection system is admirably adapted
to this type.   Take not more than 30 percent of the volume in any one
cut, less than this if at all practicable.

Where mature and overmature trees make up most of the stand, and
the younger age classes are mostly in the understory especially with

good reproduction present, some form of clear cutting followed by cultural measures in the young growth is indicated. Cutting of the overstory should be complete, cutting, girdling, or poisoning worthless trees. Stay within the allowable cut. Short-lived trees such as popple, pin cherry, red maple, and paper birch in the understory will not stop the growth of sugar maple, yellow birch, white ash, or the conifers.

For Bottom-land Hardwoods. These present special problems. The type is most common in the extensive wet overflow lands of the South. Wonderful growth and high-quality yields are possible from well-managed stands. Growth rates of 1,000 to 2,000 ft. b.m. per acre per year (and even more) are possible. A great variety of species are present, including many inferior ones. The best species commonly are red, willow, water, cow, and cherry-bark oaks, cottonwood, white and green ash, red gum, persimmon, mulberry, and cypress.

Unfortunately most stands have been cut, burned, and grazed until they now contain a great quantity of inferior species, wolf trees, and crooked and defective specimens of the better species. The soil is excellent for timber growth. In many localities markets exist for a large variety of products; hence the possibilities of profitable management are great.

Improvement cuttings are recommended to develop the most profitable growing stocks. In most stands this will require several cutting cycles, but reasonably profitable operations are possible now with greatly increased profits assured for the future. The advice of local foresters and the results of studies conducted by the forest experiment stations are essential to get the best results. The details of management cannot be given in this text.

For Other Hardwood Types. There are so many variations due to site, composition, climatic, and altitudinal range that generalized suggestions for management have little value. The more common mixtures are red, black, and white oak, hickory, beech, black cherry, with various additions on the better sites of yellow poplar, sugar maple, ash, gum, white pine, and hemlock.

On the poorer sites the oaks are prominent, sometimes with one of the yellow pines added, grading off into almost pure scrub oak, characterized by blackjack and post oak. In general a selection system or some modification of it, is applicable to most of these stands. Sometimes the scrub-oak type gradually can be converted to pine either through natural reproduction or underplanting. But normally the best plan is to accept what Nature has started, favoring the best species but making no effort entirely to eliminate the inferior species. In most oak-hickory forests, the management of the soil must be given special attention. Closed borders, complete absence of fire and grazing, encouragement of dogwood, maple, ash, and any broadleaf shrubs whose leaves improve the composition of the forest litter are all helpful. In cutting, open up the canopy as little as possible in order to accomplish what must be done. Use shelterwood and small clearcut areas to secure natural reproduction, but get a new forest cover started as quickly as possible, if need be by planting seedlings or nuts.

For Spruce-Fir. Stands of this type are often managed primarily to produce pulpwood. This means crop-tree sizes of about 12 in. d.b.h. On farm woodlands a part of the stand should be managed for saw logs to supply farm lumber. The selection system is applicable, with spruce the favored species. Where the stand is made up of tall, slender, close-growing trees with small crowns, clear cutting in small patches or in strips is necessary (Figs. 77, 81). Do this after young growth is established and has attained a height of at least two feet. If reproduction is not present, try a shelterwood cutting to induce reproduction. This must be done carefully since these species are easily wind thrown.

For Eastern White Pine. Pure stands of this species occur in the North. They are normally even aged and have originated on old fields. On the better soils hardwood reproduction comes in and is likely to take control of the site in spite of the desires of the forest manager. After the stand has been cut selectively, as long as that system is profitable, by allowing the smaller trees to reach crop-tree size, some form of clear cutting is indicated, followed by cultural work with the hardwood understory. On these sites, hardwoods will almost inevitably succeed the pine. On lighter soils, pine reproduction can be established and maintained to produce the next crop. The character of the growth will indicate the system of management. Selective cutting can often be practiced for a period of years, gradually changing to shelterwood to permit young trees to become established prior to making the final harvest cutting (Fig. 83). The blister-rust disease of white pine must be controlled in order successfully to grow this species. Consult local foresters or the state forester.

For Other Northern Pine Stands. Stands of *jack* and *red pine*, which are intolerant species, must be reproduced by some form of clear cutting.

Sometimes hardwoods will succeed the pine.   On the lighter soils pine reproduction can be secured and developed by cultural operations. There are many details of management that can only be explained by local foresters or from literature obtained from the state forester.

For Shortleaf—Loblolly Pine Stands of the South.   These can be managed, using the selection system.   This is not strictly true of all such stands, but it is true of many, especially in Arkansas, Louisiana, and Texas.   Most of this type is in reality a mixture of pine and hardwood. The latter are the inferior low-valued species.   Some cultural work to get rid of hardwoods where they occupy the ground to the exclusion of pine is necessary.   Numerous examples of successful management of such stands exist.   The most prominent is the Crossett Experimental Forest in Arkansas maintained by the Southern Forest Experiment Station at Crossett, Arkansas.   These pines have the ability to grow, when young, under the forest shade.   Slight modifications of the selection system are usually needed in every forest stand.   This type is no exception (Fig. 78).

In some places, hardwood competition becomes more severe. Extreme measures, such as cutting, girdling, or poisoning large hardwoods and destruction of ground cover by means of controlled burning or poisoning or by bulldozing, is necessary to free or establish pine reproduction.   Under such conditions, some form of clear cutting of the pine when ready for harvest cutting becomes essential.   In farm woodlands the first cutting should be on the improvement basis, using the selection system.   Get the advice of local foresters if pine reproduction fails when it is needed.   Local forestry advice also will be needed where the "little leaf" disease is slowing the growth of or killing shortleaf pine.   A very different management policy than the one suggested may be necessary.

For Slash and Longleaf Pine.   Management of these pine stands will be discussed in Chap. 10.

Virginia Pine.   This scrub-pine type occurs throughout the eastern United States, mostly in the southern half.   It is most often a farmer's problem because characteristically it occupies abandoned fields.   It is a temporary type—a nurse crop.   It is one of Nature's ways of restoring the soil on eroded fields.   Often the trees are very limby and rough, approaching the status of wolf trees, but where the stands are dense, the trees grow straight and produce fairly clean boles.

Management of such stands should take into consideration Nature's obvious plan to restore the site to better pines or the original hardwood type.   Improvement cuttings are the first order of business in order to develop the maximum number of usable or salable trees.   When the crowns of the trees begin to flatten and grow thin, the stand is mature and ready gradually to be converted to a better type. Encouragement of hardwood young growth and underplanting with one of the better species of hard pines will hasten the transition. Shelterwood or strip cuttings would seem to be the final stage.   There will still be considerable scrub pine in the new crop, but the measures indicated will greatly improve the quality of the next crop.   If conversion is attempted before the scrub pines reach their maturity, the effort is likely to fail because Nature is not yet ready for the transition.

For Ponderosa Pine.   This type covers extensive areas throughout the Rocky Mountains and the Pacific Coast states, sometimes in pure stands but often mixed with Douglas fir, true firs, hemlock, and spruce. In the northern Rockies it merges somewhat with lodgepole pine and larch and on the West Coast with sugar pine and other species.   The pine is an intolerant species and tends to grow in even-aged groups, but all ages are often mixed on small areas.   In general the character of growth lends itself to management using the selection system and the group selection modification of it.   Many of the associated species are more tolerant than the pine.   Natural reproduction is sometimes postponed many years until a good seed year and a favorable growing season are coincident.   Moderate grazing of domestic animals is the rule, and such dual uses are not seriously conflicting, provided grazing is limited to the carrying capacity of the forage.   Production of forage and timber can be successfully managed on the same area so as to yield a satisfactory crop of both.   Farmers have no difficulty in managing this type of forest on the selection system.

For Lodgepole Pine.   This type covers large areas in the central and northern Rocky Mountain states.   Normally it is a nearly pure stand, but in places it has a mixture of Douglas fir and spruce.   Characteristically, lodgepole pine grows in even-aged stands, many of them originating after extensive fires.   It is generally considered to be a temporary type, but the transition to its ecological climax type apparently will require many generations of lodgepole.   For purposes of management, it may be treated as a permanent type, since reproduction of the lodgepole and associated species is easily obtained.

Normally, most lodgepole stands contain a wide range of size classes. The stand structure is favorable for selective cutting, and practically all stands require one or more improvement cuttings. Favor spruce and Douglas fir in marking where they occur and seem to be thrifty. Continued management will eventually lead to some form of clear cutting. Research indicates that strip cutting for the final harvest will be the outcome (Fig. 81).

For Pacific Coast Douglas Fir. This type occurs chiefly west of the Cascades in Washington and Oregon and in northern California. From the standpoint of heavy yields of good-quality timber over a large area, it is one of the most important in the United States. From the standpoint of farm forestry, it is equally important because so many farms in the region include good second-growth stands. Generally market conditions are favorable. Sites vary considerably, and it is important for a farmer to understand about what his site is. Douglas-fir stands are practically all even-aged, but they contain a wide distribution of size classes admirably suited to the selective system of cutting until the time is reached for the final harvest cut (Fig. 79). That time will come after repeated thinnings and improvement cuttings when the crop trees have reached the planned maturity size. This is usually about 80 years for the average site. If preliminary cutting has continued to about that age, the stand will have developed good medium-sized saw logs, depending on the growth capacity of the site. Then it is time to get reproduction established and remove the remaining crop trees. The indicated method is clear cutting in strips, staggered settings, or small blocks.

In many stands, cutting for wood products can begin when they have reached 25 years. Cutting for Christmas trees and small poles, of course, will come earlier. Continue cuttings at about 5-year intervals (cutting cycles) until the maturity size is reached. Douglas-fir trees will grow well with close spacing. About $D + 2$ seems to be the approximate spacing generally considered desirable. This point should be checked with local foresters since continued study may show a different spacing to be desirable. If harvest cuts are needed before the stand reaches its maturity size, it can be determined by the use of Table 13. For example, $D + 2$ spacing indicates 90 crop trees per acre at 20 in. d.b.h. If this size represents 80 years on the particular site, about 1 crop tree could be marked for cutting per acre per year, after the cultural marking is completed. If the 20-in. tree can be grown in 50 years, since $90 \div 50 = 1.8$, approximately two of the largest trees could be cut annually.   Closed borders are of importance in Douglas-fir management, as in most other types.   Cut lightly or not at all near the edges of the forest.

For Other Types.   Many other prominent forest types are important in some localities.   For example, the larch-fir is important in the northern Rockies, the ponderosa-sugar pine in California.   These are successfully handled by the selective system or some modification of it. Other locally important types are northern spruce swamps, southern cedar and cypress swamps, and the redwood forests of California. Where these constitute an opportunity for farm management, the farmer should seek local forestry advice.   The problems are peculiar to these types, and any general statements would be of little value.

5. Estimating Timber by Sample Plots

As previously explained, regulation of cutting on farm woodlands so as to produce continuous crops can be accomplished by a combination of cultural treatments and harvest cuttings.   The volume to be cut, in terms of products, can be estimated by tabulating the marked trees according to sizes and, if necessary, by species and quality and multiplying the numbers thus obtained by standard or average figures of products per tree given in volume tables prepared for the purpose. Volume tables applicable to local forest types can be obtained from the state foresters.   For example, the estimate may show 9 trees 18 in. d.b.h. and each containing two 16-ft. logs.   The volume tables on pages 351–356 give the average contents of such trees.   The International rule (page 351) gives about 250 ft. b.m.   The Doyle rule (page 352) gives about 180 ft. b.m.   The result then will be 9 × 250 = 2,250 ft. b.m. or 9 × 180 = 1,620 ft. b.m. depending upon the log rule used. Other tree sizes would be totaled and the volume determined in a similar way.

The list of total products thus obtained enables the forest manager to negotiate sales for products surplus to the farm needs and to plan for the labor and equipment required to cut and process the products. It also will enable him, if necessary, to change the marking in order better to fit products to the markets available and thus ensure a profitable operation.

Cruising Timber.   This is the name commonly applied to the several methods that can be used in arriving at the total estimated volume of products in all or part of the timber stand.

1. All of the marked trees can be measured at breast height and the total height or number of merchantable logs in each estimated by eye or with an instrument. Records are kept on a "tally" sheet either clipped to a board or bound into a book.

2. Only a specified part of the total area marked is covered and a record made as explained. Another method is to mark trees for cutting and estimate the products on ¼- or ⅕-acre sample plots. Then later mark the balance of the cutting area based on the pattern developed on the sample plots. This is the sampling method. Its use makes necessary these additional facts; the total area (usually in acres) containing the marked trees (or the area of the cutting planned) and the exact area covered by the estimator's (or cruiser's) record or tally. The relation between the total area, A, and the area covered by the estimate, a, A/a is the figure to use in multiplying the totals on the tally sheets to arrive at the totals on the entire cutting area. For example, the area to be cut is 10 acres, the area actually tallied is 1 acre taken in 5 ⅕-acre plots. The cruise has been made on a 10-percent basis. The cruise data are multiplied by 10 to arrive at the total products to be cut.

The choice of methods depends upon the accuracy required by the forest manager in the total list of products. Obviously, the highest degree of accuracy will be obtained by measuring each marked tree. This gives a 100-percent estimate but never (except by accident) 100-percent accuracy. Hidden defects in the trees, breakage in falling, small errors in measuring, and necessary approximations in the volume tables all contribute to a final result that may be from 3 to 5 percent above or below the final figures arrived at by measuring the processed products. Therefore as much as 3 percent variation, more or less, in the total estimate is about the best that can be expected.

If the forest manager is satisfied with the possibility of a larger error in the estimate, the time and cost of the cruise can be reduced. The larger the forest area to be cruised and the more uniform the cover, the smaller can be the percentage cruised to attain the same degree of accuracy. Through statistical analysis of the results of a few sample plots, the total number of plots needed to give a specified degree of accuracy in the estimate of products can be determined. This process is not necessary for small woodlands. Rough guides will be sufficient. Assume an accuracy of about 20 percent in the total estimate or a variation of plus or minus 20 percent as compared to the final measurement. Then the figures in Table 16 can be used as a guide.

Of course there is a large element of doubt about what is a uniform or an irregular stand; also the cruise figures are based on the total volume of products, for example, board feet log scale.   If, for example, the estimate is broken down into trees 12 to 17 in. and trees over 17 in. or divided by species or by products, the accuracy of the estimate decreases rapidly.   Where a high degree of accuracy is required, it is best to make a 100 percent cruise especially where small areas are involved.

A 100 percent cruise is made by systematically covering the area and measuring every tree.   After measuring, each tree must be

TABLE 16. PERCENTAGE OF CRUISE TO AN ACCURACY OF PLUS OR MINUS 20 PERCENT

Acres to be cruised	Stand uniform	Stand irregular or patchy
10 or less........................	25	50
Acres to cruise in 10.............	2.5	5.0
11–20...........................	15	30
Acres to cruise in 20.............	3.0	6.0
21–40...........................	10	20
Acres to cruise in 40.............	4.0	8.0
Over 40.........................	5	10
Acres to cruise in 80.............	4.0	8.0

identified by chalk mark, bark scraper, or some other means to avoid duplication.   Less than a 100 percent cruise is made by a system of sampling.   For farm woodlands, circular plots of $\frac{1}{4}$- or $\frac{1}{5}$-acre each are recommended.   The $\frac{1}{5}$-acre plot is a little easier to handle and is preferred.   The radius of a circle containing $\frac{1}{4}$ acre is 58.9 ft.; containing $\frac{1}{5}$ acre, 52.7 ft.; containing $\frac{1}{10}$ acre, 37.2 ft.   Rounded off, the distances are 59, 52.5, and 37 ft.

A sample plot cruise involves two area factors—the area of the sample plots and the area of the timberland to which the samples apply. If a good map of the forest exists so that the acreage of that part of the forest to which the samples apply can be determined, it is only necessary to measure the area of each plot.   If no reliable map is available, the common method of procedure is what is known as the line and plot survey (Fig. 85).

By running straight lines at fixed distances apart and taking the sample plots at fixed intervals along the lines, the data for a map and determination of acreage is obtained.   In this case distances should be measured by means of a surveyor's chain or a steel tape.   Lines should

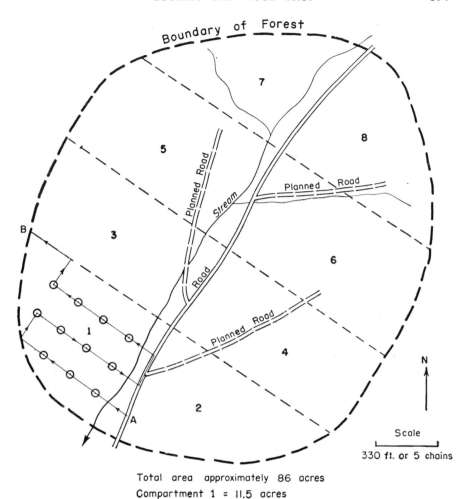

Total area approximately 86 acres

Compartment 1 = 11.5 acres

FIG. 85. Forest map showing compartments, roads, and drainage. Line and plot survey in compartment 1 starting at point A taking one $\frac{1}{5}$ acre plot every 165 ft. or 2.5 chains; 3 plots for the first line and 4 for the second and third gives 11 plots or 2.2 acres or $\frac{2.2}{11.5} = 19\%$ cruise.

be run with a pocket compass. For example, in Fig. 85 compartment 1 shows the line and plot survey. Initial point at A is 2.5 chains or 165 ft. from the southern edge of the forest. The lines are also 165 ft. apart, and the plots are at 165-ft. spacing along the lines. The line ends on the boundary at B. The square formed by the three cruise lines and the north boundary of the compartment is 10 by 7.5 chains or 7.5 acres. The triangle at the left (west) of the square contains about 1.5 acres, (7.5 × 4 chains)/2, and the portion on the southern edge about 2 acres. The calculated total is therefore 11 acres, which is sufficiently close for all practical purpose to the indicated acreage on the map. Of course there are other ways of calculating the acreage such as an acreage grid (see Appendix V, pages 359 to 362).

Measuring Sample Plots. This work must be done carefully. Errors have a tendency to multiply rapidly. Two men are essential for satisfactory and rapid sample plot work. Measurements required are:

1. Distance from center point to outer edge of circle. This should be made with a linen or steel tape along two radii and the points on the circumference plainly marked.
2. Diameter in inches at breast height (d.b.h.) of each tree, made with calipers or a cruiser's stick (Figs. 86 to 88).
3. The number of 16-ft. logs in each tree or the merchantable length in feet or the total heights in feet (depending upon what volume table is used or what products the tree contains). Heights or merchantable lengths with a little practice can be determined by eye, or the cruiser's stick or a hypsometer can be used.

Measuring fallen trees to help the cruiser's judgment is a common practice.

One man keeps the book or tally sheet and records the measurements called out by the cruiser (the man responsible for the cruise). Table 19 shows one form of tally sheet. One tally sheet can serve for one or several plots as long as the record is clear. If there is no change in the character of the timber justifying an area separation of the estimate, the only reason for changing tally sheets is one of convenience. However, great care must be exercised to keep track of the number of plots included on one tally sheet. An error here is fatal.

The next step is to add and transfer to a master sheet the total trees in each classification, for example: White oak, 14 in., 1 log; 16 in., 1 log, 2 log; 18 in., 2 log, 3 log, and so forth.

Then apply the volume-table figures to these numbers of trees. The totals are most easily converted to the basis of one acre and multiplied by the acres included in the area cruised or multiplied by the converting factor as already explained $\left(\dfrac{\text{Total acres}}{\text{Acres cruised}}\right)$. One other factor must be considered, known as the "cull," or the defect in the trees that will reduce the usable volume. Breakage in logging, especially on rough rocky ground, may be a considerable factor. These probable but unknown reductions in the final estimate are made by the cruiser on a percentage basis. Often a different cull factor is used for different species in the stand. Experience is about

TABLE 17. STAND TABLE UPLAND OAK TYPE OF NORTHEASTERN UNITED STATES *
Age class 100 years; good site

D.b.h., in.	Species, number per acre			
	White oak	Black oak	All others	Total
6	7	1	6	14
7	10	1	7	18
8	11	2	6	19
9	11	3	5	19
10	11	4	4	19
11	9	6	3	18
12	6	9	2	17
13	4	9	1	14
14	2	8	1	11
15	2	7	0	9
16	1	6	0	7
17	0	4	0	4
18	0	2	0	2
19	0	1	0	1
20	0	1	0	1
Total...	74	64	35	173

* From G. Luther Schnur, *Yield, Stand and Volume Tables for Even Aged Upland Oak Forests*, U.S. Forest Service, Allegheny Forest Experiment Station, Technical Bulletin 560, April, 1937.

the only teacher. The cull factor may be 5 to 10 percent or even larger. Usually in apparently sound timber, a reduction of 5 percent should be ample. In old trees, where broken or dead limbs, cat-faces, or holes are visible, the defects may seriously reduce the usable volume. Inquire of local timbermen about cull factors, or if there is evidence of heavy cull, employ a consulting forester or cruiser to estimate your timber.

All this sounds complicated. This is true if many species and much variation in products are involved, but a little practice helps over-come many of the seeming complications. Be sure to get suitable volume tables before starting any estimating work. In Appendix

III, pages 351 to 356, will be found two volume tables.   Others are similar in form; sometimes they are applicable to only one species. The recent trend, however, is to use generalized volume tables and use them for a large number of species.

If two or more different age classes or different types of timber are

TABLE 18. AVERAGE STAND TABLE OLD-GROWTH NORTHERN HARDWOODS, MINNESOTA*

D.b.h., in.	Species, number per acre					
	Sugar maple	Basswood	Elm	Oaks	All others	Total
6	6.15	3.11	1.89	2.90	5.41	19.46
8	4.66	2.33	1.14	1.19	3.06	12.38
10	4.60	2.78	1.36	0.90	1.99	11.63
12	3.41	2.61	2.39	0.73	1.08	10.22
14	3.47	2.33	1.53	0.91	0.57	8.81
16	2.67	2.44	1.59	0.80	0.62	8.12
18	1.53	1.59	0.85	0.74	0.35	5.06
20	0.85	1.02	0.80	0.34	0.12	3.13
22	0.34	0.40	0.62	0.28	0.06	1.70
24	0.17	0.34	0.51	....	0.06	1.08
26	0.06	0.17	0.34	0.17	....	0.74
28	0.11	....	0.17	....	....	0.28
30	....	....	0.17	....	....	0.17
32	....	....	0.17	....	....	0.17
38	....	....	0.06	....	....	0.06
Total...	28.02	19.12	13.59	8.96	13.32	83.01

* Stand and Stock Tables for Selected Forest Cover Types in the Lake States, U.S. Forest Service, Lake States Forest Experiment Station; unpublished data in library, U.S. Department of Agriculture, Washington, D.C.

involved, both the acres in each and the tally sheets must be kept separate.   Reliable estimates cannot be obtained if such radically different stands are combined as bottom-land hardwood and the upland type, or a stand to be cut only for pulpwood thinning and one to be cut for saw logs.   In this discussion there has been mentioned only the cruising of marked trees.   It is easy to understand that the trees not marked could also be included in the cruise, and with the data obtained, a stand table for the uncut forest could be prepared.   A stand table shows for the average acre (or for the entire area) the number, diameter, and species of trees present.   The stand structure, so often mentioned in this text, can then be studied on the basis of actual data (Tables 17 and 18).

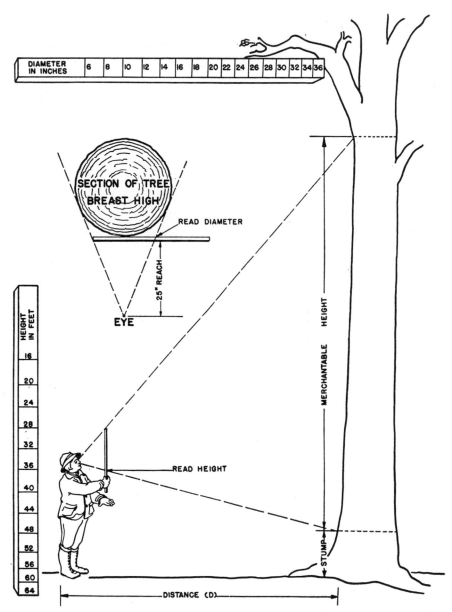

Fig. 86. Cruiser stick for measuring the diameters and heights. (*U.S. Department of Agriculture.*)

The tools needed for timber estimating are:

1. A small *pocket compass* to run lines. This is essential if a satisfactory map does not already exist. It is helpful also in making changes in the maps and in laying out roads.

2. A *surveyor's chain* or a *steel tape* for measuring distances in feet, rods, or chains. Counting steps or "pacing" is sufficient for approximations, but

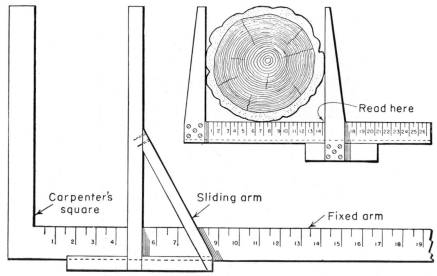

FIG. 87. Caliper for measuring tree diameters. (*U.S. Forest Service.*)

where a map is to be made, distances should be measured as precisely as possible. For measuring the radius of the circle to be used as a sample plot, there is no substitute for the steel (or linen) tape. Pacing is sufficient to determine the radius at other points *after two measurements with the tape have been made* on each plot.

3. A *cruiser's stick* (Fig. 86) for measuring diameters and merchantable lengths or total height. Tree calipers are more exact for measuring diameters, but a little practice enables a woodsman to get satisfactory results with the cruiser's stick. The latter is much more convenient and has the added advantage that it can be used to determine vertical lengths in feet.

Calipers or cruiser's sticks can be obtained from manufacturers of instruments used by engineers and foresters. Sometimes they are supplied by local agencies as a public service. Consult the state forester.

4. A *tally sheet* (Table 19) and a *clip board* (Fig. 89) or a suitable tally book. Most cruisers find the loose sheets more convenient. They are clipped to a board similar to those in use in most offices. Sufficient sheets for a day's cruise can be clipped to the board. They can be purchased or made at home.

It is important to have the tally sheet prepared as nearly ready for use as can be foreseen. Cold, heat, insects, and rain all make it difficult to

FIG. 88. Farmer in Louisiana cruising his timber with the help of his wife. He is using a diameter tape which is accurate, but the calipers or cruisers stick saves time.

rule an appropriate sheet in the woods. There should be room on the sheets for recording unexpected information and for the notes about topography, species, and quality of products.

5. Pencil, eraser, small straight edge, and chalk, or lumberman's crayon or a bark scraper, complete the list of tools. Chalk, crayon, or scraper are useful in putting temporary marks on trees as they are measured. This ensures that there will be no duplications. Chalk or crayon is usually satisfactory, but the bark scraper is more convenient. It can be purchased or made in any workshop.

Fig. 89. A clip board is convenient for tallying timber data in the woods. (*Northeast Pulpwood Research Center, Gorham, N.H.*)

TABLE 19. SAMPLE, CRUISER'S TALLY SHEET
MADE BY: _____ DATE: _____ PROPERTY OF: _____
SIZE OF PLOT: _____ NUMBER OF PLOTS ON THIS TALLY: _____

D.b.h., in.	Number of 16-ft. logs															
	White oak				Pine				Red oak				Other hardwoods			
	1	2	3	4	1	2	3	4	1	2	3	4	1	2	3	4
12																
14																
16																
18																
20																

Dot and line method of tallying by tens.

6. The *volume tables* can be obtained from the state forester or from the U.S. Forest Service, Washington, D.C. Several general tables will be found in Appendix III, pages 351 to 355.

6. Processing Wood Products

The advantages that accrue to farmers in cutting the trees and processing the products that are included in the schedule of woods operations have been repeatedly stressed in this text. Practically all publications on farm forestry emphasize these advantages. A brief summary at this point is in order.

1. The logging job is the means of carrying out the plans of woods management. No contract logger or buyer of stumpage has an interest in anything but making a profit on the one operation; the forest manager's interest is in developing a forest that will yield profits over an indefinite future. It is very difficult to prepare a contract that will safeguard the interests of the forest owner. In the cutting operation, many opportunities that cannot be foreseen in the advance planning will present themselves to take or leave trees. The forest manager who supervises his own cutting operation has complete control. He can make any changes that arc needed as the work progresses to improve either his forest or his profit. When the job is finished, he has the best growing stock that he is able to produce under the existing market and forest conditions.

2. The forest manager is learning how to grow wood as a farm crop. Whatever spare farm labor is available is being trained to do woods work. He can plan and carry out annual operations in the woods. He will gradually acquire the equipment and the skill to do this. He will learn the wood markets and adapt his management so as to produce, in the future, more profitable trees. His operations can be limited or expanded, depending on his labor and his wood markets. He does not have to sell greater quantities of products than his allowable cut permits in order to make the operation profitable to a logger. He can cut and sell whatever he chooses, not what a contractor demands.

3. Once the forest manager learns how to cut and market his wood products, his profits will be very much greater than if he sells stumpage—his income can be multiplied as much as three times over that obtainable on a stumpage basis. At the same time his labor is a stable factor; farm labor utilized in the woods annually helps keep good labor employed year long.

The following pages will discuss briefly some of the common methods of cutting and handling products in small woods operations. Many farmers are familiar with tools, equipment, and methods used

in processing wood products.   This review of the subject is intended
as a general presentation to acquaint those unfamiliar with woods
work with the major steps involved.   Cutting and processing wood
products is a relatively simple operation.   With good tools and
equipment and a little experience, it is no more complicated or
hazardous than many other farm operations.   For details of equipment and methods, the reader is referred to the manufacturers of the
equipment and to various specialized publications on the subject
included in the list of references (Appendix I).

Making the Woodland Accessible.   A *good road system* to make the
forest accessible at most seasons of the year is an asset of great value.
Trucks have done most of the hauling of wood products in recent
years.   Therefore the permanent roads should be built and maintained with this method of transportation in mind.   Cutting may be
planned for the next few years only in compartments already accessible.   However, wind or storm or insects or especially good markets
for some classes of timbers may make it advisable to cut products in
more distant places.   A good road that touches all compartments
adds a flexibility in the management obtainable in no other way
(Fig. 85).

The total rods or miles of road that can or should be built in a
particular forest depends upon the character of the timber, its age
class, and its value as well as upon the cost of a permanent road.
Naturally, a forest manager will proceed cautiously where road
building and maintenance are expensive.   In some cases, as already
mentioned, it may be worth while to sell a sizable portion of the
merchantable timber as stumpage, with the requirement that the
buyer build the necessary roads and bridges to make the forest accessible.   In such cases, the specifications for the improvements should be
carefully drawn and strictly complied with.   If at all possible, it is
better to make the investment in the roads and then sell enough
forest products to pay for them.

Woods roads need not be built to a high standard.   Four- and
six-wheel drive trucks commonly used in the woods can travel over a
fairly rough road, with upgrades against the load of 10 to 15 percent.
Curves should have radii of not less than 80 ft.   Good drainage along
and across the roads is essential.   In order to reduce skidding costs,
it is usually best to have the truck-loading point close (less than 600
ft.) to points where the wood is cut, but it depends on costs of road

building. If the road-building job seems to represent a considerable investment, the services of a logging engineer or consulting forester should be obtained.

Providing Skid Trails. A good system of skid trails to form a network connecting with loading points will make logging easier; the trails constitute the next step in developing the woodland-cutting plan. The distances between skid trails depend upon the topography

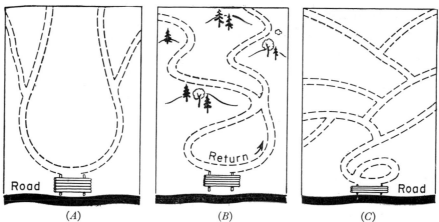

(A)   (B)   (C)

FIG. 90. Layout of skid trails: (A) good for gentle slope—straight trails, moderate curves; (B) good for steep slope—zigzag path to reduce grade; (C) a poor layout for gentle slope—sharp curves, unneccessary skidding. (*From Northeastern Loggers' Handbook, Agriculture Handbook No. 6.*)

and the skidding device to be used. Skid trails for tractors can be 150 ft. apart; for horses about 60 ft. apart. Gentle downgrades are ideal; upgrades or level stretches reduce the efficiency of skidding; swampy places, rocks, and stumps cause trouble. Usually simple grading and removal of brush is sufficient for horse trails. Well-placed fender logs help keep the load on the trail on steep slopes or to get it past an obstruction. Sometimes simple open-top culverts are needed to prevent damage from running water. After logging is completed, mats of brush across the skid trails about every 50 ft. with tops uphill in close contact with the soil will tend to preserve the trails for future use and prevent serious erosion. Figure 90 gives three sample layouts for skid trails.

Building Skidways. These are prepared places to hold logs waiting to be loaded on wagons or trucks. Foundation logs are placed firmly in the ground, usually at the base of a slope, so that logs can be piled crosswise of the skids. By blocking the front logs, the pile is held until released, when the logs can be rolled with peaveys or

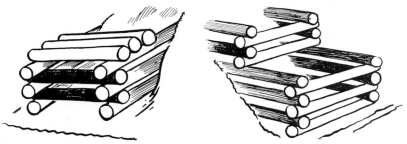

FIG. 91. A skidway on a hillside. (*From Northeastern Loggers' Handbook, Agriculture Handbook No. 6.*)

FIG. 92. A double-deck skidway. (*From Northeastern Loggers' Handbook, Agriculture Handbook No. 6.*)

cant hooks onto the wagon, sleigh, or truck. Sometimes, more or less crib work is needed to make a safe landing (Figs. 91 and 92).

Choosing Tools and Equipment. Logging tools and equipment are available in great variety. Only a few, considered to be essential for simple logging jobs, will be mentioned here.

Axes. These are of various types and weights, depending largely on individual preference. The single-bit ax is a safer tool than the double-bit, but professional loggers usually use the latter.

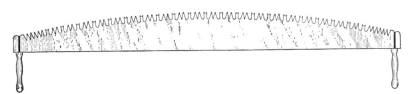

FIG. 93. Crosscut saw.

Hand Saws. Most commonly used are the bow saw (Fig. 94) and the crosscut saw (Fig. 93). The former is an efficient one-man saw for cutting timber less than 10 in. d.b.h. The latter is most useful in the two-man sizes for cutting large trees. Crosscut saws are available in straight-backed and sway-backed models. The sway-backed model is useful chiefly in small timber (10 to 15 in. d.b.h.) because a wedge can be inserted behind it in a fairly shallow cut. All hand saws are made in a variety of tooth patterns. The one commonly used for softwoods has four cutting teeth to each raker. For hardwoods, two cutting teeth to one raker is usually preferred. For dry wood, a saw without rakers is satisfactory (Fig. 95).

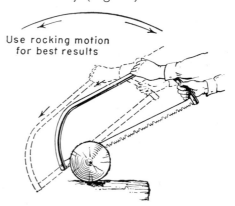

FIG. 94. Bow saw. For best results use rocking motion as indicated by arrows. Hold saw frame just above the blade with one hand, put other hand at middle of bow bend with palm facing down. Tilt the blade forward a little on the forward strokes and backward on the backward strokes. This gives the saw a rocking motion and makes it cut faster and easier.

Power Saws. Several types are available; for example, circular saws, drag saws, and chain saws; all are useful in many farm woods. No detailed description of power saws and only a little discussion of them is appropriate in this text. Manufacturers of such equipment will furnish all details of construction and necessary instructions for

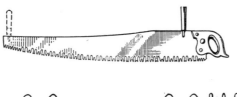

(A)   *(B)*

FIG. 95. Tooth patterns. *(A)* For hard wood and knotty timber. Preferred for farm use. *(B)* For soft woods, four teeth per raker. Teeth with sharper points.

operating each piece of equipment. Detailed discussion of this type of equipment will be found in publications listed in Appendix I, page 335.

This can be said here. This is a mechanical age. Farmers do more and more of their work with power equipment. Work is easier and faster with it. If woods work is planned as a regular part of the farm business, it is certainly worth while to consider carefully the advisability of using power equipment wherever its use can be justified by the volume and regularity of the work. All such equipment is expensive and requires careful handling. If the volume of work in sight is not sufficient to justify the purchase of the equipment by one farmer, its rental can often be arranged through dealers, farmers cooperatives, or through soil-conservation districts. Or for heavy cutting jobs, a contractor with power equipment may be hired for the days required to do the major part of the sawing.

FIG. 96. Logger's peavy.   (*From Northeastern Loggers' Handbook, Agriculture Handbook No. 6.*)

Wedges. These are small but indispensable tools in woods work. They prevent saws from pinching, they are useful in felling trees to make them land where the operator desires, and they are extremely helpful in splitting wood.   Wedges can be made out of dry hardwood, preferably, if available, dogwood, ironwood, hard maple, or beech. Steel wedges last longer and are preferred by many woodsmen. Splitting wedges are usually longer and thicker in the shank than those

(*A*)   (*B*)   (*C*)

FIG. 97. (*A*) Logger's cant hook; (*B*) hog-nose toe ring; (*C*) crowfoot for handling square timbers. (*From Northeastern Loggers' Handbook, Agriculture Handbook No. 6.*)

used for felling.   Steel wedges can be homemade or purchased; the steel is left untempered.   Wedges are driven with a wood chopper's maul.

Other Small Tools. Among those most useful are *peaveys* and *cant hooks;* the former are more useful in the woods (Figs. 96 and 97), the latter on rollways. Pulp hooks are useful in handling small bolts (Fig. 98). *Log chains* (Fig. 99) are indispensable for many purposes. Grapple hooks (Fig. 100) and *log tongs* (Fig. 101) are convenient in skidding logs.   Log skid sleds (go-devils) (Fig. 102) are useful to elevate the front end of logs to facilitate skidding and to keep the

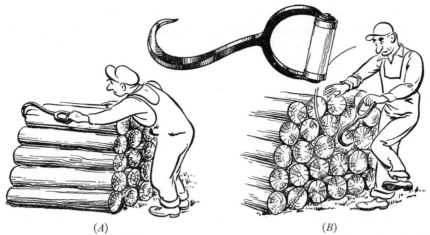

(A)   (B)

FIG. 98. The pulp hook: (A) the safe way is to hook the end of the stick, not the side (B) where the hook may glance off. (*From Northeastern Loggers' Handbook, Agriculture Handbook No. 6.*)

FIG. 99. Log chain.

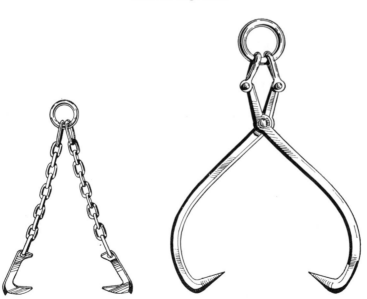

FIG. 100. Grapple hooks.   FIG. 101. Log tongs.

logs free from dirt and grit.   *Log jacks* (Fig. 103) are useful in lifting small logs off the ground and supporting them while being bucked. There are also numerous types of *peeling tools* available on the market useful in removing bark for products salable only in a peeled condition.

Horses.   Horses are still used in the woods, mostly for skidding logs or hauling light loads for short distances.   Some patience and

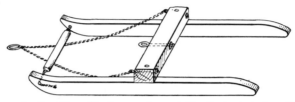

Fig. 102. The go-devil.   (*From Northeastern Loggers' Handbook, Agriculture Handbook No. 6.*)

training are required to get them habituated to the work.   Strong, heavy harness is needed.

Wheeled Tractors.   These are available on most farms, and are frequently used for skidding and hauling.   They are somewhat top heavy and cannot safely be used except on level ground or gentle slopes.   Since they do not have the necessary traction, their use is also

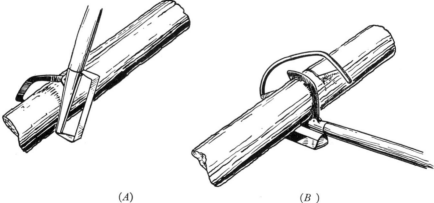

(*A*)   (*B*)
Fig. 103. The log jack: (*A*) position 1; (*B*) position 2.

limited to dry or frozen ground.   Under these conditions they can be used successfully.   Their usefulness can be increased greatly by mounting a winch on the rear end.   Hydraulic lifts also increase their usefulness in handling logs.   With the winch and cable, logs can be dragged out of places where a tractor cannot be driven.   Some sort of safety hitch should be used to free the load from the tractor in an emergency. Several good hitches are manufactured, or one can be improvised by using a wooden breakaway pin in a clevis.

Light Crawler Tractors. Because of their greater traction and low center of gravity, these can be used where the wheel-type tractors are not safe. Many types are available. The crawler-type tractors do not compact the soil on cultivated fields as much as do wheeled tractors or horses, and they have greater pulling power. They can be used for both woods work and the usual farm work. A farmer who has several weeks' work in the woods every year could advantageously use this type of tractor intead of the wheeled type. Rental of crawler-type tractors may be possible in some cases from farmers' cooperatives or soil-conservation districts. A winch and cable is also highly useful for woods work in connection with the crawler tractor.

Felling. To fall a tree where it will do the least damage to unmarked trees and young growth and will not break in the fall is the first consideration. Trees sometimes break, ruining one or more logs, if they fall over rocks, stumps, or very uneven ground. A smooth bed on which to fall will avoid this danger and is especially important for the larger, more valuable trees. Things that interfere with a free fall can sometimes be avoided, for example, large dead limbs on trees likely to be touched in the fall or any limbs or crotched tree apt to lodge the tree being felled. Dead limbs knocked off in the fall are dangerous to woodsmen. A tree felled straight up the slope may kick back when it hits the ground, endangering the felling crew. Lastly, each tree, where possible, should be felled where it can be handled most easily, especially where the logs or tree stem can be pulled directly to the skid trail without turning.

All of this is easier to talk about than to accomplish in the woods. For small trees, 12 in. d.b.h. and less, it is not very difficult. For larger trees and especially those that lean the wrong way, it is not easy to drop them where the fallers intend them to go. The steps in the process are, first, an undercut on the side toward which the tree is intended to fall. The undercut is made with a horizontal saw cut; then, with an ax, a V-shaped cut is made above the saw cut. The depth of the undercut should be about one-fourth of the diameter of the trunk. The back of the undercut should be at right angles with the direction of the fall. Second, start the back saw cut about 2 in. higher than the base of the undercut. If all is well, keep on sawing, inserting wedges behind the saw to prevent pinching and to start tipping the tree slightly. Stop sawing before completely severing the trunk, leaving an inch or two of wood to act as a hinge to guide the direction of fall.

If the tree leans the wrong way, some guidance can be accomplished by leaving uncut wood on one side to hold the tree while cutting and wedging on the other to force the tree in the direction of the wedging. This is a matter of skill born of experience. The felling crew should have a clear space a few yards from the tree to which to retreat as the tree begins to fall, taking the saw with them. Watch for falling limbs and yell "Timber-r-r!" in a loud voice. This is the traditional warning to all who may be in the woods to look out—*a tree is coming down.*

Limbing. The next step is to limb the tree after it is down and clear the way for the "bucking," or sawing the stem into logs or bolts. The ax is most commonly used for this purpose. Safety rules suggest that the axman stand on one side of the trunk and cut limbs on the other. Cut flush with the bole of the tree leaving no stubs and with a stroke parallel with the trunk from the base of the tree upward. Smoothly trimmed boles are important in both saw logs and such products as pulpwood. They enhance the value and facilitate handling. Saplings bent into a bow by the fallen tree must be cut carefully lest a sudden release cause them to spring up suddenly and with great force.

Bucking. Cutting the stem of the fallen tree into suitable log lengths calls for a knowledge of specifications for different classes of logs. The higher grades are usually the long logs, 12 ft. and up, and the smooth, sound straight ones of large diameter. Find out what the specifications are. Select places to saw the stem to give the maximum volume in the higher-grade logs. The butt logs usually bring the highest price. Careful selection of log lengths will avoid unnecessary crook. Defects such as catface can often be placed at the butt end of a log where they will be removed in the slab. For most trees, especially hardwoods, the first step is to mark the total merchantable length of the tree. Then subdivide the stem into logs so as to get maximum scale and grade. Divide on the basis of products, for example, saw logs, veneer logs, peeler logs (Douglas fir), pulpwood. Small trees often can be skidded full length to a landing where they can be bucked into suitable lengths cheaper and much more advantageously than in the woods. Long lengths, however, are more diffi-

cult to handle without injury to the trees left.   One good horse or a
wheeled tractor easily can handle tree lengths of small softwoods or
second-growth hardwoods, even by ground skidding.   All log lengths
should be measured, including the trimming allowance universally
applicable.   Find out what it is (usually 3 or 4 in.) before bucking
the tree.

Skidding and Yarding.   These words are almost synonomous.
Logs are skidded to a landing or a skidway.   The latter usually

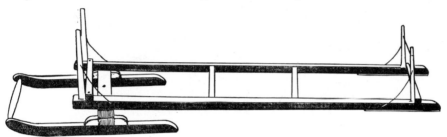

FIG. 104. The travois, or dray.   (*From Northeastern Loggers' Handbook, Agriculture Handbook
No. 6.*)

provides for one tier of logs.   The former is a more extensive collection area, hence a landing.   A yard may be a larger collection area
than a landing to which logs and other products are hauled as well
as skidded.   Yards, landings, and skidways are all places where wood
products are collected preparatory to transporting them by water,
trucks, or other types of transportation.   A landing often means a
place on a stream bank preparatory to driving a stream.

Skidding with horses is commonly used in small operations.   One-
horse skidding is preferred unless the logs are too heavy.   One log at
a time is the rule for ground skidding.   Logs are attached to the
whiffle tree by a log chain (Fig. 99), by a grapple hook (Fig. 100),
or by log tongs (Fig. 101).   Sometimes the front end of one or more
logs is fastened to log sleds (Fig. 102), sometimes called "lizards" or
"go-devils."   Such devices facilitate the skidding and protect the
logs from dirt and gravel that detract from their value.   For hauling
short bolts, a modification of the log skid sled is called a "travois" or
"dray" (Fig. 104).   A bunk is provided with the front end on the
sled while the rear end drags on the ground.   In level country a
bummer (Fig. 105) is used for skidding or yarding logs.   There are
many other types of sleds and contrivances for handling logs and other
products from the stump to the point of major transportation.

Horses under most conditions are expected to skid or yard wood products for distances up to about 300 to 400 ft. They will handle from 2,000 to 4,000 ft. log scale per day per horse or team. Longer distances are better adapted to tractor skidding. For farm woodlands,

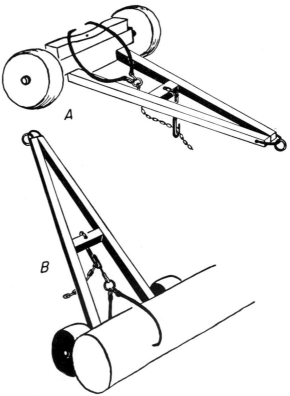

Fig. 105. (*A*) The bummer; (*B*) method of loading. (*From Northeastern Loggers' Handbook, Agriculture Handbook No. 6.*)

except for the larger areas, it is probably better to develop main roads and skidways or landings at sufficiently close intervals to permit horse skidding at reasonable costs.

Loading. If farmers do not own suitable trucks or wagons for hauling products to market, sales may be made at the loading point, in which case the loading and hauling will be done by the buyer. Often greater profit can be made by renting equipment and hauling the products to market or even by contracting the hauling and selling products at the delivery point.

Loading small wood such as pulpwood and fuel is usually done by hand with the aid of a pulp hook (Fig. 98). Often such products are sold in the piles in the woods and the buyer takes over the job of yarding the products to the loading point and transferring them to trucks. Loading on trucks can be done by a simple conveyor-type loader propelled by gasoline engines or electric motors. The wood is elevated to the truck endways or sideways depending on the type of loader used. These types of loaders can be homemade.

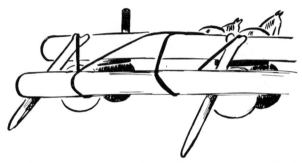

Fig. 106. Crosshaul method of loading. (*From Northeastern Loggers' Handbook, Agriculture Handbook No. 6.*)

Logs and poles must be loaded with the help of some kind of mechanical contrivance. The simplest type, when skidways are on gentle slopes, is merely to bridge the gap from the skidway to the truck with "skids" (poles or logs) over which the logs are rolled onto the truck. Logs are propelled by means of cant hooks or peaveys (Figs. 96 and 97). Two men should work together on the logrolling job, one to hold a log on an upgrade while the other gets a new grip.

The next type of loading device commonly used is the crosshaul (Fig. 106). It consists of a chain or cable passed from the vehicle bunks around the log and back across the bed of the vehicle to the motive power on the other side. The motive power can be a horse, a motor, a gasoline engine, or a winch powered by the truck being loaded.

Crosshauling requires two skid poles at least 6 in. d.b.h. and any suitable length to reach from the ground to the bolster of the truck or wagon. These skids should fit firmly in the ground and be properly notched to avoid slipping at the point of contact with the vehicle. The chain or light cable is usually about 30 to 40 ft. long. Fasten one end to the front and the other to the rear bolster of the vehicle to be loaded.   Pass the chain under the log to be loaded and over the vehicle to the motive power.   The pull is then at the middle point of the chain or cable.   The skids must be raised after the first layer of logs is in place so that the top ends rest on the loaded logs. Only one log is loaded at a time, and the chain or cable must be released from the motive power and pulled back by hand to engage

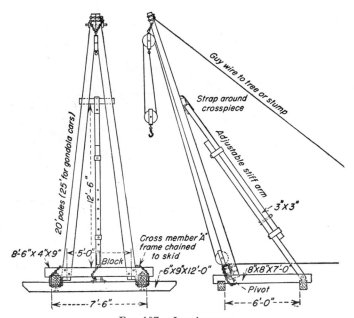

Fig. 107a. Log-jammer.

each separate log.   This method of loading is therefore a slow process as compared with the highly mechanized types.

There are many other types of loading devices from the simple stationary gin pole to various types of movable "jammers" including high-powered ponderous machines.   For farm jobs, a gin pole or an A-frame loader may be justified (Figs. 107a and 107b).   Specifications and drawings for homemade structures can be obtained from state foresters or from the U.S. Forest Service.

Hauling.   This is ordinarily done by trucks, but where snow roads are practicable, horse- or tractor-drawn sleds are used.   The sleds are especially made for hauling heavy logs.   For short bolts, sleds are fitted with racks with the wood placed at right angles to the direction of haul.   The ordinary flat-bed truck, commonly used on farms, readily can be equipped to haul a variety of wood products. Even if the bulk of the products are sold at the roadside, farmers frequently will haul short logs to a mill for custom sawing or other products to market or to the place of use on the farm. Where logs are to be hauled in a flat-bed truck, it should be equipped with two steel or wooden bunks placed across the truck bed. These will give

Fig. 107*b*. An A-frame loader. Short Douglas-fir logs loaded with a team. The logger's wife served as "mule skinner." (*Soil Conservation Service.*)

a firmer support to crooked logs and save the truck bed from wear. Stakes can be installed in the ends of the bunks to help hold the wood. Additional safety is secured by fastening the load with chains.

If this type of truck is to be used for very much hauling, it may be necessary to reinforce the rear end with supplementary springs or an additional axle and wheels. A cord of green hardwood easily may weigh 2½ tons and a cord of coniferous wood 2 tons. One thousand feet log scale of logs may weigh as much as 6,000 to 7,000 lb. With average-sized logs, trucks rated at 1½ tons are reported to handle 700 to 800 ft. b.m. of logs; 2½-ton trucks 1,200 ft. b.m., 5-ton trucks 2,500 ft. b.m.

Scaling or Measuring. This is the process of determining the total volume or amount of products in terms of the unit in which they are sold. Posts, some classes of poles, and mine timbers are sold by the piece; each piece has specifications indicating its length and thickness. Amounts are determined simply by counting the pieces that measure up to the specifications.

Railroad ties are classified into grades (usually five), with specifications for each grade. These products must be counted according to the grades they will make. Most mine timbers, poles, and piling are sold at prices per foot of length, but each piece must conform to the specifications of the buyer as to top diameters, crook, defects, and species. It is highly important, therefore, that the forest manager not only knows these specifications before cutting but sees that the cutters abide by them in the woods operations.

Pulpwood, firewood, and acid wood normally are sold by the cord of stacked wood measured either in the woods or on the truck. The standard cord is, of course, a pile of wood 4 ft. high, 8 ft. long, and 4 ft. wide, containing 128 cu. ft. Other units are used such as the 5-ft. cord (4 by 8 by 5 ft.) or the pen, a loosely ricked pile of approximately the amount of wood in a cord or agreed-upon fraction of a cord.

Cords of wood piled in the woods require careful measurement of heights and lengths, and the sticks must be piled evenly. Pulpwood sold by the cord has strict specifications as to species, lengths, crook, defect, and so forth. Simple measurement to arrive at the total cords is not difficult under favorable conditions. However, if the wood does not meet the buyer's specifications, it may be rejected entirely or deductions made in the number of cords because of defective bolts or poor piling.

Saw logs are sold by the number of board feet they contain. A board foot is a piece of lumber 1 in. thick, 12 in. wide, and 12 in. long. The number of board feet in logs is determined by the use of a log rule, which is a table giving the calculated contents of logs for different lengths and top diameters inside the bark (see Appendix IV, pages 356 to 358). There are numerous log rules in use, such as the Doyle, Scribner, International, and many others. They are all approximations of the board feet that logs will produce when sawed at the mill. They attempt to allow for loss in saw kerf but make no allowance for defects in the logs that reduce the number of board feet obtainable. For convenience in measuring, scale sticks are made on which the log-rule table is transplanted so that the contents of any log can be read directly from the stick according to its length and diameter.

It is important to know what log scale is to be used before selling logs. There are considerable variations in the figures given by the different rules for the same logs, and a great many give results that are considerably less than the mill tally (Table 21, page 236). The latter is, of course, the actual output of board feet and is the standard by which the accuracy of the log rules are determined. The difference

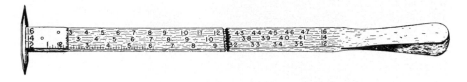

Fig. 108a. Log-scale stick.

between the "scale" (measurement of board feet by log rule) and the mill tally is known as "overrun." It is an important element in appraising the value of standing saw-log timber where values are determined using the price of sawed lumber as the base.

Logs are scaled at the loading point, at the mill, in the woods, or any other convenient concentration point. The entire log should be available for inspection at the time of scaling, except for logs scaled in water, where special log rules apply. A scale stick is a necessity where very many logs are to be measured, but logs can be scaled simply by measuring the lengths in feet, the diameter inside bark at the top end in inches, and referring to a printed table to get the contents. A scale stick provides the means of measuring lengths in feet, diameter in inches, and reading the result in board feet (Figs. 108a and 108b). Each log is usually numbered with lumberman's crayon and the board foot contents recorded in a book opposite the log number. The record looks something like that shown in Table 20.

Logs are scaled on a "straight and sound basis." That is, the figures in the log-rule table or on the scale stick are calculated for logs that are straight and sound. Only the saw kerf is deducted. The scaler must make appropriate deduction for crook and for defect. The amount of deduction varies from culling the log because it has too many defects to a reduction in the number of board feet. For

FIG. 108*b*. Scaling a log in the woods (Pennsylvania). (*Soil Conservation Service.*)

example, a 16-ft. log 16 in. in diameter at the small end scales 160 ft. b.m. (Scribner decimal C rule). It contains heart rot in the center measuring 3 in. across. The scaler estimates that the rot (it shows at both ends) will ruin 6 boards 16 ft. long and 6 in. wide, or 48 ft. b.m.

TABLE 20. PAGE FROM A LOG BOOK

DATE: _____   LOCATION: _____

SCALED BY: _____   LOG RULE: _____

Log number	Length, ft.	Diameter, in.	Net scale, ft. b.m.
1			
2			
3			
4			
5			
etc.			
Total....			

Probably he would reduce the scale by 40 ft. and record the net scale as 120 ft. b.m.   It requires some practice and experience to become expert in scaling logs, but any farmer can learn enough about it to satisfy himself that the buyer's scale is fair and honest.   Where logs

Fig. 109.   Girdling a tree preparatory to the application of chemical.   (*Northeast Pulpwood Research Center, Gorham, N.H.*)

are sold at the truck-loading point, sample loads can be scaled and compared later with the buyer's scale at the delivery point.

Removing Bark with Chemicals.   Experiments in removing bark by application of a chemical to standing trees have been conducted by the Armstrong Forest Company, Johnsonburg, Pennsylvania; the Northeast Pulpwood Research Center, Gorham, New Hampshire; the Chemical Debarking Research Project at the N.Y. State College of Forestry, Syracuse N.Y., sponsored by commercial organizations; and perhaps by other agencies.   The results, applicable to the northeastern and Lake states, and to Eastern Canada, promise to revolutionize the methods of peeling trees to produce pulpwood and poles. They are especially important to farmers because, by use of the chemical, only a small part of a peeled pole or pulpwood operation needs to be done during the peeling season, which normally is a busy season on farms.

FIG. 110. Applying the chemical to girdled area with a paint brush.   (*Northeast Pulpwood Research Center, Gorham, N.H.*)

During the sap season (about June 1 in Pennsylvania), remove a complete girdle of bark, with a minimum width of 6 in., from the standing trees marked for cutting. Make the girdle at a height of 2 to 4 ft. above the ground. Use a light single-bit ax. Remove only the bark. Be very careful not to cut into the sapwood. This technique for removing the bark without injury to the sapwood is subject to constant revision as the result of research. The latest development indicates that it is best to loosen the bark by gentle pounding with the heel of the ax, using the cutting edge only as a spud. Attempts are being made to develop a special tool that will be superior to the ax for this job (Fig. 109).

With a 3-in. brush, apply a weak solution of sodium arsenite (about 4 lb. per gallon of water). A gallon costs (1950) about $1. It is sufficient to treat 300 to 500 trees at a reported cost of less than $0.05

per cord of pulpwood. The chemical can be obtained from any manufacturer of such products (Fig. 110).

The chemical is poisonous to both animals and humans, so it must be handled carefully. It is quickly absorbed by the tree; leaves and buds

Fig. 111. The effects of the chemical on a large beech tree a year following treatment. Note that the bark is loose at the top of tree. (*Northeast Pulpwood Research Center, Gorham, N.H.*)

die in a few days or weeks and so become unattractive to birds. No injury to wildlife has been reported. Wash your hands thoroughly after handling the chemical. If by accident it is taken internally, use an emetic of mustard or anything to cause vomiting; then swallow olive oil or white of egg. *See a doctor at once.*

Both hardwoods and conifers have been studied. Hardwoods have included oak, aspen, cherry, elm, beech, maple, birch, and ash. Conifers include spruce, balsam, hemlock, pitch, and Scotch pine.

Following treatments, the bark becomes set in much the same way that it is in any tree following the close of the sap or growing season.

Tests have been successful on all species tried, both hardwood and conifers, except ash. Results with this species have been poor. Elm, aspen, and oak after poisoning will again peel readily within three to four months after treatment. Other hardwoods will not peel readily until about six months after treatment. In moist and humid locations, loosening of the bark will take place within a shorter period of time.

FIG. 112. Pulpwood from chemically treated trees yarded to strip road. Nearly all the bark fell off during bucking, skidding, and piling. (*Northeast Pulpwood Research Center, Gorham, N.H.*)

In a year following treatment, large sections of the bark in some species have begun to fall from the standing trees, and in most cases the felling and handling incident to processing the products will cause most of the bark to drop away. There are some exceptions. During the winter when the temperature is below freezing, the bark is not easily removed (Fig. 111).

Experience indicates fewer difficulties in felling and swamping treated trees as compared to normal operations. Limbs become brittle and easily break, causing fewer "hang ups." Less work in limbing is reported. There is, however, more danger to the woods workers from falling limbs.

Because of seasoning, the peeled pulpwood weighs less than sap-peeled wood and hence is cheaper to handle and to transport. Bark removal costs are considerably reduced.   As much as 85 to 90 percent of the bark drops off without any effort by woods workers.   The actual loss in weight has not been determined for many species.   In the case of pitch pine, weight loss was 23 percent.

The advantages to a farmer of being able to produce peeled wood at any season of the year are obvious (Fig. 112).

As already indicated, new tools soon may be available to lessen costs and enable you to do a better job of girdling and applying the poison.   Keep in touch with your nearest forest experiment station for the latest developments applicable to your locality.

SUPPLEMENTARY ACTIVITIES

Pacing

Timber cruisers use a pocket compass to keep directions and to follow established lines in the woods.   They measure distances (except where exact measurements are required) by counting their steps.   This is called "pacing."   They measure in terms of chains—80 chains = 1 mile, 1 tally = 5 chains, 16 tallies = 1 mile.   Usually they count only one foot; hence a pace is the average distance in 2 steps.   They constantly practice pacing by stepping distances on measured lines.   In rough country, they make allowances for the fact that paces are likely to be shorter than on smooth ground.

1. Carefully measure two distances of 5 chains each, or 1 tally; (a) 5 chains (330 ft.) between stakes across a field or along a road; (b) 5 chains in the woods partly uphill and down, blazed and marked at each end.

2. Step off the distances along each course several times.   (Wear your woods shoes.)   Count and record your paces and find the average number per tally.   Walk naturally as you would on a stroll except that you consciously try to keep your steps of even distance.   Keep on practicing, morning and night, for several days until your paces are approximately the same every time for each course.

Now you have a reasonably accurate way of determining distances. Divide 330 by the number of paces per tally to get the feet per pace.   For distances less than a tally, multiply paces by feet per pace.   Usually a cruiser will use the same number of paces per tally on any ground but take a few more (uncounted) paces where the going is tough.   Or he may count more paces on rough ground; this is a matter of choice.

Measuring Trees

1. Locate a woods containing trees from 16 to 24 in. d.b.h.

2. Choose 10 trees of saw-log size; label them so that you can easily see the labels at a distance.

3. Measure the diameter breast high of each tree in inches.   Use calipers or a cruiser stick; take two measurements at right angles and average the two.   If you have to use an ordinary tape measure, take the circumference and divide by 3.14 to get diameter in inches.

4. Now measure the number of 16-ft. logs in each tree.   Cut a pole 18 ft. long; stand it alongside the tree you are measuring.   Allowing for a 2-foot. stump, the top of the pole marks the top end of the first 16-ft. log. Now stand back and count the other logs above, to the point where the bole is no longer merchantable.   The upper point is determined by big limbs, defects, or by diminishing size of the bole.   (The latter is likely to be 10 to 12 in. for hardwoods and 8 in. for conifers.)   You must decide this point. Estimate the number of logs to the nearest $\frac{1}{2}$ log (8 ft.).

5. Use a local volume table or one of those in the appendix.   The latter are for trees of Form class 80.   You may assume that your trees fall into this class.   "Form class" is explained in Appendix III, pages 344 to 350.   Make a record like this:

Tree number	Species	D.b.h., in.	Number of 16-ft. logs	Volume, ft. b.m.
1				
2				
3				
4				
5				
etc.				
Totals.....				

Scaling Logs

1. Locate a skidway or pile of saw logs—usually found at a sawmill or along a railroad ready for loading.   Pick out 10 logs that are visible along the entire length and at both ends.   Number them with a soft pencil, chalk, or lumberman's crayon.

2. Borrow a log-scale stick if you can; if not use a yardstick.   Measure each log.

The length in feet: lengths are measured in even units as 6, 8, 10, 12 ft., and so forth.   Three or four inches is allowed for loss in sawing due to slanting saw cuts.   If the logs are cut to odd lengths, measure to the nearest even length.

Diameter inside bark to nearest inch: for example, record $11\frac{1}{2}$ to $12\frac{1}{2}$ in. as 12 in.; $12\frac{1}{2}$ to $13\frac{1}{2}$ in. as 13 in.   If the end of log is not exactly round, take two measurements and average.

3. Note any defects in each log. Defects are anything that will reduce the volume of usable lumber that can be sawed from the log. For example, excessive crook, rot, wormholes, shake, fire scars, or catface. If the defects will be removed in the slab, no deduction is made. The log-rule table assumes that the log is straight and sound; the scaler has to make deductions in the scale (volume) for defects that reduce the scale. Use your judgment and deduct $\frac{1}{10}$, $\frac{1}{5}$, $\frac{1}{4}$, or $\frac{1}{2}$ from the figure given in the table or on the scale stick. If the log will not produce at least $\frac{1}{2}$ the full scale, it is culled.

4. Keep the record of your scale something like this:

Log number	Length, ft.	Diameter, in.	Gross scale, ft. b.m.	Net scale, ft. b.m.
1				
2				
3				
4				
5				
etc.				
Total......				

5. What log rule did you use? Compute the scale of these logs by two other log-rule tables and note differences in the total scale of the logs.

Marking Timber for an Improvement Cutting

1. Use an assistant. Locate a woods containing trees of different sizes, particularly from 12 to 16 in. d.b.h. Choose one that has not had any major cutting operation for ten years or longer.

2. Get permission from the owner to mark the trees that you think should be removed in an improvement cutting. Read the instructions in the text.

3. Mark the boundaries of an area of about 5 acres. Mark the outside lines by pinning colored cloth to the bark of trees along the line. (Ten chains by five chains, or 660 ft. by 330 ft. makes a convenient rectangular plot.) Use a pocket compass or a carpenter's square to make right-angle turns at the corners. Measure distances with chain or tape.

4. Now select the trees to be cut; mark them with white paper or cards fastened to the bark with tacks or a stapling machine. Go through the woods beginning at one side and cover a strip about 2 rods wide (33 ft). One person selects the trees, the other labels them. Keep on in parallel strips until the entire 5 acres is marked.

Cruising a Stand of Timber

(Two or three persons make a crew.)

1. Use the 5-acre plot already set up in the activity "Marking timber for an improvement cutting."

2. Start in the middle of the short side of the 5-acre plot and walk parallel to the long boundary (a pocket compass is a great help). Pace or measure the distance; stop at 1-chain distance (66 ft.) and take the first ⅕-acre sample plot. Use the end of the first chain as the center of the plot. (Read instructions in the text to be sure that you know how to proceed and that you have the proper tools.) Take plots at succeeding distances of 3, 5, 7, and 9 chains. That will give you 5 plots or 1 acre actually measured. This amounts to a 20 percent cruise of the 5-acre woods.

3. Use two tally sheets, similar to Table 19 in the text, one for trees marked (to cut) and one for trees not marked. Tally for each sample plot the trees marked and those not marked on the appropriate tally sheet. Tally the marked trees by diameter breast high and number of logs; the trees to leave may be tallied by diameter breast high only. If you can recognize different species, separate the more important ones from the others on the tally sheets.

4. Now take the tally sheet for marked timber and apply the volumes from a local volume table or use one of those in the appendix. Add up the total board feet by species; deduct what you think appropriate as a cull factor. This will be the net volume log scale for one acre (which you measured). Multiply by 5 to get the total volume to cut on the 5 acres. Can you figure the cords of pulpwood or fuel in small trees or tops (see Appendix III, pages 351 to 355)?

5. Now put the figures on the two tally sheets together to make a stand table (see Tables 17 and 18 in the text) for the original stand.

6. Now use the tally sheet for unmarked trees and make a stand table for trees to be left after the cutting.

7. Talk to the farmer who owns this 5-acre tract; show him the trees in the woods marked for cutting and your figures of products to cut. He will be interested; he may give you some helpful advice, and he may want to follow your marking when he cuts his timber.

7. Marketing Wood Products

W OOD PRODUCTS, unfortunately, are not marketed on the same basis as are other farm products. That is partly because wood has failed to become generally recognized as a farm crop. To keep in touch with markets for most farm products, the farmer needs only to turn on his radio at the scheduled time or look at the proper place in his daily or weekly paper. Wood-product markets are not organized to supply such up-to-the-minute information. This subject will be discussed according to the following headings:

1. Finding the Basis for Wood Markets
2. Using Available Marketing Services
3. Taking the Preliminary Marketing Steps
4. Becoming Familiar with Specifications for Different Products
5. Making Use of Organizational Aids
6. Developing Farm Wood Industries

1. Finding the Basis for Wood Markets

Prices for forest products either as stumpage, processed logs, or bolts are related to selling prices of lumber and other finished products. They are also related to the competition among buyers for the raw products needed by wood-using industries. This is another way of saying that the price of raw products of the forest is determined by the law of supply and demand.

No industry pays more for its raw materials to keep the factories busy than it is forced to do to ensure an ample supply. Where forests contain plentiful supplies of good timber, the value of standing timber (stumpage) is low, and the price of logs is about the cost of production plus a moderate profit. As the demand for timber increases in relation to the supply, competition among buyers raises the price of stumpage and increases the profit margin in producing logs.

The quality of the raw wood material required by industry to make the products demanded by consumers is an important element in determining prices for stumpage or logs or bolts. To make high-

231

grade lumber for furniture, for floors, for paneling and trim in our homes and offices requires large-size clear logs that come only from big trees with clean straight boles. Good construction timbers can be made only from logs reasonably straight, sound, and free from serious defects.

In terms of board feet, about 70 percent of the products cut from out forests are used for lumber. Another 17 percent goes into pulpwood (9 percent) and fuel (8 percent). Thus 87 percent of forest products cut are lumber, pulpwood, and fuel. There are a large number of other products, such as fence posts, railroad ties, poles, piling, veneer, cooperage, mine timbers, distillation wood, and many, many others. Some of these may be highly important as a market outlet for local products or for the particular type of timber under management. But by and large, the chief dependence of the forest manager for profitable products from his forest must be on those which produce lumber. As already pointed out, however, only the big trees 18 in. d.b.h. and up will make the high-class lumber so much in demand and becoming more and more difficult to find.

Saw logs are often graded 1, 2, and 3. Grade 1 includes the big logs 12 in. or more inside bark at the small end, 12 ft. and longer in length, largely free from knots and other defects (Figs. 62 and 113). Usually grade 2 must be 8 in. and more inside bark, 10 to 16 ft. long, reasonably straight and sound. Grade 3 includes all others usable for ties, timbers, and low-grade lumber for such uses as rough construction, boxes, and crates. The forest that can produce harvest cuts of grade 1 and 2 logs is in the high producing class, but it takes good trees. Grade 3 logs are plentiful, low-grade products—produced from small inferior trees—selling for relatively low prices.

The point to this discussion is that if your forest is still in the low-grade class, you will have to face the fact that profits are likely to be small. Furthermore, it may not be easy to sell all the products you would like to dispose of. The supply of low-grade products generally is greater than demand. Two remedies are available: (1) Hoard the high-grade trees. Sell them gradually to increase the average income from the woods. Save those trees that will be high class a few years hence, the 14- to 16-in. class that show promise of making grade 1 logs. In other words, manage carefully to put your forest into the upper-grade quality as rapidly as possible. (2) Watch the market for salable products that can be made from the low-grade trees in need of cutting to improve the growing stock. Wood markets often change suddenly. Products not salable today may be salable tomorrow. Often further processing or grading of logs or bolts will enable a forest manager to sell products that are not otherwise in demand. For example, fence posts or timbers treated with preservative, rough lumber instead of rough logs, seasoned and graded fireplace wood, wood chips instead of poor fuel wood can be sold.

Fig. 113. A No. 1 red-oak log, 16 ft. long 22 in. top diameter (Ohio). (*Soil Conservation Service.*)

Most forest owners have to struggle with a surplus of low-grade products, especially when beginning to develop a previously mismanaged woodland. The farmer is in a better position than any other forest owner to cope with a surplus of low-grade products, first, because he has a market on the farm for many products, second, because he can earn a labor income in producing and selling many products even if the profit is very small, and third, because he is not only building a more profitable forest for future income but he is increasing the value of his farm as his woodland improves. The latter value may become apparent before his increased woods income becomes a reality.

So marketing problems are worth struggling with. The forest manager who has no worries on this score is fortunate indeed.

2. Using Available Marketing Services

Some states maintain a marketing service for wood products supervised either by the state forester or the extension forester or, in some cases, by cooperative arrangements between them. Bulletins are issued annually or monthly. Get in touch with the county agricultural agent and request that your name be placed on the mailing list to receive such information. Probably it will not be long before all states will provide this service. Even with this help, however, farmers who expect regularly to market wood products will have to undertake more or less of a local market survey in order to get acquainted with the buyers of wood and the specifications and conditions under which they purchase wood products. More of this later.

3. Taking the Preliminary Marketing Steps

The importance of knowing about what is to be offered for sale has already been emphasized. If a rough plan of management has been decided and sample marking completed, it will be relatively easy to express what is to be sold in terms of number and size of trees and in terms of such units of measure as board feet log scale, cords, ties, and so forth. You will have a good idea from the size and character of your timber whether or not you have some upper-grade logs to sell.

If a local farm forester is available, get him to look at the timber you want to cut and have him check your figures on quantity and grades. He will know what can be sold easily and at good prices and the portion that will offer some difficulties. Write down names and addresses of buyers and users of timber. You probably have already decided whether to sell stumpage or products. Sometimes it is wise to sell some standing trees (stumpage). For example, you may have a few very large trees that will make nice clear logs, too big to handle with any equipment available, or you may have a few black walnut trees 20 in. or larger, or you may have white ash of high value. Walnut buyers often want the stump attached to the first log. These trees are best sold on the stump. They bring high prices, and unless they are very difficult to get out of the woods, even a few trees can be sold. Get the farm forester's advice or call in a consulting forester if you have many such trees. But do not be in a hurry about selling them. If you can, let them stand for a year or two while experience is gained in selling products that can be handled with your equipment. They are money in the bank.

Be sure to estimate the farm needs for products—fence posts, rough lumber, poles. Surveys have shown that average annual farm needs often run 75 to 100 posts, 5 to 15 cords of fuel, 800 to 1,200 ft. b.m. (feet board measure) of lumber. For surplus material, here are some of the industries likely to be interested. Sawmills buy logs but often will not pay the real worth for quality logs. Lumberyards and many different factories buy rough lumber. Railroads and streetcar lines buy ties. Light, telephone, telegraph, and power lines buy poles. Piling is usually bought by contractors who sell to railroads, shipyards, and construction firms. Mining companies buy rough lumber and all sorts of rough, hewed, and squared timbers. Pulp and paper mills buy pulpwood and often rough lumber and white-oak timbers. Veneer and woodworking plants buy specified grades and species of logs and lumber. Wood-distillation plants use large quantities of low-grade wood. Brickyards, bakeries, lime kilns, creameries, packing houses, and fuel dealers buy fuel wood, and of course homeowners in the towns prefer to buy ordinary fuel and fireplace wood from reliable farmers.

These are the potential buyers of what you have to sell. Visit or write to those most likely to need products that you can make from your trees. Get acquainted with the buyers; examine the stock of wood products on hand; and inquire about prices paid at delivery point or at the roadside, the method of measurement and payment, and the minimum quantities accepted. Lastly inquire of neighbors who have sold wood products to get the benefit of their experience and their opinion about the reliability of different buyers. Make a record of this information. You may want it later.

4. Becoming Familiar with Specifications for Different Products

It is a good practice to keep a complete list of specifications of buyers for different products for ready reference even if all products are not likely to be found in your woods. This is especially important for high-priced products such as poles, piling, veneer logs, furniture logs, and special products from dogwood, ash, maple, or white oak. You may find trees suitable for high-grade products. It would be too bad not to recognize them.

Here are a few broad classifications of specifications for a few major forest products. Actual detailed specifications vary in different parts of the country, and it is necessary to find out what they are in any particular locality.

For Saw Timber. This is a general term indicating trees suitable for sawing into lumber and major timbers. Practically all species that grow to sufficient size, if the trees are sound, are usable. Except for those cut as part of an improvement cutting, trees to be cut for saw logs should be a minimum of at least 16 in. d.b.h. (diameter

TABLE 21. COMPARISON OF THE NUMBER OF BOARD FEET IN 16-FT. LOGS OF DIFFERENT TOP DIAMETERS, ACCORDING TO THREE SCALE RULES*

Scale rule	Average diameter inside bark at small end of log, in.														
	10	11	12	13	14	15	16	17	18	19	20	21	22	23	24
Scribner decimal C	60	70	80	100	110	140	160	180	210	240	280	300	330	380	400
Doyle	36	49	64	81	100	121	144	169	196	225	256	289	324	361	400
International (¼-in. kerf)	65	80	95	115	135	160	180	205	230	260	290	320	355	390	425

* Logs less than 16 ft. long have a proportionately smaller scale. For example, an 8-ft. log scales one-half, a 12-ft. log three-fourths as much as shown in the table for 16-ft. logs.

breast high), should contain at least one 16-ft. length of stem clear to the nearest branch of appreciable size, and should be reasonably straight and sound. Based on logging and milling studies in both pine and hardwoods, the costs of production of saw logs from trees smaller than indicated normally exceeds the selling price. The significance of log grades has already been mentioned. Log grades are not generally recognized by buyers in all localities, but the seller should recognize them and insist on higher prices for the better grades. Usually he will do better to keep the high-class logs separate and sell them in a lot after getting bids. Insistence on this point will soon force buyers to pay better prices for good logs. Needless to say, the aim of management, consistent with farm economics and the desirability of getting an annual income, should be to produce a maximum quantity of grade 1 and 2 logs. Top-grade logs normally are worth three or four times grade 2 logs and six to twenty times grade 3 or common-run rough logs. The results of pruning when the stands are young show up in the higher proportion of upper-grade logs at time of harvest cut.

Saw logs are measured in terms of estimated lumber contents by log rules. Many different ones are used. They should be carefully considered in relation to the price offered and the average size of logs to be sold. Table 21 gives a comparison of three log rules in common use. (See Appendix IV, pages 356 to 358 for complete log-rule tables.)

For Lumber. Lumber is graded in accordance with a variety of lumber-grading rules based on the amount of clear material in each piece and sometimes the use for which it is to be put. For an understanding of lumber grades locally applicable, one must get copies of the rules printed by lumber associations operating in the region in which the timber is located. In general, lumber is divided into grades based on minimum width and length and percentage of clear, sound material in each piece. A sample of the grades often used (beginning with the highest) are F.A.S. (Firsts and Seconds), Select, No. 1 Common, No. 2 Common, and No. 3 Common.

Sometimes the F.A.S. grade may be omitted and Select subdivided into several grades, and the Common grades may include more than three subdivisions. Timbers and dimension stock may be kept separate from 1- or 2-in. lumber. The number of board feet in each piece is determined by multiplying length in feet, width in inches, and thickness in inches and dividing by 12, or $(L \times W \times T)/12 = $ ft. b.m. Thus a board

$$1 \times 12 \times 16 = 16 \text{ ft. b.m.}$$
$$3 \times 8 \times 10 = 20 \text{ ft. b.m.}$$
$$3 \times 10 \times 14 = 35 \text{ ft. b.m.}$$

A lumber tally stick similar to a log-rule stick can be purchased; it greatly facilitates measuring lumber. If you have lumber to sell, by all means get one and use it.

For Pulpwood. This product is purchased either rough or peeled; (Fig. 112), that is, with the bark on or off. Specifications usually include, in addition to species; length of bolt (usually 4 ft., 50 in. or 5 ft.) cut from sound live timber free from fire scars or burned wood, limbs closely trimmed; and minimum size of bolts ($3\frac{1}{2}$ to 4 in.) at small end. For peeled wood, the specifications usually require removal of all inner bark. This normally means cutting during the "peeling" season, when the bark slips easily, or the use of some sort of mechanical peeler. The use of the latter is not likely to be feasible for small operations (Fig. 117). The use of chemicals to facilitate peeling operations was discussed in Chap. 6.

Shrinkage in volume from rough wood to the peeled state, when hand tools are used, is usually 10 to 15 percent, but if a machine is used to remove the bark, the shrinkage may be considerably greater. This is an important factor where there is a choice of selling either rough or peeled wood. For example, the price for rough wood at delivery point may be $12 per standard cord, for peeled wood $15. If shrinkage is 10 percent, it requires 1.11 standard cords of rough wood (1/0.90) to make 1 cord of peeled wood. If shrinkage is 15 percent, it requires 1.176 cords of rough wood (1/0.85) to make 1 cord of peeled wood. Therefore,

For 10 percent shrinkage;

$$1.11 \text{ cords} \times \$12 = \$13.32$$
$$\text{Margin to cover cost of peeling, } \$15 - \$13.32 = \$ 1.68$$

For 15 percent shrinkage;

$$1.176 \text{ cords} \times \$12 = \$14.11$$
$$\text{Margin to cover cost of peeling, } \$15 - \$14.11 = \$ 0.89$$

The cost of peeling largely depends upon the species, the season, and the average size of bolts. It is, of course, cheaper to peel wood that averages 7 in. per bolt than wood that averages only 5 in.

For Railroad Ties. The relative suitability of various species of wood used for ties depends on strength, wearing qualities, susceptibility to preservative treatment, and natural resistance to decay. No

TABLE 22. SUITABILITY OF WOODS FOR RAILROAD TIES

GROUP U-a	GROUP U-b	GROUP U-c	GROUP U-d
Black locust (heartwood)	Hard pines (heartwood)	Cedars (heartwood)	Catalpa (heartwood)
White oak (heartwood)	Larch (heartwood)	Cypress (heartwood)	Mulberry (heartwood)
Black walnut (heartwood)	Douglas fir (heartwood)	Redwood (heartwood)	Sassafras (heartwood)

GROUP T-a	GROUP T-b	GROUP T-c	GROUP T-d
Ash	Same species as U-b	Beech	Any of U-d group
Hickory	and U-c with	Birch	with sapwood
Honey locust	sapwood	Cherry	Butternut
Red and black oaks	Hemlock—spruce	Gum	Elm
Any of U-a group with sapwood		Hard maple	Hackberry
			Poplar
			Sycamore

single species has all these favorable characteristics, but the oaks, hard pines (two-and three-needled), Douglas fir, and larch (tamarack) are used in the greatest numbers.   Species are commonly grouped together, as shown in Table 22.   These groups, when considered with the various sizes (grades), dictate the acceptability and value of

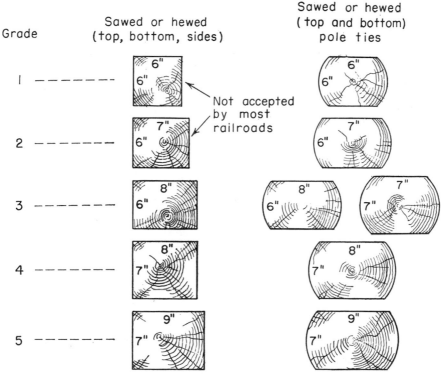

FIG. 114. Standard specifications for railroad crossties.   (*Soil Conservation Service.*)

the product.   Group U ties may be used untreated, group T ties require treatment.

The minimum standard railroad-tie length is 8 ft., although many roads demand 8½-ft. or 9-ft. ties.   The minimum diameter of a tie cut is about 12 in. outside the bark at the small end, although it will be seen from the diagram of grades that this may be variable, depending on the size which the market accepts.   Trees must be reasonably straight, sound, and free from decay and large knots.

The demands by different railroads are variable in respect to grades of ties.   However, the grades shown in Fig. 114 are standard, and it remains only for the seller to determine grades that the market will accept.

For Piling. Oak, pine, and Douglas fir are most commonly used for piling. The market, however, is variable and irregular in its demands, and for many purposes, sound straight trees of any species are acceptable. Sizes also are variable, depending on special uses. Soundness, freedom from crook and excessive sweep, and gradual taper from butt to tip always are essential requisites for good piling. Sizes range from 15 to 60 ft. or more in length, and between 6-in. tip and 20-in. butt. Table 23 gives the specifications established by one state highway department.

TABLE 23. SPECIFICATIONS FOR FIRST-CLASS PILING (OAK, PEELED) ESTABLISHED BY A MIDDLE WESTERN HIGHWAY DEPARTMENT

Length, ft.	Diameter 6 ft. from butt, in.		Diameter of tip, in.
	Minimum	Maximum	Minimum
Less than 30	12	18	10
30 to 40	12	18	9
More than 40	12	18	8

For Poles. Treated pine is the most widely used species, although tamarack, cedar, and some of the more decay-resistant hardwoods are used locally when available. Both poles and piling are sold by the linear foot.

As shown in the Table 24, there are ten classes of poles, based on top diameter and length. The first seven classes also specify minimum circumference of the butt. Freedom from short crooks, excessive sweep, decay, cracks, and bird holes are required in addition to size. Shakes and checks are also considered as defects if located at the top or above the butt of the pole, and prior to treatment the surface must be free from bark and projecting limb stubs.

Table 24 gives the classes of southern pine poles and their minimum dimensions, as specified by the American Telephone and Telegraph Company.

For Veneer. Usually the best grade of timber will bring the highest price if sold to veneer manufacturers, but the specifications are about the same as for grade 1 logs. Veneering—the cutting, slicing, or sawing of timber into thin sheets—is not a new process.

Veneered caskets and plywood furniture have been found in the tombs of Egyptians who lived 1,500 years B.C. Since then, improved machinery, modern waterproof glues, and new methods of laminating have greatly expanded the use of veneer to many fields of construction.

TABLE 24. SPECIFICATIONS FOR SOUTHERN PINE TELEPHONE POLES

Length of pole, ft.	Class 1	Class 2	Class 3	Class 4	Class 5	Class 6	Class 7	Class 8	Class 9	Class 10
	Minimum top diameter, in.									
	8.6	8.0	7.3	6.7	6.0	5.4	4.8	5.7	4.8	3.8
	Minimum circumference at 6 ft. from butt, in.*									
16	....	....	....	....	21.5	19.5	18.0			
18	....	....	26.5	24.5	22.5	21.0	19.0			
20	31.5	29.5	27.5	25.5	23.5	22.0	20.0			
22	33.0	31.0	29.0	26.5	24.5	23.0	21.0			
25	34.5	32.5	30.0	28.0	26.0	24.0	22.0			
30	37.5	35.0	32.5	30.0	28.0	26.0	24.0			
35	40.0	37.5	35.0	32.0	30.0	27.5	25.5			
40	42.0	39.5	37.0	34.0	31.5	29.0	27.0			
								No butt requirement		
45	44.0	41.5	38.5	36.0	33.0	30.5	28.5			
50	46.0	43.0	40.0	37.5	34.5	32.0	29.5			
55	47.5	44.5	41.5	39.0	36.0	33.5				
60	49.5	46.0	43.0	40.0	37.0	34.5				
65	51.0	47.5	44.5	41.5	38.5					
70	52.5	49.0	46.0	42.5	39.5					
75	54.0	50.5	47.0	44.0						
80	55.0	51.5	48.5	45.0						
85	56.5	53.0	49.5							
90	57.5	54.0	50.5							

* To reduce to diameter at breast height of standing trees, divide circumferences by 2.76. Thus a tree 50 ft. above the stump to an 8-in. top diameter must be 15.6 in. d.b.h. (43.0 ÷ 2.76) to produce a class 2 pole. On the same basis, if a tree of that height is in excess of 16.6 in. d.b.h., it will produce a class 1 pole, etc.

Because of the wide variety of uses, most species in large-sized bolts are usable for some purpose. The more common are black walnut, the oaks, birch, yellow poplar, basswood, cottonwood, elm, maples, gums, sycamore, and pine. The fact that manufacturers want clear, unbroken pieces of veneer emphasizes their demands for large logs without defects. Trees below 16 in. in diameter or logs that have

SPECIFICATIONS FOR VENEER
OR GRADE NO. I LOGS
(Wisconsin and Northern Michigan Hardwoods)

All logs shall be 12" and larger in diameter at the small end, the small way. Logs must be cut in 10,12,14,or 16' lengths. Logs 6,7,8,and 9' long may be cut but are optional with buyers. Add 4" to length for trimming allowance.

Below is diagramed the maximum number of defects allowed in the various lengths of logs. Knots, worm holes, shake, cat-faces, dead or dozy spots, bird pecks, brown spots, pin-holes, or seams are considered defects.

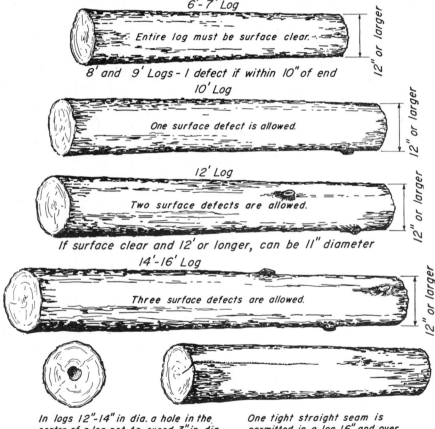

6'-7' Log

Entire log must be surface clear.

12" or larger

8' and 9' Logs - 1 defect if within 10" of end

10' Log

One surface defect is allowed.

12" or larger

12' Log

Two surface defects are allowed.

12" or larger

If surface clear and 12' or longer, can be 11" diameter

14'-16' Log

Three surface defects are allowed.

12" or larger

In logs 12"-14" in dia. a hole in the center of a log not to exeed 3"in dia. is allowed. In logs 15"-16"dia. a 5" hole allowed. In logs over 16" a 6" hole allowed.

One tight straight seam is permitted in a log 16" and over in dia. No seam allowed in logs 15" dia. or smaller.

Fig. 115. Specifications for veneer logs.   Wisconsin and Northern Michigan hardwoods. (*Soil Conservation Service.*)

visible knots, rot, wormholes, and shake ordinarily are not marketable for veneer.

Logs are sold by the board foot the same as saw timber, even though manufactured veneer is sold by the square foot of surface. Specifications for veneer logs vary according to locality and species. Figure 115 shows the maximum number of defects allowed in various sizes of veneer logs in Wisconsin and northern Michigan. Although

FIG. 116. Veneer logs being loaded on a railroad car in Wisconsin. (*Soil Conservation Service.*)

standards in other parts of the United States are somewhat different, the same principles are applicable.

For Fuel Wood. Although any reasonably well-seasoned species may be used as fuel, its value for heating purposes is roughly equivalent to its dry weight, that is, its specific gravity. This relationship is shown by figures supplied by the Forest Products Laboratory, giving the weight per cord (80 cu. ft. solid wood) of air-dried wood (20 percent moisture) and the gross fuel value in B.t.u. (British thermal units). See Table 25.

For comparison with other fuel, the range of values for bituminous coal produced in Indiana, Illinois, Iowa, Missouri, and Ohio is between 18 million and 30 million B.t.u. per ton, and an average grade of fuel oil furnishes 120,000 B.t.u. per gal. Hence, roughly speaking, a cord of good dry wood is about equal to one ton of coal or 200 gal. of fuel oil, assuming comparable efficiency of the heating units.

A ton of hardwood burns to about 60 lb. of ash; hard coal, 200 to 300 lb.; and soft coal, up to 1,000 lb. of ash per ton.

The above values are for seasoned wood—wood cut for 6 to 12 months and properly dried. Green wood of some species like aspen

TABLE 25. WEIGHT OF AIR-DRIED FUEL WOOD AND GROSS FUEL VALUE*

Species	Weight per cord, lb.	Total heat value per cord, B.t.u.
Shagbark hickory.......	4,240	24,600,000
White oak............	3,920	22,700,000
Beech...............	3,760	21,800,000
Sugar maple..........	3,680	21,300,000
Red oak.............	3,680	21,300,000
Birch................	3,680	21,300,000
Ash.................	3,440	20,000,000
Red maple...........	3,200	18,600,000
American elm.........	2,960	17,200,000
Shortleaf pine........	2,900	18,500,000
Red pine............	2,880	18,200,000
White pine...........	2,080	13,300,000
Aspen...............	2,160	12,500,000

* From Forest Products Laboratory.

and elm may burn with only 60 percent of this heating value, depending on the amount of natural moisture in the cells. However, since the heartwood of other species like white ash, beech, pignut and shagbark hickory, black locust, Osage orange, red pine, and tamarack is naturally dry, such species will improve but little on drying.

There are no standard grades or specifications for fuel or cord wood. It is sold by the cord or rick. State laws in some states define a cord as 128 cu. ft., and even though local usage is commonly indefinite, the courts, in absence of statutes, have upheld the dictionary definition which says a cord is a pile of wood 4 by 4 by 8 ft., or 128 cu. ft. A rick of wood (sometimes called a "short" or "face cord") generally designates fuel or fireplace lengths, 4 ft. high and 8 ft. long.

For Mine Timbers. These are a good outlet for rough logs, small poles, and sawed or hewed products. If a local market exists, it is worth consideration. A large variety of timbers are needed, such as lagging, props, ties, stulls, and large timbers. Lagging are usually small poles less than 5 in. top and of variable length.   Props are round timbers usually up to 16 ft. long and 3½ to 10 in. and larger at the top.   Ties are smaller than railroad ties hewed or sawed on two sides. Stulls and other large timbers are needed in various sizes and degrees of "framing."   Purchase may be by linear foot, green weight, or by the board foot.

5. Making Use of Organizational Aids

Individual farmers are at a disadvantage in selling forest products partly because the buyers know so much more than farmers about wood products and their uses and partly because they are well organized.   On the other hand, farmers are usually well organized to sell all farm products except wood.   Yet farmers potentially have great power in influencing both the growing and marketing of wood products.   Half of all commercial forests and more than three-fourths of all private woodlands are in ownerships of less than 500 acres each. Besides 50,000 to 100,000 operators of small sawmills and wood-conversion plants, these owners include more than 3 million farmers and nearly a million investors.   In other words, small owners control over three-fourths of the private commercial forest land of the United States, and farm owners represent 75 percent of the total ownership.   When you add the important factor of accessibility to market, farmers are in a position to grow the products in demand, and by organizing to protect their interests, they can ensure fair prices for their products.   Good timber is in short supply and promises to continue in that status for an indefinite future.

Farm cooperatives help farmers sell eggs, fruit, grain, livestock, and many other products.   There are relatively few that sell forest products but one organized to handle other products could also sell wood, if farmers need the service.   A few general farm cooperatives successfully handle wood products now.   Wood grown as a farm crop needs the help of organized selling.   As soon as farmers appreciate the opportunity that exists in growing and selling wood as a farm crop, the way to profitable marketing is clear.

Organization can solve many problems of equipment needed for cultural operations, for reforestation, and for harvesting timber. Many organizations already exist, such as cooperatives, soil-conservation districts, and less formal types of cooperation among farmers. This help takes the form of ownership of equipment for rental to farmers, pooling of products for shipment to distant markets, and organized crews to plant trees and to do woods work at contract rates. Organized farmers, through cooperatives or soil-conservation districts, can also influence contractors and agents who wish to work for farmers as well as buyers of products, by approving or, in effect, "licensing" those who are reliable and responsible.

Then, of course, there are the public aids. The farm foresters, increasing in numbers as farmers find their services helpful, are one example. The marketing information service previously mentioned is another. The forest experiment stations and the Forest Products Laboratory of the U.S. Forest Service are constantly working not only to increase knowledge of how to grow wood but to improve techniques of wood handling and marketing and to find new uses for wood products. The employees of the Extension Service and of the Soil Conservation Service, also assist farmers in problems of growing and marketing wood. Other organizations offering aid to small woodland owners in all phases of forestry, including marketing, were mentioned in Chap. 1.

So there are many aids in marketing wood products. Farmers need only to take the same interest in this problem that they take in marketing other farm crops. Wood crops produced annually become a part of the farm business. The way to grow wood and to market it is a part of that business. Farmers can solve the problem, if they make use of the present aids available to them and of their strategic position as owners of such a large part of the private timber-producing land.

6. Developing Farm Wood Industries

The thesis around which this text is built is that wood is a farm crop, subject to the rules of farm economy. That means that as a rule selling stumpage is the least profitable way for a farmer to sell his wood crop. The labor and profit value that is added by converting stumpage into logs or bolts is not only worth while but in accordance with the principles of farm economy. High-grade trees will return a good profit if sold as stumpage; low-grade trees have very little stumpage value. The value of the latter consists largely of what is added by the investment of additional capital or labor or both. This is also true of many other farm crops.

Therefore, carefully consider the possibilities of adding values to your low-grade products by further processing and handling. If farmers can find the time, and the capital needed, to do this, worth-while labor returns, interest on investment, and profit often can be made from forest products of little values as stumpage or as logs or bolts.   A few examples will be given to illustrate what is meant.

Producing Fence Posts.   Buyers of posts made from durable woods want to purchase at the lowest price, but they also want to be assured

FIG. 117. Peeling larch posts in Pennsylvania.   (*Soil Conservation Service.*)

of good value.   Grade your posts into two or more grades and carefully season them.   The buyer is then sure that he is getting full value for his money.   The top grade would, of course, be straight sound full-dimension posts, chiefly or entirely heartwood; the second grade would be those that are serviceable but slightly under full size and with some sapwood.   Still another grade would be 10-ft. posts, 7 in. thick or larger.   These are only suggestions for grades. A stock of such posts priced fairly, a reputation for honesty, and a little advertising are the elements that result in satisfactory sales of any product, even where competition is keen (Figs. 59 and 117).

Producing Fuel Wood. This product is always in plentiful supply and therefore not easy to sell at satisfactory prices. Nevertheless, from the standpoint of the consumer, good fuel wood is hard to find. The consumer wants well-seasoned sound wood cut to specified lengths and properly split, and *he wants full measure* at the point of delivery. For fireplace wood, especially, he is glad to pay a fair price to a seller who can be relied upon to deliver exactly what he offers to sell. Too often the consumer buys, for example, what he is told is oak-hickory seasoned wood 24 in. long at an agreed-upon price per cord. When the wood is delivered, he finds most of it is 20 to 22 in. long with more or less basswood, poplar, soft maple, or even pine mixed with the oak and hickory. When he laboriously ricks it up and measures it, he finds only 58 sq. ft. (side measurement) instead of 64 sq. ft. The seller tells him that he measured the wood stacked in standard cords (4-ft. lengths) and that the difference represents the shrinkage in cutting and handling. The consumer is not satisfied, but he pays the bill. When he tries to burn the wood, he finds it full of moisture. It sizzles and sputters and refuses to burn without adding undue quantities of dry kindling. The heat of the burning kindling is used in burning the wet logs, and so there is little or no net heat to warm the consumer's living room or cheer his heart. On the contrary, he feels bitterly that he has been cheated. He will not buy another batch of wood from the same seller.

The farmer who wants to sell fuel wood year after year for a satisfactory price must take the trouble to build a clientele of satisfied customers. That means careful processing, grading, seasoning, full measurement, and proper labeling of the goods offered. The seller must not demand a greater price than his product is worth in competition with other sellers, but once his reputation for honesty and fair dealing is established, he will have no difficulty in getting a price that compensates him for the extra trouble. The selling price of most low-grade products leaves only a narrow margin for profit. A fair labor return normally is about what the price of fuel wood represents. However, good salesmanship plus superior methods of processing will result in a small profit on the operation.

Table 25 indicates that oak-hickory-maple wood (air dried, 20 percent moisture) weighs close to 4,000 lb. per standard cord, conifers from 2,000 to 3,000 lb. The green weight, usually about 70 percent moisture, would be at least 1,000 to 3,000 lb. greater. It is difficult to air dry fuel wood below 25 percent moisture, but this means a loss in weight of 800 to 1,500 lb. per cord, depending upon species.   If the moisture content is reduced to only 40 percent instead of 25, an increased handling weight of 300 to 500 lb. per cord results, with consequent increased costs of handling and transportation, and the product has poor burning qualities.

Size of sticks is the important factor in drying fuel wood.   Splitting increases the rate of drying.   To ensure uniform rapid seasoning, split sticks above 8 in. in diameter once and those above 12 in. twice. To ensure seasoning in northern climates, cut and pile fuel wood not later than June; it will be fairly well seasoned by October.   If left outdoors over winter, it will reabsorb moisture to the extent of as much as 300 lb. per cord.   In piling wood for seasoning, keep all bolts off the ground and allow free circulation of air.   Open spots, of course, permit more rapid drying than shaded areas.

Producing Rough Lumber.   There is always a possibility of selling lumber at retail prices instead of logs at wholesale prices. Where small or inferior logs are difficult to sell, they can be custom sawed either by hauling logs to a mill or by a small mill temporarily set up near the woodland.   Such lumber, 2 by 4's, 2 by 6's, 2 by 8's, 4 by 4's, 6 by 6's, and larger sizes are always in demand for farm construction.   Some of it can be used without seasoning, but to ensure against warping and undue checking, it must be properly piled.   The sawing is equally important.   Select a sawmill that has a reputation for sawing to uniform thickness.

Piling Lumber (For seasoning).   This consists of the following steps: (1) Select a good location, well drained, level, and exposed to air currents.   Remove weeds, brush, and trash.   (2) Provide a solid foundation.   Seasoned white-oak posts 8 to 10 in. in diameter or 6- by 6-in. timbers are good, but any durable wood will do.   Set rear posts 3 ft. in ground and about 15 in. above ground.   Other posts from rear to front should be set to about the same depth, approximately 3 ft. apart, to give a down slope of 1 in. for each foot of length front to rear.   Two or three rows of posts are used, making piles 6 to 10 ft. wide.   The length is determined by the length of the longest board.   Substantial timbers, 6 by 6 in. or 6 by 8 in., and the length of the pile, are laid on the posts with crosspieces 4 by 4 in. or 4 by 6 in.

(3) Build the pile of lumber and timbers so that the ends of each piece are supported and each layer is of one thickness.   Stickers, lined up

with the foundation supports, are placed between each layer.   Stickers
are sawed and seasoned pieces 1 in. thick and about $1\frac{1}{2}$ to $2\frac{1}{2}$ in.
wide (the wide ones for softwoods).   Wide stickers are used at the
front end of the pile and should project beyond the ends of the boards
to decrease end checking.   The front of the pile should pitch forward
1 in. for each foot of height.   Leave "flues" from top to bottom
through the pile for air circulation.   Almost two-thirds of the seasoning process is due to vertical air movement through the pile.
Full length boards should be used on the outside of each layer, short
lengths on the inside.

(4) Place covers on piles to provide protection from snow, rain, sun,
and the effects of exposure.   Extend them over the front of the pile
at least 12 in. and over the back $2\frac{1}{2}$ ft.   Low-grade boards are satisfactory for the roof.   Tarred building paper over the roof makes the
roof tighter, and it's use requires fewer boards.   Anchor the roof to
the pile with wire to ensure against wind damage.

(5) Allow time for seasoning.   This is from 4 months to a year,
depending upon climate, seasons, exposure, and other factors.   Thin
lumber dries faster than thick pieces.   Moisture content of green
lumber properly piled is reduced in air seasoning from around 70
percent to 20 percent.   After seasoning is complete, the contents of
the pile can be sorted and transferred to a shed for more convenient
handling.

Other details of lumber piling for air seasoning are shown in Fig.
118.

Selling Wood Chips.   This offers a possible market for low-grade
wood, limbs, and small trees from thinnings.   Wood in the form of
chips has been used for many years in commercial processes, such as
the manufacture of paper, roofing felts, floor mats, linoleum, and
other products.   Recently portable chippers have been used to produce chips for agricultural uses, such as bedding for cattle and poultry;
mulch for orchards, berries, and gardens; and as organic matter to be
added to the soil for use in pastures and in cultivated fields.

Research has established the fact that sawdust or wood chips added
to the soil directly or after use as bedding do not sour the soil.   No
additional lime is needed because of the use of wood particles.   The
addition of any organic matter to the soil uses up nitrogen in its
decomposition, and hence nitrogen must be added with the organic
matter; otherwise the current year's crop will suffer.   About 2 lb. of a

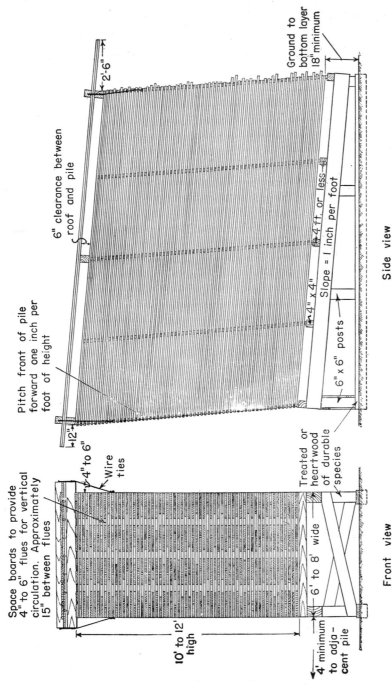

Side view

Front view

Fig. 118. Details in piling lumber for air seasoning. (*Forest Products Laboratory, U.S. Forest Service.*)

nitrogen fertilizer such as nitrate of soda or ammonium sulfate per 100 lb. of wood chips is recommended. After the first year, crop yields show improvement in succeeding years without any further applications of nitrogen.

Even the smallest chippers available are expensive and require large quantities of wood for economical operation. It would not be feasible for a farmer to own a chipper just to convert his own waste wood into chips for use on the farm. Reports, however, indicate more and more chippers are becoming available on a custom basis. Where they can be used locally at a fixed rate per cord of wood or per ton of chips, this method of utilizing wood waste, and at the same time greatly improving soil conditions by adding this form of organic matter, should be investigated.

There is no doubt that wood chips added to the soil will increase crop yields and lessen erosion and that the effects last much longer than organic matter in the form of green manure crops. In localities where many farmers use such products as sawdust and wood shavings, the supply is soon exhausted. Hence, the use of wood chips is a logical next source of supply. Chips are being produced experimentally for from $4 to $6 per ton of chips, including machine operation and wood handling. One standard cord of wood produces about 2 tons of chips (Fig. 119).

The maintenance of organic matter in the soil has always been one of the big problems of agriculture. Whether or not wood chips can be produced and applied cheaply enough to meet the requirements will be answered by future developments. Possibly less acres of cultivated and pasture land well supplied with organic matter from wood will produce greater crop yields than present acreages. Perhaps the future farm will have less acres under cultivation and in pastures and an increased acreage of woodlands. Perhaps such a farm will yield a better income to the farmer with less expenditure of labor. Every farmer will do well to watch for such possibilities and to take advantage of opportunities to test the new organic methods of farming.

Preserving Wood. The addition of toxic substances to the wood preserves it against decay. This is another important way of adding value to low-grade wood products. Fence posts are the products most commonly and easily treated with preservatives on the farm. It is possible to treat small trees removed in thinnings to make them suitable for bean poles. Construction timbers, especially those to be used in porches or other places exposed to damp conditions, if treated, will last much longer than untreated wood of nondurable species. Great progress has been made in recent years in methods and details of treating wood with preservatives. There are many details of treating and handling which should be learned by one who undertakes any operation in wood preservation. Many bulletins

FIG. 119. Wood chipper being used to convert tree tops and other wood waste material into chips. In this case the wood chips are used for mulch in an orchard. (*Soil Conservation Service.*)

and pamphlets are available for free distribution by state agencies and the U.S. Department of Agriculture, and new ones are constantly being published. These give details and cost of wood preservation by different methods. The reader, if he contemplates any such operation, should ask for appropriate literature from his county agricultural agent, the Extension Service, or the state forester.

This text will attempt to classify the general principles and methods of wood preservation and leave the details of actually conducting the operation to other publications easily obtained as above indicated. *Decay in wood* is caused by fungi, which feed upon the wood and gradually break it down. The method of control is to poison the wood with toxic chemicals so that the fungi are deprived of their food supply. The same effect is obtained by withdrawal of air (as when wood is submerged in water), by withdrawal of moisture (when wood is well seasoned and kept dry), or reduction in temperature below the point where the fungi can live. Obviously poisoning the food supply is the most practicable method for wood to be used under conditions where other factors cannot be controlled.

Sapwood of all kinds of timber has low resistance to decay. The heartwood of some tree species is so resistant to decay that preservative treatment is considered unnecessary. General comparisons of the relative decay resistance of different species must be estimates. They cannot be exact, and they may be misleading if interpreted as being mathematically accurate and applicable to all cases. Comparative figures may be useful, however, if their limitations are understood and if it is understood that they have application only when wood is used under conditions that favor decay. Tables 26 and 27 classify wood into groups in accordance with the above limitations.

TABLE 26. COMPARATIVE DECAY RESISTANCE OF THE HEARTWOOD OF NATIVE TREE SPECIES WHEN USED UNDER CONDITIONS THAT FAVOR DECAY

High	Intermediate	Low
Bald cypress	Douglas fir	Ash
Catalpa	Honey locust	Aspen
Cedars	Larch	Basswood
Chestnut	Chestnut oak	Beech
Juniper	White oak	Birch
Black locust	White pine	Cottonwood
Mesquite	Southern pine	Firs (true)
Red mulberry	Sassafras	Hemlock
Osage orange		Sugar maple
Redwood		Northern red oak
Black walnut		Spruce
Pacific yew		Willows

The *heartwood* is all important in untreated wood. In wood treated with preservatives, the sapwood is all important. The reason is simple. Sapwood absorbs the preservative with relative ease, while the heartwood is penetrated only with difficulty, usually only under pressure. Since only nonpressure methods of treatment are feasible for small operations, the treatment is usually limited to round timbers —posts and poles.

Sawed timbers, for use in buildings or structures not actually in

TABLE 27. APPROXIMATE COMPARATIVE LIFE OF UNTREATED FENCE POSTS (HEARTWOOD)

(1) At least 20 years	(2) 10 to 15 years	(3) Less than 10 years	(4) Remarks applicable to col. (3), years
Osage orange	Catalpa	Eastern ash	7
Black locust	Mulberry	Oregon ash (split)	6
Red cedar	Chestnut	Red elm	7
Alaska red cedar (split)	Northern white cedar	Red and black oak	6
	California incense cedar	Red alder (split)	5
Port Orford white (split) cedar	Bur oak	Willow	5
	White oak	Aspen cottonwood	4
Sierra juniper	Walnut	Pines	4
Redwood	Sassafras	Hickory	4
Pacific yew	Tamarack	Maple	3
	Cherry	Birch	3
	Oregon white oak	Cascara	5
		Douglas fir	4 to 7
		True firs	Western grand fir 8 (split)
		Hemlock	6
		Western larch	6

TABLE 28. RELATIVE PENETRATION OF WOOD PRESERVATIVES, SAPWOOD ONLY

Good	Moderate	Poor
Beech	Aspen	Ash
Red elm	Birch	Basswood
Red gum	Black gum	True firs
Red oak	Cherry	Butternut
Pines	Cottonwood	Hemlock
Sycamore	White elm	Sugar maple
Tupelo gum	Hackberry	Yellow poplar
	Hickory	Spruce
	Soft maple	Tamarack or larch
	White oak	Douglas fir
	Willow	

contact with the soil but subject to considerable moisture, can be treated by brushing, spraying, or dipping. The preservative does not penetrate the wood to any extent, but even a surface treatment will add to the life of the timber. Examples of uses of wood where this treatment is worth while are in brooders, hog and poultry houses, feed troughs, stakes, racks, roosts, and stable floors.

Treating Unseasoned Green-cut Wood. Four methods commonly used are briefly described here. All of them introduce water-soluble chemicals, in solution, into the water-conducting tissues of the wood. They penetrate the sapwood quite well but usually fail to get

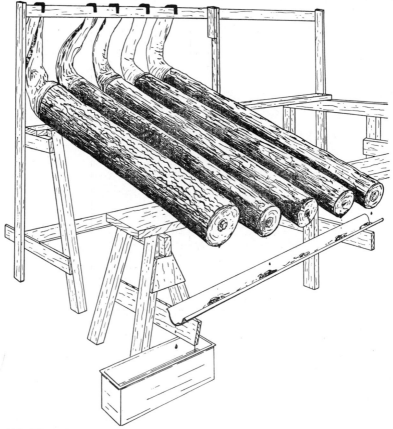

FIG. 120. Tire-tube method of treating green-cut rough fence posts with zinc chloride. (*Forest Products Laboratory, U.S. Forest Service.*)

into the heartwood. Zinc chloride or chromated zinc chloride is the chemical commonly used to treat only woods that show good penetration of the sapwood by preservatives (Table 28). Since the preservative used is soluble in water, these methods are not suitable for wood to be used in excessively wet situations.

The *tire-tube method* is suitable for posts 4 to 8 in. d.b.h. (Fig. 120). Pull a section of old inner tube, 2 to 3 ft. long, over the butt end of the post and secure it firmly to make a tight seal. The bark at the end should be removed and the tube fastened with wire or rubber bands. The preservative solution is poured into the tube. It penetrates in about 24 hr. The posts may be used immediately.

The *stepping method* is applicable to small trees, either hardwood or

FIG. 121. The stepping method for treating small trees, either conifers or hardwoods. Treat immediately after cutting while in full leaf. (*Photograph by Richard H. Fenton, from University of Connecticut Extension Service Bulletin* 415.)

conifers. They are cut and immediately set in a barrel or pail containing the preservative solution. The trees must retain all or most of their green crowns since the leaves draw the preservative into the sapwood (Fig. 121). A variation of this method is its application to thinnings in plantations where the trees are too heavy to handle directly. Trees are cut and "hung up" against adjacent uncut trees. The butt ends of the trees are then eased off into a pail or half drum which is then filled with the preservative solution (Fig. 122).

The *barrel method* has been used to treat green-cut unbarked posts.

The posts are set vertically in the vessel containing the solution, and the liquid is drawn through the submerged end. The amount of solution absorbed by the posts is small; therefore, a concentrated solution is used. It is reported that the solution will rise to only about

FIG. 122. Variation of the method shown in Fig. 121 applicable to larger trees. (*Photograph by Richard H. Fenton from University of Connecticut Extension Service Bulletin 415.*)

1 ft. in the submerged end. Posts are removed from the container and placed vertically with the treated end up and left for two or three months. This method is more or less experimental at the present time (Fig. 123). It is usable, in most climates, only between May 1 and Sept. 1, which coincides with the peeling season.

The *osmose process* compares favorably with other nonpressure methods, according to tests with southern pines. Sodium fluoride and sodium or potassium carbonate are the basic ingredients that are applied to green and freshly cut material in the form of a thin paste.

Posts must be peeled, but it is not essential to remove all of the inner bark. Then place the wood in close piles and cover with watertight paper; leave it for two weeks to three months, depending on the thickness of the wood. During this period, the salts in the paste gradually diffuse with the water in the wood cells by osmosis. The entire length of the sticks or only parts of them may be treated by this method.

Fig. 123. Treating posts by the barrel method. (*Photograph by Richard H. Fenton, from University of Connecticut Extension Service Bulletin* 415.)

The chemical may be applied with a brush or the timbers may be dipped in the solution (Figs. 124 and 125).

The osmose process has been used commercially in the United States since 1930. It is sold under proprietary names. It's desirable features are that it is easy to apply without special equipment, there is no fire hazard, and the treated wood is odorless, paintable, and clean.

Treating Seasoned Wood. The commercial *pressure methods* of impregnating wood with preservatives are efficient and satisfactory. They require large capital investments, however, and are not suitable for small operations. The *hot and cold creosote bath treatment* has been used for fence posts for a very long time. It has proved to be effective. It has the disadvantage of leaving a bad odor and a messy oil and tar residue on the outside of the wood. The treated wood is highly flammable and does not take paint readily. Wood to be treated is heated in coal-tar creosote in an open tank to temperatures ranging from 180 to 220°F. for two hours or more, depending on species. The wood is then removed and placed in another tank containing cold

Fig. 124. Piling peeled posts immediately after dipping in Osmosalts. (*Soil Conservation Service.*)

Fig. 125. Covered pile of posts treated with Osmosalts. In this case the penetration of the salts was over one inch after being covered for 15 days. (*Soil Conservation Service.*)

creosote, although "cold" is used only in a relative sense. The "cold" temperature should be about 80 to 100°F.—high enough to thin the oil. This cooling process allows the preservative to enter the wood cells from which air and moisture have been expelled. The hot and cold baths require about the same length of time. Equal parts of fuel oil and creosote can be used in the cold bath. If only a small quantity of wood is to be treated, one tank is sufficient. The wood is left in the tank overnight, the fire is withdrawn, and the preservative is allowed to cool gradually. The next day the process can be repeated with a new batch of wood.

Thoroughly season posts or poles to be treated with creosote and completely remove outer and inner bark. The surface of the wood must be dry at time of treatment (Fig. 126).

Pentachlorophenal is a relatively new process, but it is rapidly replacing creosote. If used with a light petroleum oil such as kerosene, the

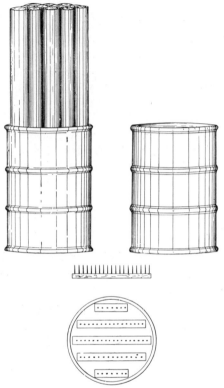

Fig. 126. Tanks for treating posts using the hot and cold bath method. Note method of holding the posts at the bottom of the tanks.

treated wood will easily take paint. The chemical can be purchased as a liquid concentrate to be diluted with a petroleum oil as recommended by the manufacturer. Treatment is simply to soak the wood in the solution in tanks for 48 to 72 hr. depending on species (whether easy or difficult to treat, Table 28). The hot- and cold-bath method can be used. It hastens the time of penetration of the chemical and possibly gives a maximum penetration. Completely peel all outer and inner bark from posts and poles and thoroughly season before treatment.

SUPPLEMENTARY ACTIVITIES

Checking Quality Products

One of the activities in Chap. 6 was cruising a stand of timber.

1. Look up the stand table that you made, and, if necessary, revisit the plot.

a. How many trees per acre are there 20 in. d.b.h. and up?

b. How many of these had smooth clean boles for the first one or two logs?

c. What proportion of the saw logs that you marked for cutting came from these logs?

2. The first two logs from trees 20 in. and up make a high percentage of grade 1 saw logs. These bring the high prices. Let's take an example.

a. Suppose that you marked about 2,000 ft. b.m. per acre to be cut, none of them better than common logs worth, say, $30 per M ft. b.m. on the skidway at the edge of the woods. That would amount to $60.

b. Now suppose that 25 percent of the 2,000 ft. b.m. would make grade 1 logs worth $100 on the skidway. How much would the farmer then get for the same quantity of logs?

3. Will it pay this farmer to manage his woods so as to produce at least some high-grade logs?

Examining the Market for Fuel Wood

1. Ask ten people who use fireplace wood the following questions, and record their answers.

a. Do you have trouble buying well-seasoned wood, sound, cut to proper lengths, largely body wood as opposed to limb wood?

b. Do you always get full measure a cord of 128 cu. ft. or a full rick, if you buy it that way?

c. Would you like to secure your wood from a reliable farmer who would deliver exactly what he promises and give full measure?

d. Would you like to haul your wood on a two-wheel trailer from a near-by farm and thus save part of the hauling cost?

e. Would you be willing to pay a premium price of, say, a dollar per cord extra if you could find a thoroughly reliable farmer who would furnish the kind of wood you want as described in question 1*a*?

2. What conclusions do you draw from the answers to these questions about the opportunity for farmers to market surplus fuel wood?

8. Managing the Farm Woods for Maple Sap

THE SUBJECT MATTER of this chapter is the management of the woods so as to produce profitable quantities of maple sap. The latter is the raw material for a farm industry. The processes and techniques used in converting raw sap into the finished products— sirup and sugar—are discussed only as they influence the volume or quality of the raw sap. The success of any industry depends upon the abundance and cost of the raw material, the cost of manufacture, and the margin for profit between these costs and the selling price of the product.

The price of the product, in this case, apparently need not cause much worry. Maple sirup or sugar is a luxury product in demand by a sufficient clientele who are willing to pay any reasonable price. The product is in short supply in relation to demand, and the trend in production is downward. There is likely to be less rather than more maple sirup produced in the future because the number of trees tapped is steadily declining. In 1935 the number of trees tapped in the United States was 12,341,000; in 1950, 7,713,000, a reduction of 38 percent in the 15-year period. From 1935 to 1940 the loss in Vermont was about 40 percent, in New York 20 percent, in Pennsylvania 50 percent.

Reduced costs of processing due to better methods and improved equipment generally have been offset by increased costs of getting the sap. This in turn has been due to failure of most farmers, over the years, to take care of their woodlands which contain sap-producing maple trees. Costs vary tremendously from farm to farm. For example, a study of 20 farms in New York showed 1947 costs ranging from $2.24 to $4.74 per gallon of sirup.

The well-managed sugarbush will be the one that will show low costs of sap production in the future. The farmer who produces sap at costs below average is assured not only of a good labor return but of a good profit as well. The management of farm woodlands where maple sap production is an important product therefore deserves a separate chapter. The subject is discussed here according to the following outline of jobs:

1. Determining the Place of Maple Sap Production in Woodland Management and Farm Economy
2. Providing Conditions Suitable for Growth of Maple Trees
3. Managing the Sugarbush
4. Watching the Costs

1. Determining the Place of Maple Sap Production in Woodland Management and Farm Economy

Maple sap production on a commercial basis is not feasible throughout the range of the hard maple tree. Its range covers most of the United States east of the Mississippi River. It is most prominent as a forest tree in the forests of New England, New York, Pennsylvania, and the Lake states, and in the adjacent parts of Canada. In order to produce sap in sufficient volume to justify its conversion into sirup or sugar on a commercial scale, the northern climate seems to be as necessary as the presence of maple trees. A slow transition from winter to spring with an alternation of cold nights and warm sunny days seems to be required. These conditions occur in the states named above and to a limited extent in other states. Current statistics of maple sap production are maintained by the Crop Reporting Board, Bureau of Agricultural Economics for 10 states as follows: Maine, New Hampshire, Vermont, Massachusetts, New York, Pennsylvania, Ohio, Michigan, Wisconsin, and Maryland. Many sugarbushes are operated in other states, such as Indiana, Illinois, Minnesota, Virginia, and West Virginia. The trend of production in Minnesota in recent years is upward.

Whether or not the local climate is suitable for a maple sap operation can be determined largely by past experience of farmers. If there is no record of successful local operation, it would be well to test the volume of flow and length of season on a few trees for several seasons before making the investment in equipment needed for commercial operation. There should be enough maple trees to support a minimum of about 500 buckets. Sap of sufficient sugar content to makes its use practicable for manufacturing sirup or sugar is obtained from the sugar or hard maple (*Acer saccharum*) and the black maple

(*Acer nigrum*).   Other species of the genus Acer contains too small a concentration of sugar in the sap to justify the expense of converting the sap to sirup or sugar.

Maple sap, within the range of optimum growth of sugar maple trees combined with suitable climatic conditions, furnishes the raw material for an important and profitable farm industry.   At least

FIG. 127. A sugar house in Michigan.   Maple sap operation utilizes man and horse, or tractor, power in early spring that may not otherwise be profitably engaged.   (*Soil Conservation Service.*)

half, and usually more, of the cost of producing maple sirup is the labor involved.   The work comes in early spring (usually February or early March in the northern country) before work in the soil is possible.

A maple sirup operation can be fitted into the labor schedule of a great many farms; it utilizes man, horse, or tractor labor that may not otherwise be profitably engaged (Fig. 127).   For an ideal setup, there would be 50 to 60 tappable maple trees per acre, capable of carrying 80 to 100 buckets.   A 20-acre sugarbush on this basis could support a 2,000-bucket operation.   Using average figures from Michigan of 1 gal. of sirup from 5 buckets, the yield in sirup would be about 400 gal.   A price of $4 per gallon would indicate a profit on the average operation of about $1 per gallon or $400 on 20 acres.   This would be an average profit of $20 per acre each year from the 20-acre woods. The labor return would amount to $1.50 per hour or more. Actually most sugarbushes that carry 2,000 buckets cover three or four times the 20-acre figures used in the foregoing example. The point is that good management over a period of 30 to 40 years could change a 2,000-bucket operation from a 75- or 100-acre woods to a 20-acre

FIG. 128. A good stand of well-developed maple trees in an Indiana woods. (*Soil Conservation Service.*)

woods. The result would be considerable savings in costs of operation and maintenance so that the profits would be larger than in the average operation. If a sugarbush pays, now, to the average farmer, it will pay even better if attention is given to woods management—to the development of a growing stock adapted to the requirements of maple sap production (Fig. 128).

The income to be obtained from a sugarbush that is part of a farm woodland is an important factor in making the entire undertaking a success. Maple sap is a premium product, like grade 1 saw logs. The more of the premium product that can be produced, the greater the woodland profits. The conversion of maple sap to sirup requires large quantities of fuel, about 1 cord of well-seasoned wood for every 75 sap buckets. For a 2,000-bucket operation this means 27 cords of fuel. Here is a market on the farm for a low-grade product not easy to sell at a profit.   This is much more wood than could be obtained from cultural operations in a 20-acre sugarbush, and so the sugarbush helps the woodland economy by increasing the premium product revenues and by furnishing a home market for a considerable volume of low-grade products otherwise not salable or salable only with difficulty.

Where woods and climate are suitable, woodland management on the farm is greatly benefited where maple sap can be included as a forest product.   With hard-surfaced roads kept free of snow, maple sap has been successfully transported for distances up to 40 miles to a central processing plant.   The sap is very perishable; it must be converted to the finished product soon after it leaves the trees; also it is very bulky.   Some operators report storing sap successfully in underground tanks for 24 to 48 hours.   In one instance, it is reported that 5,000 gal. were held for 4 days without deterioration.[1]   Such examples are undoubtedly exceptional.   A safer plan would seem to be to increase the evaporator capacity so as to process the sap as fast as gathered.

Notwithstanding these possibilities, the great majority of the maple sap is processed on the farm.   There are very few sugarbushes operated except as part of a farm business.   If those farmers who have the opportunity to operate a sugarbush will pay the same attention to woodland management as they do to the details of processing the sap, the maple sap industry will soon cease to be classed as a vanishing industry.   If they will also treat the sugarbush as one unit of the farm-woodland enterprise, it will be possible for farms in the north-woods country to secure a very substantial part of farm income from the farm woodland.   Many north-woods farms, because of physical conditions, cannot make sufficient income without the help that the woodland can give.   Many farms, long since abandoned, would be successful going concerns today if the farm woodland had been made a partner in the farm business.

2. Providing Conditions Suitable for Growth of Maple Trees

The sugarbush is, or should be, essentially one unit of the farm forest.   Maple trees are forest trees.   In the well-managed forest they

---

[1] A letter to the author from F. E. Winch, Jr., Associate Professor of Forestry, Cornell University, Ithaca, N.Y., Nov. 13, 1951.

find the conditions that promote their best growth.   The more closely
the sugarbush conforms to the general outline and physical conditions
of the well-tended forest, the more likely it is to produce maple sap
abundantly and continuously.   There are some special measures
needed in the management of a sugarbush that will be discussed in the
next section, but they do not change the essential fact that forest conditions best promote the growth of maple trees whether grown for wood
products or the production of sap.   It is, of course, barely possible
that maple orchards, similar to apple or peach orchards, could be
successfully maintained.   If so, their management would be in the
field of the horticulturist and the agronomist rather than the forester.
The fact remains, however, that so far the bulk of the maple sap has
come from forest-grown trees.

Often farmers find that roadside maple trees, where they have large
well-developed crowns and plenty of soil moisture, produce larger
quantities of sap per bucket with a higher percentage of sugar than
forest-grown trees.   This is another way of saying that for sap production, management by farmers of roadside maple trees has been more
successful than management of trees grown in the woods.   This has
been more or less of an accident.   Full crowns exposed to sunlight and
abundant moisture plus the necessary soil nutrients are the elements
that seem to produce large quantities of sweet sap.   As long as roadside trees enjoy these advantages, farmers should of course include
them in their operations.   The same conditions, however, can be provided for woods-grown trees, with the assurance that woods management will perpetuate the sugarbush and furnish a continuous and
uninterrupted flow of sap.

The difficulty about dependence upon roadside trees is that there
are seldom enough of them in places where good soil conditions prevail; they are subject to more accidents of storm, insects, and disease
than are forest trees; there are no young trees to replace the old ones
as they die; and there seldom is any control over soil conditions which
may be changed by the character of use of adjoining fields.   Well-
planned silvicultural practices offer the best assurance of growing
conditions suitable for maple trees intended to produce continuous
crops of wood products or sap or both.   More about management
later in this chapter.

What are the conditions in the woods that give optimum growing
conditions to maple trees?   In Chap. 6, the forest soil was described

and the processes and agents that take part in its building and maintenance were outlined.   The hardwood forest was portrayed as the
best example of Nature's handiwork in building the forest soil.
Undisturbed by destructive agencies, the hardwood forest builds a
mellow, crumbly, moist soil.   The litter from the forest canopy passes
into humus and becomes part of the colloidal soil mass without undue

Fig. 129. Maple trees growing under good woods conditions in Michigan.   Note the young
growth and evidence of good litter and humus.   (*Michigan State College, East Lansing,
Mich.*)

delay.   Plant nutrients are continually replaced and made available
for plant growth through the activity of myriads of creatures that live
in the forest soil.   Here maple trees are at home.   They find conditions to their liking.   From the soil they obtain moisture and plant
nutrients, and from the sun they get the power to enable the leaves of
the crowns to manufacture the things that make wood tissue.   Sap is
one of these things.   Maple trees, it will be remembered, are tolerant
trees.   They are tolerant of shade; in other words, they can get along
in the forest with smaller quantities of light than some of their neighbors.   This means that they can stand very close together with relatively small individual crowns, but under such conditions they grow
slowly.   Both for quality wood production and for sap production,
fewer trees per unit of area than Nature is apt to maintain give better

results.   The individual trees with more space grow faster because they have better crowns.   They use the increased light to good advantage.   Up to a certain point, the forest manager who wants grade 1 maple logs uses the same silvicultural practices that he would if he wished only maximum sap production.   In either case, he must maintain the forest canopy without too much disturbance because from

FIG. 130. A sugarbush in Vermont showing a large number of trees but poorly developed. There are indications of a lack of woods conditions; no young growth, probably poor litter and humus, trees short and limby. Compare with Figs. 128 and 129. (*U.S. Forest Service.*)

that comes the litter that builds the forest soil.   Soil moisture is perhaps the most important single factor influencing the growth and vigor of maple trees.   Big crowns exposed to sunlight produce large volumes of sap, only if the trees remain healthy and vigorous.   They cannot remain healthy and vigorous if soil moisture declines.   And this leads us to the third section (Figs 129 and 130).

3. Managing the Sugarbush

If the reader has followed the previous discussion of silvicultural factors in the management of farm woodlands, he will know pretty well, from what has been said before, the substance of what is to be said here. Nevertheless, it is well to repeat briefly the essential steps and add the particular measures most applicable to the management of sugarbushes.

For example, the common practice of *grazing domestic animals* in the sugarbush destroys the forest litter, compacts the soil, and wipes out the ground cover and the forest tree seedlings. These things destroy the life-giving forest soil that maple trees require, reduce soil moisture, and slowly but surely bring the end to the profitable production of the sugarbush. A grazed sugarbush has the death penalty hanging over it from the day grazing animals first are allowed free access to it. For one thing, young trees are not allowed to grow. There are no replacements for the tappable trees. For another, the health and vigor of the large trees, grown under forest conditions, slowly decline. Maple trees, even under such conditions, have great stamina. They persist for a surprisingly long time, but one by one they drop out. There are no young vigorous trees to replace them. The costs of gathering sap increase because fewer buckets can be hung per acre. The average volume of sap for the remaining trees grows less as their vigor declines. Conservative students of the subject tell us that an ungrazed sugarbush will produce on the average about 6 percent more sap per bucket than a comparable sugarbush that is grazed. Again costs are increased in the grazed sugarbush.

A study was made a few years ago of two Ohio sugarbushes. They lay side by side and had the same number of tappable trees per acre, the same-sized trees, the same type of soil, and the same tapping practices were used in each. One was grazed, the other was not. Measurements over a five-year period gave the following results: 21 gal. of sirup per acre on the ungrazed bush, 16 gal. on the other, a loss of nearly 25 percent production seemingly attributable to the ill effects of grazing. This may be an exceptional case, but the loss in sap production caused by grazing animals is very real. In the grazed sugarbush, production of sap slowly declines, costs of gathering sap go up; the trees lose vigor, there are no replacements; the end of profitable operation comes nearer each year.

Ground fires are seldom of importance as a destructive agency in sugarbushes, but if they do occur, they must be stopped as quickly as possible. Fire lines are occasionally needed to protect the sugarbush against encroaching fire from known sources of danger. Repeated fires can be as destructive to the forest soil and to the health and vigor of the maple trees as is continued grazing.

Other *protective measures* to conserve soil moisture in the sugarbush fall into the same category as for any woodland. For example, a closed border to stop drying winds, good ground cover to protect the soil, and maintenance of the overhead canopy are important. Such measures are justified for a sugarbush at greater cost than for the usual type of woodland because of the relatively high income obtainable from the former. Conservation of soil moisture is the keynote of silvicultural management of the sugarbush. The items enumerated above are of first importance.

Other *management measures* are aimed at increasing the productiveness of the sugarbush per unit of area and keeping it continuously productive. A sugarbush that produces 20 gal. of sirup or more per acre is obviously more profitable than one that produces only 5 gal. To put it another way, a 2,000-bucket operation from a 20-acre woods will produce cheaper sirup (and greater profits) than if the operation is spread over 80 acres or more. The factors involved are spacing of tappable trees and volume and sweetness of sap from individual trees. Simply stated, then, the objective of management peculiar to the sugarbush is to concentrate the operation on the smallest practicable area—to get the largest sirup production per acre of sugarbush. This is a long-time objective. It requires 30 to 40 years to grow a maple tree from seedling to minimum tappable size (about 10 in.).

Increasing the spacing of trees is easy; simply remove some of them. Decreasing the spacing can be accomplished only by growing additional trees on the area. That involves natural reproduction or planting or seeding, appropriate soil conditions for young seedlings, and removal of some overhead shade to permit the young trees to grow. In an established sugarbush with too few tappable trees, it means starting new maple-crop trees at appropriate intervals and guiding them from infancy to maturity, making holes in the overhead canopy as they reach for the upper air. Of course, it means starting a great many more young trees, including some nonmaple species, than will ever reach the top story. The process involves the removal of nonmaple trees to make room for the maples and the gradual removal of tappable trees as they lose vigor or become injured. Carried on over a period of years, the old trees will finally be replaced by the new crop.

In fact, consistently carried out, such management will result in a constant but very gradual turnover of the growing stock of tappable trees.

Is such a system of management which takes so long to bring about tangible results worth while?   That question can be answered only by each individual farmer.   If a farmer can see no immediate profit in such a long-time system of management and is not interested in building something worth while for the next generation, he probably will not undertake it.   He will lose a degree of satisfaction that comes from any steps to build a better farm.   Perhaps, however, even the monetary returns will not be so long delayed.   Ten years of conservation management of the sugarbush will make a decided difference in its appearance.   The young crop trees will be in evidence, the litter and soil humus easily can be felt underfoot, and the sugarbush begins to show signs of permanence even to the uninitiated.   The value of that farm has already been enhanced because the sugarbush is a growing, increasing asset.   But what is even more important, the farmer has been working at the job of improving his sugarbush.   He has helped Nature start new seedlings.   He has picked out likely crop trees from sapling stands and freed them from stagnating competition. He has cut into the overhead canopy to allow thrifty pole-size maple trees that he had never before noticed to push their crowns up where the sun shines.   He has a new interest in that sugarbush, a new joy in its development.   No, the rewards are not postponed for 40 years. They come every year.   And what is the cost?   Certainly not much actual cash; it is mostly thoughtful planning and work, with the goal ahead in clear perspective.   Why worry about the costs?   After all, maybe the results are tangible and worth while from the beginning of the development.   Each farmer who has the opportunity to manage a sugarbush must decide for himself.

The foregoing is an attempt to present a general picture of what is involved in the management of a sugarbush.   What are the details?

First of all, a farmer should realize that maple trees in the virgin forest rarely grow in pure stands.   The northern hardwood forest is a mixed forest, traditionally known as the maple-beech-birch mixture. Hard maple is often a very prominent member of the association, and with a little help from the forest manager, it easily can take over most of the space formerly occupied by other species.   If a farmer wants a pure maple woods, he can probably get it by continually favoring the maple at the expense of other species. From the standpoint of the most economical operation of a sugarbush, such an objective undoubtedly is correct.

There is, however, another side to the story. Our best guide in forest management is to follow Nature's lead, to work with rather than against her. The question, therefore, is whether or not the development of a pure stand of maple is desirable from the standpoint of the health and welfare of the forest. A dual-purpose forest can be maintained from which will come maple sap and wood products. Over relatively small areas of 15 to 20 acres, probably no harm will come from the attempt to develop a pure maple stand. If in spite of the forest manager's efforts only 80 percent of the stand turns out to be maple, it would seem wise to accept the result with the thought that Nature knows best.

The purpose of this discussion is not to discourage efforts to produce pure maple stands to be managed as a sugarbush but to point out possible dangers connected with the attempt. There are a great many different conditions encountered in the northern forest where maple trees form an important component of the forest. Study local conditions and get the advice of local foresters; you may be safe in attempting to force the development of a pure maple stand. In fact, it may be very easy to do. If it is easy, it is probably right for your situation.

Nature likely will not resist attempts to favor maple trees in the forest association, but we are dealing with a forest, not an orchard. A minor percentage of ash, cherry, basswood, and birch may help to bring about conditions most favorable for maple, and in the end, perhaps, the forest will earn more money because of the presence of these other species. Perhaps, in Nature's economy, part of the crop from a good sugarbush will be fuel to fire the evaporator and part will be saw logs and poles salable, when they are ready, for more than you can get for maple sap. Perhaps safe sugarbush management would be woods management with a very strong emphasis on the production of maple sap (Fig. 129).

It has been pretty well established that the sap flow of individual trees depends upon the size of the crowns and their exposure to sunlight. Very likely the sweetness of the sap is related to the same factors. Many operators carefully test the sugar content of the sap of individual trees as a basis for selecting trees to remain in the stand.

Of course, the vigor of the trees also is an important factor. The latter is favorably affected by the healthy condition of the stand—the maintenance of good forest conditions. The size of the crowns is influenced chiefly by providing ample growing space to relatively young trees at the time of vigorous growth, usually between the sizes of about 8 to 12 in. d.b.h. Freeing the crowns of vigorous growing trees will place them in the dominant class with as much crown spread and access to sunlight as is consistent with the maintenance of forest conditions. To attempt to go beyond this point in freeing maple-crop trees of competition will destroy the forest canopy and react unfavorably on the health of the tappable trees. The effort should be to develop and maintain a good crown, exposed to sunlight, covering the upper one-third to one-half of the total height of each tree.

Direct all cultural operations toward the main goal of producing a large number of dominant sugar maples. But do not sacrifice good young trees and other species, straight and sound, especially the better species such as ash, cherry, and basswood, without very good cause. If no maple trees of equal vigor and promise are competing with them, it will be best to let them grow until they reach saw-log size, or at least until they can be replaced by young maples. Besides, the profit from letting them grow may exceed the possible advantage of a few more maple seedlings or saplings (Fig. 132).

On the other hand, mature trees of species other than maple should be removed where the ground cover of seedlings and saplings is satisfactory. Cutting should be on a selective basis, removing single trees or small groups, never so as to create large openings. Then would follow weeding and thinning in the understory so as to favor sugar maple where the site is favorable to this species. Some spots may be better adapted to ash or other hardwoods than to maple. The growth of evergreens, such as pine, spruce, and hemlock, in the sugarbush is believed by many farmers to insulate the soil, tending to hold frost in the ground too long. This tends to shorten the sap season. Their dense foliage also may shade the maples. The evidence seems to indicate that evergreens, especially hemlocks, lessen the volume of sap and may adversely affect its sugar content. Therefore, it is probably wise to keep such coniferous growth to the minimum (Fig. 131).

In weeding operations to favor maple, it is generally recommended simply to cut back the tops of competing trees so as to give the maples a chance to take the lead. This leaves a ground cover of subordinate growth which protects the soil.

Naturally, the tappable maple trees will be watched for signs of decadence and tested for volume and sweetness of sap flow. When

Fig. 131. Too many conifers, especially hemlock, is generally believed to reduce the volume of sap and adversely affect the sugar content. In this New Hampshire woods, the hemlocks should be cut to make room for young maples. (*U.S. Forest Service.*)

they begin to show inferiority in volume of sap or other signs of decline, the forest manager will remove them as rapidly as they can be replaced by younger trees.

Starting a new sugarbush on old fields or cutover land by planting was covered in Chap. 2. That discussion covered the planting of seedling stock. Experiments indicate the desirability of using rooted cuttings instead of seedlings. The use of cuttings makes possible the choice of mother trees on the theory that good sap-producing trees, especially those with records showing sap of consistently high sugar content, will be able to transmit the same characteristics to their progeny. There seems to be very good evidence to show that this is not only possible but probable. Gather cuttings in June preferably from young twigs. A convenient size would be 6 to 8 in. long and less than ½ in. in diameter. Plant them in a mixture of 2 parts peat and 3 parts sand. Completely cover the cuttings at first, then gradually uncover the tops after the roots develop. Keep the cuttings covered with cheesecloth and keep moist by daily watering. Up to 50 percent of the cuttings have successfully rooted by following the above methods. The rooted cuttings should remain in the nursery bed until the following spring before being transferred to the planting site.

Creating a sugarbush from natural young growth of hardwood or a mixture of hardwood and conifers is governed by the principles already set forth in Chaps. 3 and 4. In this case, the emphasis will naturally be on selecting all possible good maples as crop trees. The final distribution of the maple trees when they reach tappable size should be about 30 by 30 ft., but early selection should follow the principles for weeding and thinning any young forest. However, there is one factor in thinning young maples that is different. The sweetness of the sap is believed to be due in part to inherited characteristics. Some trees tend to produce sweeter sap than others. Therefore, hydrometer tests of the sap of promising young trees may enable the forest manager to select trees that will produce sap with better than average sugar content. There is some prospect that a quicker and more satisfactory test for sugar content of sap than by use of the hydrometer will soon be available. Keep in touch with your Agricultural Experiment Station. The nearer the thinning reaches the stage of final selection of crop trees, the more important this factor becomes.

There is no apparent good reason for changing the $D + 6$ spacing rule in thinning young maples to grow into a sugarbush. Some authorities advocate selecting crop trees in early thinnings on a 12- by 12-ft. spacing. There may be good reason for this exception. Therefore, follow the advice of local foresters in this matter. If no thrifty maples are present at the spots where crop trees are needed, select other species. Obviously, in successive thinnings, some maples previously chosen as crop trees will be found to have suffered from porcupines or wind or ice or disease. Other species will have to be selected in their stead. Where this happens frequently, it may be a warning that the site is not favorable for maple. Perhaps it is best to follow

Nature's lead and be satisfied with the species that seem to thrive best. There will still be plenty of maples in the places best suited to their growth.

Managing an Open Stand of Mature Sugar Maples Heavily Grazed. Here the problem is primarily one of restoring forest conditions and gradually replacing the worn-out trees with young ones. This is not an easy transformation to bring about, and it requires a long period of years. The damage that has been done over many past years can be repaired only by carefully planned steps. Restoration of soil conditions as found in the undisturbed forest is the first consideration. Stop the grazing, keep out the fires. Plant conifers and shrubs along exposed borders. Disk or plow or otherwise break up the sod. Get young growth established by natural reproduction or by planting. Wait patiently for Nature to take hold and repair the damage of past mistreatments. Watch the results. They come gradually.

Begin to weed out the trees already past their usefulness, whether maple trees or other species, as the young growth comes along. Then weed and thin to speed up the growth of the trees that show promise. A new forest with maple in the lead is replacing the old grazed sugarbush. Life and vigor and productiveness again become characteristics of the new forest, the new sugarbush. The forest manager working with Nature has accomplished the transformation.

The Harvest Cut. From the sugarbush it is mostly maple sap. At least that is the forest manager's objective. Not in every case, however, will all of the area of the sugarbush be covered with tappable maple trees. Some parts may be chiefly species other than maple. To these parts, the previous rules (Chap. 6) of one tree or fraction of a tree per acre per year represents the harvest cut, *in addition to whatever is taken in cultural operations.* Where maple trees constitute the dominant stand, the harvest cut is made up of maple trees removed because they are no longer efficient sap producers, plus the annual harvest of sap from those retained. In a woods sugarbush the maple trees (except for a few feet of the butt logs) no longer useful for sap will have high value for saw logs.

The Road System. In the sugarbush, roads if well planned and maintained in good condition, aid in handling wood products as well as in collecting sap. The ground cover and the young growth, so essential for the health and permanence of the forest, must, of course, be kept out of the road.   If this is done, there will be little added expense in sap collection due to this factor.   Spraying the undergrowth along roads with 2,4-D or 2,4-5T has proved effective in road maintenance and in keeping open paths to individual trees.   In any case, the future productiveness of the woods is dependent on this understory and it

Fig. 132. Sugar house and sawmill in a Michigan woods indicates management for both wood products and maple sap. This kind of management, where the woods is large enough to justify it, has proved to be profitable. (*Michigan State College, East Lansing, Mich.*)

must be maintained.   In the long run, its benefits will far outweigh the disadvantages.

Other Factors.   Among those that influence the health and vigor of the sugarbush are the following.

The minimum tappable size without noticeable effect on the growth of the trees is considered to be 10 in. d.b.h.   The rules commonly accepted are: trees 10 to 16 in. d.b.h., 1 bucket; trees 16 to 20 in. d.b.h., 2 buckets; trees over 20 in. and up to 26 in., 3 buckets; trees over 26 in., 4 buckets.

There is no pronounced difference in the volume of sap obtained by tapping different sides of trees.   Experiments in Michigan over a four-year period showed that the variations of the average sap flow between south, west, north, and east are not sufficiently great to warrant concentrations of tapholes on any one of the four positions. It is better for the trees to rotate the tapholes around the circumference. Tapholes should be 2 to 3 in. deep. Bore them on an upward slant into the trees to obtain good drainage. Since the sap comes exclusively from the sapwood, it is useless to bore into the heartwood; 3 in. is a maximum depth for any tree. Use a $\frac{3}{8}$- or $\frac{7}{16}$-in. sharp tapping bit especially designed for the purpose; it will remove all shavings from the taphole and leave a clean smooth bore. If warm weather stops the flow of sap, tapholes can be reamed out with a $\frac{1}{2}$-in. reamer. Some operators claim that reaming tapholes is wasted effort because sap produced after reaming is likely to be of such low quality that it will not prove to be worth while.

Select tapholes 2 to 4 ft. above the ground. If the tree has been previously tapped, place the new hole 6 to 8 in. distant from the old scar. Remove loose bark from the surface where the hole is to be bored, but do not injure or remove the firm bark. After use, the taphole dries out, and an area a little wider than the width of the hole becomes stained and may show some decay. This stained portion extends up and down the tree for 1 to 2 ft.; it will not produce sap again until a new thick layer of wood has been laid over the dead wood. Therefore, it is essential that no more tapholes be bored into the tree in this stained area for approximately ten years. In the first tapping of a tree, it is recommended that holes be made around the tree at a height of 2 ft. above the ground. Make the second circle of holes, alternating with the first, 8 in. above, the third circle 8 in. above the second. This will bring holes to a height of 4 ft. By that time begin again at the 2-ft. level. In this manner tapping may continue indefinitely without serious injury to the trees. When a tapped tree is cut, the lower 4 to 6 ft. of the butt log will have been rendered useless except for fuel.

4. Watching the Costs

The farmer who develops and maintains his sugarbush as part of his farm-woodland enterprise is building for future low costs of operation of his maple sap industry. At the same time, he is at no disadvantage because of present high operating costs that are directly traceable to his woodland-management program. The elements of cost that his management will favorably affect are:

1. The volume of sap produced per tree and per acre. Volume will be increased by maintenance of the best growing conditions, thus keeping individual trees healthy and vigorous; by increasing the number of tap-pable trees per acre; and by giving ample crown space to each one.

2. The concentration of the business of gathering sap in smaller areas will result in shorter hauling distances or more sap per mile of haul road.

3. Careful tapping practices will extend the life and vigor of individual trees. This will tend to keep up production and lower gathering costs.

4. The sweetness of the sap is a variable factor. Not too much is known about the things that make maple sap consistently sweet. Obviously, the richer the sap the lower the costs of producing sirup. It seems rea-sonable to expect that good conditions for growth—abundant soil mois-ture, maintenance of soil nutrients through natural biological processes, and well-developed crowns exposed to sunlight—will result in the maxi-mum of sweet sap that Nature is capable of producing. There is, of course, the added factor of an inherited tendency to produce sweet sap, but good growing conditions are the first essential in any case.

Other factors in the costs of operation of the maple sap industry are related to efficiency of business management which are, strictly speak-ing, outside the scope of this text. However, in order to complete the picture, some important factors of cost will be mentioned.

Modern equipment is probably most important, such as a sugar house well located, well built, and equipped with a modern evaporator large enough to handle the sap quickly.

Good *spile* and *bucket* equipment. Great improvements have been made in recent years. New portable power tapping machines reduce the labor cost of tapping and enable the farmer to set up all the buckets quickly to catch the first run of sap. New materials are used for mak-ing collapsible buckets, lightweight, easily cleaned and stored.

Plastic pipe for conducting sap from field tanks to the sugar house instead of iron pipes.

These things increase the investment for sirup making, but if they reduce the costs, they are worth while. In New York State the aver-age investment in buildings and equipment was found to be $1,986 per farm.

Other items that affect costs are: having everything ready to go in early spring to catch the important first-run flow; cleanliness of sap buckets, storage tanks, and evaporator; ample supply of dry wood fuel to boil the sap. Many operators prefer wood for fuel in contrast to gas, oil, or coal. For a farmer who is managing his woodland to furnish part of his farm income, wood is the logical and cheapest fuel because he needs a market for low-grade products. Cut and season the wood fuel a year in advance of expected use. There is, however, no inherent reason why gas, oil, or coal will not give satisfactory heat with evaporators designed for their use. The question seems to be which fuel will supply heat at the cheapest cost. Wood fuel will normally be plentiful and should be cheaper than other fuels unless labor to produce it is the deciding factor.

TABLE 29. AVERAGE COST OF PRODUCTION OF MAPLE SIRUP IN NEW YORK
20 farms in New York: 1947 averages per farm, 2,009 buckets, 482 gal. of sirup;
1935–1937, 295 gal. of sirup

Item	Cost per gallon		Percent of total	
	1935–1937	1947	1935–1937	1947
Fixed costs				
Interest: buildings, equipment............	$0.12	$0.23	9	8
Depreciation and repairs................	0.20	0.26	16	9
Use of bush...........................	0.20	0.39	16	14
Insurance: fire, theft, and compensation....	.....	0.02	...	1
Total fixed costs.......................	0.52	0.90	41	32
Other costs				
Man labor............................	0.42	1.24	33	44
Fuel (wood)...........................	0.25	0.40	20	14
Horse, truck, or tractor.................	0.07	0.29	6	10
Total fixed and other costs..............	1.26	2.83	100	100
Marketing (at the farm).................	0.14	0.19		
Total costs............................	1.40	3.02		
Selling price..........................	1.50	4.83		
Profit margin..........................	0.10	1.81		

Range in costs in the New York study for 1947 were as follows: Total costs varied from $2.24 per gallon to $4.74 with an average of $3.02. Labor costs varied from $0.60 to $2.38 per gallon, with an average of $1.24. Fuel costs varied from $0.17 to $0.73 per gallon, with an average of $0.40. Margin for profit varied from a loss of $0.61 to a gain of $2.56 per gal. with an average of $1.81.

The average man-labor time per gallon of sirup was 96 min. total, divided as follows:

LABOR	MINUTES
Preparation...................	18
Gathering....................	36
Boiling.......................	27
Filling can or drums...........	5
Clean up.....................	10
Total.....................	96

Michigan State College has published cost records covering 14 years' operation of a sugarbush at East Lansing, Michigan. The 1947 cost was $3.44 per gallon as compared to $3.02 in the New York study, but the sale price was $5, and so the profit was $2.56. The record shows a range of profits from $0.08 to $2.56 over the 14-year period with two years showing a loss.

In Ohio, a study of 58 sugarbushes showed in 1946 an average net labor return per hour of $0.57. (A very poor sap flow year.) In 1947 an average net labor return per hour of $3.54 was recorded.

TABLE 30. COSTS OF MAPLE SIRUP PRODUCTION IN VERMONT 1947 *

Items	Cost per gallon			
	Average of 80 farms studied	Farms with		
		80–500 buckets	501–1,000 buckets	1,001–3,300 buckets
Value...................	$5.15	$5.03	$5.25	$5.12
Cost of production:				
Interest.................	0.52	0.51	0.58	0.50
Taxes..................	0.10	0.08	0.10	0.12
Depreciation.............	0.60	0.72	0.64	0.55
Labor..................	1.44	1.82	1.98	1.00
Wood fuel...............	0.48	0.67	0.46	0.45
Cans and strainers.........	0.16	0.21	0.18	0.13
Power (horse and truck).....	0.15	0.20	0.21	0.10
Other costs..............	0.02	0.01	0.02	
Total costs.............	$3.47	$4.22	$4.17	$2.85
Profit margin..............	1.68	0.81	1.08	2.27
Gallons sirup per farm........	171	70	146	323

* Labor returns per hour ranged from $0.98 for a small operator to $2.77 for a larger one.

The general conclusion reached by practically all investigators is that the labor return from maple sap operations is very good and that, on the average, a profit on the operation is reasonably assured. The better than average operation is practically assured of a good profit.

SUPPLEMENTARY ACTIVITIES

Examining a Sugarbush

1. If you live in the sugarbush country, visit a farm and examine the sugarbush critically.

  a. Is it grazed?

b. Is it an open stand where the wind blows through freely?

c. Is the soil soft and spongy or hard? Is there plenty of litter on the ground?

d. Approximately how many trees 10 to 16 in. d.b.h. and larger are there per acre?

e. Are the maple trees short and limby with signs of defect or are they tall with big crowns and clear boles?

f. Is there a mixture of some coniferous growth in the sugarbush?

g. Are there plenty of maple trees from seedlings to 8 in. d.b.h.?

2. What are your conclusions about this sugarbush? Write a report of your findings telling what is good and bad about it. Make recommendations about steps that this farmer might take to improve his sugarbush so that it will produce abundantly and continuously. Will the steps that you propose eventually reduce the costs of gathering sap?

Boring Tapholes and Inserting Spiles

The general practice is to do this just before the sap starts to flow. Some operators think that the trees can be made ready weeks ahead of the time the sap actually starts to run.

1. Select three groups of 10 maple trees as close together as practicable; select the trees in each group so that they are approximately the same size (in d.b.h. and crown spread, and otherwise about equal). Tack a card to each tree giving the group (*A,B,C*), number, date of boring tapholes.

2. In group *A*, bore holes about Jan. 1. In group *B*, bore holes about Feb. 1. In group *C*, bore holes at the same time that other trees are tapped.

3. In the succeeding sap season, keep a record of quantity and condition of sap from each tree. The following form may be helpful:

Group	Tree no.	D.b.h., in.	Date tapped	Gallons of sap produced	Condition of sap and remarks

4. What do the results indicate?

9. Managing Farm Woods for Christmas Trees

M OST OF OUR Christmas trees come to market from long distances. The total number used annually in the United States is estimated to be about 28 million; 21½ million from the forests of the United States, most of the remainder from Canada. A few come from Labrador, Newfoundland, and the Dominican Republic. Of the trees cut in the United States, the heavy producers are 11 Northeastern and Middle Atlantic States, 6½ million (30 percent); the 3 Lake states, 5 million (23 percent); 14 Southern states, 3 million (14 percent); Pacific Coast and Northwest States, 6 million (28 percent). These account for about 95 percent of the production. About 13 percent, or about 2.8 million trees, comes from public lands, 1 million from national forests, 1½ million from state and county land, and the balance from other Federal lands. Established Christmas-tree plantations are reported to produce 1½ million trees annually.

The species cut are as shown in Table 31. The balance consists of

TABLE 31. SPECIES CUT FOR CHRISTMAS TREES

	PERCENT
Balsam fir	30
Douglas fir	27
Black spruce	11
Red cedar	10
White spruce	5
Scotch pine	3
Southern pines	3
Red spruce	3
Virginia pine	2
White fir	2
Norway spruce	1
Total	97

red fir, red pine, alpine fir, white pine, grand fir, Arizona cypress, jack pine, Colorado blue spruce, pinyon pine, hemlock, juniper, Engelmann's spruce and some others not identified.

285

It will be noted that the choice of species depends much upon what are available locally or offered on local markets. Probably the price and the form of the trees are more important than the species.

In the thickly settled parts of the United States, farmers have many advantages in growing Christmas trees over commercial growers. They are also in a position to compete successfully with the sellers of trees shipped from long distances. These advantages are: (1) Land can be used to produce Christmas trees that is not suitable for other uses either because of size, location, or soil condition. (2) Most of the labor required (except for planting) can be applied at seasons not in conflict with the labor schedule for seeding, cultivating, and harvesting of the usual farm crops. (3) Greater attention than is possible by most commercial growers can be given to producing thoroughly first-class trees. (4) By virtue of the preceding plus a strictly local market, they can command better than average prices. (5) They avoid costs of bundling and packaging, and they are able to deliver fresh-cut trees to consumers. (6) Once the outlet to market for Christmas trees is established, many opportunities not previously available will be found to market the thinnings from parts of the woodland primarily devoted to growing other forest products.

The business of producing and selling Christmas trees will be discussed under the following headings:

1. Determining the Economic Possibilities
2. Planning the Enterprise
3. Managing Christmas-tree Plantations
4. Harvesting and Marketing the Crop

1. Determining the Economic Possibilities

A good case could be made to show that the growing of Christmas trees is a very profitable farm enterprise. However, there are some "if's" involved. Chiefly these concern the prices at which the trees can be sold and the difficulties and the costs encountered in growing the trees. No one can prophesy accurately about future prices, and no one can predict what unforeseen costs or losses may occur. Theoretically Christmas trees can be grown at the rate of at least 1,000 per acre in from 5 to 12 years at costs, including labor, interest, depreciation, rent, and all others, of about $0.25 per tree or $250 per acre. If the trees bring an average price of $1 each, a very good profit results.

If costs are double the estimate or the price is only half, there is still a good margin.

There are many records of successful Christmas-tree enterprises. Doubtless there are also many failures, but these are rarely reported. One grower in Ohio planted 12,000 trees on 4 acres in 1927. In 1936 he began harvesting, and during the next 9 years he sold 2,000 trees (on the stump, which is not usually the most profitable way) for $0.60 each or $300 per acre. He reported net earnings amounting to more than 7 percent compound interest, leaving a good stand of potential saw timber. Another owner in New York State reported on a 15-acre plantation. Over a 15-year period, his gross earnings were $7,000, selling trees both wholesale and retail. He estimated his costs at $0.30 per tree for planting, pruning, harvesting, and marketing. His total costs were $2,700, his net earnings $4,300 or about $286 per acre.

Determining Size of Plantation. Competition is likely to be greater in the future than in the past, but there would seem to be a good opportunity for a profitable operation for farmers who grow trees on a scale that does not demand too much of their time yet still justifies careful attention to details. For the average farmer that probably would be an annual harvest cut of 500 to 1,000 trees. This would mean a plantation of 5 to 10 acres planted at the rate of from ½ to 1 acre per year for approximately 10 years. If first-class planting stock was purchased from commercial nurseries, this scale of operation might represent an annual investment of $100 to $200. The first returns could be expected 5 to 7 years after the first planting. Thereafter, if replacements were made each year, the income would be annual, gradually increasing to a maximum about the tenth year.

If the woodland already includes evergreens, part of the Christmas-tree harvest could come from thinnings of natural or planted trees (Figs. 133 and 134). This, of course, would necessitate planning the thinning operation to coincide with the marketing season for Christmas trees. The tops of coniferous trees cut for poles and other products sometimes are suitable for Christmas trees. The record of Christmas trees used, previously given, indicates that coniferous trees of any species, if well shaped and reasonably priced, can be sold.

On farms where there is an opportunity to cut trees for the Christmas trade from thinnings or from old pastures, the strictly Christmas-tree plantations could well be on a smaller scale than where such supplemental sources of trees do not exist.   However, if a farmer decides to undertake to sell Christmas trees as part of his woodland enterprise, a plantation devoted exclusively to this crop is well worth while.   For one thing, the business requires that he develop a clientele of customers for his trees.   If he does not have an assured annual supply, he is likely to run out of trees to sell.   He has that assured supply

Fig. 133. Young Douglas fir in Montana. There is plenty of opportunity here to cut Christmas trees with benefit to the remaining trees.   Northwestern Montana ships more than 3 million trees annually, three-fourths of which are cut from farm forests. (*Soil Conservation Service.*)

in his Christmas-tree plantation.   For another thing, the plantation gives him the opportunity to produce a variety of species and to shape them, as they grow, into nearly perfect specimens.   A quality product is perhaps even more important in selling Christmas trees than most other forest products.   The consumer wants as nearly a perfectly shaped tree as he can find.   The price drops rapidly for second-grade specimens.

Developing Management Plans.   There are several ways of growing Christmas trees in plantations.   One is to plant completely whatever acreage is available in one or several years and await the time when they are large enough to begin harvesting.   Meanwhile, of course, they must be tended, as will be explained later.   Harvest time

is when the trees reach salable size.   That may mean table trees 2 to
3 ft. tall or the usual size of 6 to 7 ft.   Nature does not grow all trees
uniformly.   Some reach merchantable size several years ahead of
their fellows of the same species planted on the same area.   This gives
the opportunity to harvest, perhaps, 1,500 trees on an acre, of different
sizes, over a period of 3 to 4 years.   If the holes created by this system

FIG. 134. Douglas fir in Montana.   To the right of the sign, the woodland has been thinned
for Christmas trees and the remaining stand pruned; to the left, no treatment.   (*Soil Conservation Service.*)

are promptly planted with new trees, a continuous production can be
maintained.   Most commercial growers do not follow this plan
because of increased costs of planting and harvesting, but many
farmers do (Fig. 135).

The plan sometimes recommended and considered by some authorities to be the best is to plant as many plots each year as the number of
years on the average required to grow 6- to 7-ft. trees.   Christmas
trees reach this height generally in from 7 to 14 years.   Depending on
the species planted, this might be an average of 10 years.   If the total
area is to be 10 acres, 1 acre would be planted each year for 10 years.
By that time, the first plot would be ready for harvest, and theoretically all trees almost regardless of size would be cut, harvested, and the
plot replanted.   This would give a continuous annual yield of approx-

imately the same amount. The newly planted trees would not be handicapped by the trampling and accidents incident to harvesting or by the shade of larger trees. Actually, it is doubtful if any grower is able to adhere strictly to any such rigid plan. Its success would depend upon a market for trees of different sizes or upon sacrificing many trees not of marketable size. Probably the result would be a

Fig. 135. Planted Douglas fir Christmas trees in Connecticut managed under the continuous yield system. Prompt replanting of holes made by harvest cuttings results in this type of plantation. The larger trees are held for special orders. (*Photo by Hartford Courant, Connecticut Extension Service Bulletin* 409.)

compromise by extending the harvesting period for each plot over 2 to 3 years. Harvesting would be in progress in two or more plots at a time, and the second planting would be delayed by 2 to 3 years. This would permit the slower trees to reach harvest size. Such a compromise plan has many advantages, the most important being the opportunity to produce a large percentage of high-quality trees (Fig. 136).

A further modification of the foregoing plans is to plant trees primarily for wood products but plan the thinnings for Christmas trees. This is a little different from simply using thinnings from existing thick stands. Planting would be about the same as for the usual Christmas-tree plantation but at closer spacing than used for a wood-product planting, say, 5 by 5 ft. instead of 6 by 6 ft. This would permit removal, theoretically, of 500 Christmas trees at 8 to 10 years of age and leave 800 or more trees per acre to grow into a normal woods. Rarely is it feasible to plant a variety of species, in this case, unless they are placed in pure stands in separate blocks. The differences in growth rates of different species make equally spaced mixed plantings very difficult to handle.

Fig. 136. Christmas-tree plantation in Pennsylvania. Norway spruce four years old. (*Courtesy W. W. Simonds, State College, Pa.*)

It is, however, entirely feasible to combine the growing of small ornamental trees with Christmas trees where a market for the former exists. If the ornamental stock could be harvested at five years of age, the original planting could be made at 3- by 3-ft. spacing. The removal of the ornamentals would leave the Christmas trees spaced 6 by 6 ft.— a distance permitting ample growing space for well-formed trees. Upon removal of the Christmas trees, the plot would be immediately replanted.

All these different plans of management deserve consideration before finally deciding what kind of plan best fits the situation on your particular farm. Undoubtedly, one of the most important elements is the potential market for Christmas trees and such supplemental sources of income as ornamental stock and even Christmas greens. In many places, extra boughs can be bundled and sold as Christmas greens.

If your farm is located at a distance from possible local markets and the only prospects for selling trees is to buyers for shipment to distant markets, there will be little prospect of high profits. Perhaps good wages can be made in growing trees, but the enterprise is not likely to return more than that. In such a situation, good profits may be possible in cutting trees already available from old fields or pastures or from thinnings in natural stands (Fig. 134), but probably not from trees planted solely for the Christmas-tree market. The costs and the risk in the latter case appear to be too great.

2. Planning the Enterprise

As already indicated, there is a considerable choice of species to plant. First choice are those species more commonly used in the locality, if they can be grown successfully. This is because people have previously used them and are prejudiced in their favor. Good trees of species with which the consumer is acquainted require no sales talk. They sell readily. However, the big factor is a nicely formed tree of good foliage. If a new species looks nice and really proves satisfactory, it is not difficult to introduce to the public. For example, eastern and western white pine make excellent Christmas trees. They have good foliage of blue-green color, and the needles have unusual ability to stay on the tree indoors and to retain their color. These, like other pines, are likely to grow too fast, but their growth can be held back by pruning. If this is done, the result is a nearly perfect Christmas tree. In spite of the record that shows relatively little use of white pine for Christmas trees in the past, if they are properly trained, there is no reason to hesitate in growing at least a proportion of these pines in plantations. The consumer, once he has tried a well-formed white pine for a Christmas tree, is sure to return in successive seasons for more (Fig. 137). Of course, white pine must be grown in territory free of the blister rust and weevil, but there are many such localities.

There are other species, equally good potential Christmas trees, that have not been extensively used in the past because consumers are not acquainted with them or because in their natural growth in the wilderness they normally do not have the compact form which is so desirable. You, however, are undertaking to produce a special product. You can control the growth to make just the kind of tree

that the consumer wants.   There also is this added factor in your
case.   You are producing a different Christmas tree not usually
available to consumers who buy on street corners from assorted lots
shipped from wilderness areas.   A little advertising of this fact may
be a big asset in your business.

Choosing Species.   In considering what species to plant, consider
the recommendations of the state, extension, or local farm forester,

FIG. 137. White-pine Christmas trees being loaded on a truck.   (*Soil Conservation Service.*)

but also visit a good commercial tree nursery and look at the different
coniferous trees in stock and try to picture what you could do in
shaping some species not previously recognized in the Christmas
trade.   Of course, you want to be conservative and not plant untried
species too generously, but in growing Christmas trees, it will pay to
venture a little on a small scale.   Perhaps you will find that you can
grow some Christmas trees, and very excellent ones, that no one else
in your locality can offer.   The price?   Well, think of the possibilities.
If the new ones fail?   Do not try too many until you are sure that
you can grow them.   Make sure that somebody has already grown
at least specimen trees under climatic conditions similar to yours.

The characteristics of Christmas trees that seem to please most
consumers are these:

1. Good color of the foliage—dark or slate-green or blue-green.
2. Compact dense appearance.
3. Symmetrical shape; inclined to be pyramidal, but with a fairly wide crown.
4. Ability to retain needles (and their color) indoors for at least two weeks.
5. Branches stout enough to hold the ornaments, lights, and small presents.
6. Nonprickly foliage, preferably with fragrant odor.

Probably no one species of evergreen tree is perfect from the standpoint of its growth habits or all of the above characteristics. Here listed are the species commonly considered best for planting for Christmas trees together with some notes about each one. Be sure to check with your local or state forester to make sure that the species you would like to grow are suited to your climate and soil.

Douglas fir (Pseudotsuga taxifolia). This tree is native to the Pacific Coast and the Rocky Mountains states. It has proved to be adapted to the climate of the Northeastern states. The Rocky Mountain variety is most likely to succeed. It has good foliage, it retains its needles well, and it grows naturally with little or no pruning into a compact form. Its chief drawbacks are its site requirements and its relatively slow growth. Plant it on cool moist sites preferably on north and east slopes. It requires usually from 12 to 15 years to become marketable at the 6- to 8-ft. height. It is subject to frost damage; therefore avoid frost pockets. The higher elevations are better than low-lying land. Very little insect damage is reported (Fig. 135).

Douglas fir is equally good as a Christmas tree in its native home in the West. The cheapest trees are obtained from the wilderness or from managed natural stands. It is also planted for Christmas trees on open land. On the poorer sites, it grows evenly much as it does in the East. This is the chief tree shipped in quantity to eastern markets from the Northwestern states (Fig. 133).

Balsam fir (Abies balsamea). A very satisfactory Christmas tree as shown by the record of use. It has good form and color, fragrant odor, and good needle retention. However, it has proved to be very difficult to grow in plantations. It requires a cool moist site; it is subject to loss from drought; it requires from 10 to 15 years to reach marketable size of 6 to 8 ft. There are few insect enemies, and it requires little or no pruning. This species should be planted sparingly because of the risk, but if your climate and site appear to be favorable, try it.

Naturally this species is not likely to succeed south of the Mason and Dixon line except in the higher altitudes. There are several other species of fir, some of which promise better results than the balsam. Among these are the western firs—concolor fir, grand fir, California red fir, and in the East, the Fraser fir, native to high altitudes of the Southern Appalachian mountains.

Norway spruce (*Picea abies*). This is a European species extensively planted in this country for both wood products and Christmas trees. It grows well in a wide altitudinal and latitudinal range. It is relatively easy to grow, but it requires some pruning and it is subject to damage by the white-pine weevil, the spruce gall aphid, the spruce sawfly, and the red spider. Like most other spruces, the needles drop rapidly indoors unless the tree stands in water. Even then, needle retention is not as good as Douglas fir, the true firs, or the pines. Eight to fifteen years are required to reach 6 to 8 ft. in height, depending upon the site and locality (Fig. 136).

Norway spruce grows slowly for the first four or five years then shoots up rapidly. This necessitates pruning and shaping to make satisfactory trees. In spite of these handicaps, Norway spruce is a dependable species for Christmas-tree growers. Its insect enemies cause some failures but not enough to ruin any large percentage of the trees. Cutting and burning affected parts is usually sufficient to hold insect damage to a reasonable amount.

Other Spruces. The white spruce (*Picea glauca*) is similar in its characteristics to Norway. It is inclined to grow more uniformly and hence requires less pruning; also it tends to be more cylindrical in form and seems to suffer less damage from insects. Probably it should be planted as readily as Norway.

Colorado blue spruce (*Picea pungens*) promises good results. Its needles are sharper than those of other spruces, but reports indicate that needle retention is a little better. It probably grows at about the same rate as the two previously mentioned spruces. It has the advantage of good sale prospects for ornamental stock.

Many other spruces, such as Engelmann's, Black Hills, other western spruces, and eastern red spruce, may prove to be equally good.

The Pines. All the pines grow faster than the species already discussed. They reach merchantable size in 6 to 10 years. They are not nearly so sensitive to soil conditions, especially soil moisture, as the spruces and firs. Their shape is inclined to be globular rather than cylindrical. Unless carefully pruned, the crowns are not sufficiently compact to make first-class Christmas trees. A big advantage of the pines is their ability to retain their needles indoors. It is not easy to select pine trees of suitable compact form from the wilderness. For this reason, they have not been very extensively cut and delivered to the market places. This fact offers opportunities to the plantation grower if he will spend the necessary time in pruning and shaping his product.

Red pine (*Pinus resinosa*), when properly pruned, makes an acceptable tree. The coarse framework of the tree is likely to show through the foliage. In some years the color of the foliage is not good. It is subject to snow damage and injury from mice and rabbits. The pine sawfly sometimes causes serious damage.

Scotch pine (*Pinus sylvestris*) in some localities is preferable to red pine. Its growth habit is less coarse, the needles are shorter (and sharper), and the whole appearance is better. It seems to suffer less injury from insects (but this is not certain), but it suffers from snow damage and sometimes tends to lose color in late fall. It grows rapidly and hence must be pruned regularly to make a good tree (Fig. 138).

White pine (*Pinus strobus* or *monticula*). This pine has already been mentioned. The chief objection to its use is its vulnerability to the blister rust disease. Control of the disease is to keep the territory within about 1,000 ft. of the planted pines free of gooseberry and currants (Ribes). The Ribes are alternate hosts of the blister rust fungus; the fungus cannot hurt the pines where Ribes are absent. Many localities do not suffer from the disease. Consult your local forester or county agricultural agent for information about this disease in your locality (Fig. 137). The white pine is also subject, in some localities, to injury by the white pine weevil.

Other Conifers. Such trees as red cedar, hemlock, jack pine, Virginia pine, pinyon pine, and a variety of cedars are used in various localities in the United States. Red cedar is often grown in plantations. It is a fairly satisfactory Christmas tree. The others are satisfactory also, especially where they can be obtained from the wilderness and sold at prices below those long established in the market. That is a vastly different thing from growing them for profit in a plantation.

Most of the southern pines are satisfactory Christmas trees, and they are suitable for plantations if pruned and shaped. In the South, these pines with red cedar, white pines, and pitch pines (in some parts of the South) are the chief trees adapted to the climate available for Christmas-tree plantations.

FIG. 138. Scotch-pine Christmas trees in Michigan—six years old. (*Soil Conservation Service.*)

Deciding on Source and Age of Planting Stock.

In most states, planting stock of the common species are available to farmers from state nurseries at less than commercial prices. Restrictions usually are placed on such trees forbidding buyers to sell them for ornamental stock. Their use for Christmas trees to be sold by severing the stem from the roots is allowed in some states. In other words, sale of living Christmas trees or ornamental stock is forbidden by contract.

Commercial nurseries have no such restrictions. If you are not sure just what your market will be, buy the stock from commercial nurseries. In any case, investigate what they have to offer. You may find some species worth trying that state nurseries do not grow.

Most pines can be planted as two- or three-year seedlings (in the

South one-year seedlings).   Transplants of other species 2—1 or 2—2
are usually advisable.   The transplants are sturdier, and growth
response is much faster than in seedlings of most species.

If you are undertaking a planting program for several years in
advance, costs can be reduced by buying seedling stock (2—0) and
replanting in transplant rows and allowing it to grow for one or two
years more.   Such a program has the advantage of making the
planting stock immediately available near the planting site when the
time to plant arrives.   Chap. 2 discussed the details of actual planting.   These are in no way different in starting Christmas-tree plantations except that greater care in planting is justified than for the usual
wood-product planting.   Good profits on Christmas trees are expected
in 7 to 12 years.   Delays in getting the trees started are costly.

Selecting Suitable Land.   Most any soil except poorly drained
land or coarse sand is suitable for Christmas trees.   Most old fields
or pastures are acceptable.   For Douglas fir or any of the true firs,
a moist site preferably facing north or east is best.   The pines will
do well on the drier sites.   Red cedar prefers a limestone soil.

The location of the plantations with respect to accessibility to hard
roads and ease of protection and harvesting is important.   Locate
the plantations, if possible, where a truck can get in easily.   A rough
terrain makes harvesting more expensive.   The maintenance of fire
lines between blocks also is more difficult and expensive.   If there is
a choice, place the plantations where they can be observed from the
house.   Both fire and trespass must be prevented.

Recently cutover hardwood land is not a good place for a plantation because of the expense of holding back the hardwood growth.
Old fields adjacent to established woods will seed in rapidly to volunteer growth that interferes with the growth of the planted trees.   However, if the site is a good one for Douglas fir or balsam—moist and
free from frost damage—this adverse factor may be worth discounting.
But land where advance growth of trees and brush is already established will give no end of trouble.   The best bottom-land soils will
grow Christmas trees very rapidly, but they also grow weeds and
grass very prolifically.   Such sites should be cultivated for a year
before planting to get rid of the competing grass and weeds.   Cultivation or annual mowing may be required for a few years until the trees
are able to take care of themselves.   If such a site is selected, plant
only sturdy transplant stock of all species used.

For most old-field land no preparation for planting is needed. For heavy sod land, planting in previously plowed contours or in "scalped" spots is often necessary. If the slope is gentle or level and supports a heavy growth of grass or weeds, plow and harrow before planting (Fig. 139).

Spacing. The farmer must judge for himself, by considering the purposes he has in mind, what spacing to use. A plantation designed

FIG. 139. Old fields are usually suitable places to plant Christmas trees.   A four-year-old Scotch-pine plantation in Pennsylvania.   (*Courtesy W. W. Simonds, State College, Pa.*)

to yield only 6- to 8-ft. trees will do best at 5 by 5 ft. or 6 by 6 ft.   If ornamental stock or table-size trees are to be marketed, 3 by 3 ft. or 4 by 4 ft. is best.

Different species should be planted in separate blocks.   These may be in a checkerboard or in irregular shapes, suiting species to site. Plowed or disked fire lines separating blocks or groups of blocks is a good safety measure.   Lay out the hauling roads before planting begins and maintain them as fire lines; space them so that cut trees will not be dragged more than 20 to 25 ft.

Fencing. If livestock are likely to get into the plantations, build temporary or permanent fences to keep them out.   The damage is likely to be much greater than the cost of the fence.   You cannot do much about deer browsing, but you can about livestock grazing.

3. Managing Christmas-tree Plantations

Well-managed Christmas-tree plantations pay the best dividends.

Weeding. If the plantation is located in the hardwood country, sooner or later hardwood seedlings and brush will begin to appear. The land was originally in hardwood forest, and inevitably, in the absence of surface tillage, Nature will strive to restore the land to its original cover. A soil-building process is under way, and the faster the process is accelerated by the treatment you are giving the land the more rapidly will Nature take advantage of the opportunity. A plantation on poor soil and some distance away from sources of seed will likely be invaded more slowly than one on good rich soil or one near an established hardwood forest.

The pioneer species come first—popple, wild cherry, raspberries, blackberries, various brush species, usually some scrub pine. Unless war is made against this invading army, the Christmas-tree plantation will last for only one or several rotations. The method of fighting the enemy is to go over the plantation systematically each year and pull out or mow those volunteers that lend themselves to this treatment, and get rid of the others by poison spray on the foliage or by cutting and applying poison to the cut stump (see Chap. 3 for details). The farmer may have to use his own ingenuity in devising methods of control.

In the western country, where hardwoods do not present the same problem, there will still be plenty of effort in holding back the foreign invasion of alder, salal, wild cherry, serviceberry, ceanothus, and numerous others, plus unwanted conifers.

After the first crop of Christmas trees is harvested from a block, it is time to do a thorough job of ridding the land of foreigners before replanting to Christmas-tree species. Obviously, the most serious competition is likely to be when the planted trees are very young.

Mention has already been made of the necessity of either cultivating or mowing of heavy competing grass and weeds on sites where such vegetation is rank. Usually, if transplant stock has been planted, annual mowing for a few years is sufficient.

Watching for Fire and Trespass. Just before the holidays, keep a close watch of the plantations even when the trees are not yet large enough for market. Unfortunately, there are plenty of potential thieves who are satisfied with a small Christmas tree when it costs nothing.   In the spring and fall, keep watch for thieves who may lift small trees for landscaping.

Fire is usually an ever present risk during the dry season.   In addition to maintaining fire lines by disking or plowing, keep a man-pack water tank (Fig. 140) filled and ready to use in case a fire starts. Also keep fire tools handy, especially a fire rake and a flapper (Figs. 141 and 142).

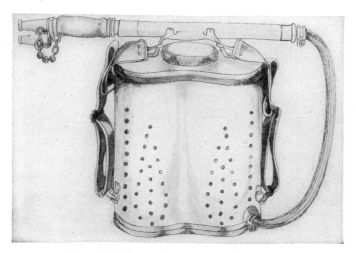

Fig. 140. Man-pack water tank and pump.

Meeting Bad Weather Conditions.   There is not much you can do about the weather.   Heavy wet snows and ice storms sometimes cause damage.   Try to avoid locations likely to suffer, but when the storms come, mostly you have to "grin and bear it."   Of course, with a wet snow, it is possible to go through the plantation with a heavy club and knock the snow off the trees.   In the case of ice, you may do more damage than good.   Pines are more likely to suffer than spruces and firs.   Later pruning may satisfactorily reshape some trees.

Unseasonable dry weather following planting or heaving caused by alternate thawing and freezing sometimes causes severe losses.   It is less likely to happen if transplant stock has been used and the planting job has been well done.   Nevertheless, losses do occur from these causes.   Replant the failures and hope for better luck next time.

Controlling Rodents.   Damage is usually most severe with pines. Rabbits, mice, and ground hogs are the worst offenders.   Trapping and shooting the animals is one way to handle the situation.   Another is to put out poison bait as is often done in orchards.   In most cases, this is probably not necessary.   The damage is usually localized, and on the whole only a small percentage of the plantation may be expected to suffer much damage.

Controlling Insects and Diseases.   Insects may cause considerable damage.   *Bark beetles* have been known to attack Christmas trees,

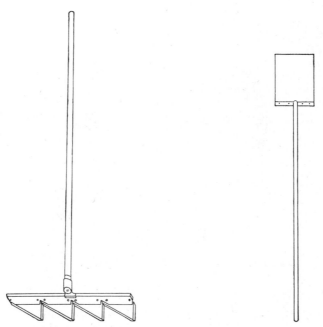

FIG. 141. A fire rake.   FIG. 142. A fire flapper made of flexible composition material.

but they are not at all common.   These insects bore into the bark, and worms hatch from eggs in the cambium layer just under the bark. The worms kill the trees by girdling.   They can be detected by the presence of pitch tubes on the trunks.   Cut and burn the affected trees.

Weevils attack white pine, the spruces, and sometimes Scotch pine. These insects bore into the terminal leaders, causing them to die. Cut off the affected terminal shoots in June and July and burn them. This will keep the damage to a minimum.   Affected trees, in the succeeding year, send up new terminals.   A lead arsenate spray on the leaders applied in March is reported to be effective (Fig. 143).

Gall aphids are sucking insects causing conelike galls on the twigs of the spruces (Fig. 144). They cause premature leaf shedding and browning of the ends of the twigs. Seldom do they endanger the life of the trees, but they spoil their appearance. Cut and burn the affected trees or use a contact spray if the attack is bad. Get advice

Fig. 143. Weevil injury on Norway spruce. (*Photo by Richard H. Fenton, Connecticut Extension Service Bulletin* 409.)

from state or Federal entomologists for the latest directions about time and method of application of the spray and how to mix it. Fortunately, reports indicate few really serious infestations.

Sawflies are defoliating caterpillars on jack (*banksiana*) pine, pitch pine, Scotch pine, and red pine, Norway spruce, and perhaps on a few other species. The larvae hatch in early summer and, on the pines, cling to the branches in great masses. If unmolested, they will completely defoliate branch after branch. Clip off the affected branches and destroy the worms preferably by fire. Dusting or spraying is also effective, but usually removing and destroying the insects is sufficient.

On Norway spruce the green larvae appear singly.   It is difficult to detect them because of their color.   Branches stripped of their

FIG. 144. Gall-aphid injury on Norway spruce.   (*Photo by Richard H. Fenton, Connecticut Extension Service Bulletin* 409.)

needles are the best indication of their presence.   So far as reported, this species does not seem to suffer very serious injury except on trees larger than 6 to 7 ft.

Spittle bug has been reported on Scotch pine, causing numerous brown twigs.   This is a sucking insect that protects itself, while feeding, with a globule of spittle.   If the infestation is bad, use a contact spray.   The brown twigs spoil the appearance of the tree unless removed.

Red spider sometimes affects spruces; it is difficult to detect.   When the foliage looks stunted and has an unhealthy appearance, the trouble probably is due to red spider. Cut and burn such trees to prevent spreading the infestation.

Diseases. Except for the white-pine blister rust, already discussed, the conifers seem to be almost free of disease. Other rusts have been reported on Scotch and red pine, but the damage so far has been negligible.

Pruning. Growers will probably have only about 50 percent of the trees in their plantations acceptable as Christmas trees unless they are systematically pruned and shaped as they grow. There are only about three exceptions—Douglas fir, balsam, and red cedar. These grow uniformly and rarely need pruning. To be successful, pruning may be necessary every year after the first few years of growth. This type of cultural work is the price you have to pay for fast-growing trees. The three species mentioned grow slowly and evenly and produce the pleasing effect the consumer wants.

Other trees either grow too rapidly most of the time or the growth is uneven. Only by holding back the growth where it is too fast can the grower approach the uniformity that Nature reaches in Douglas fir as it has grown in Christmas-tree plantations in the eastern United States. In its native habitat, Douglas fir, when grown for Christmas trees on average or better sites, requires pruning to get the even growth desired. On the poorer sites of the West Coast region, this species produces satisfactory trees without pruning (Fig. 145).

There are two types of growth in conifers which require different treatment. *The spruces* and other short-needled evergreens have buds and branchlets along the stems between the whorls that mark each year's growth. This type of conifer can be pruned either with pruning shears or hedge shears. The result with the former can be more selective and is likely to produce a more pleasing effect than can be obtained with hedge shears. With pruning shears, the leader is cut back to the length desired (usually 10 to 15 in.), and the side whorls also cut proportionately to maintain balance. If cut just above a bud, no stub is left and the tree picks up growth at that point the next season. Pruning can be done at any time after the season's growth is complete. Spruces incline to grow slowly for the first few years, making a compact growth, and then begin to grow rapidly. If not cut back, the tree presents a spindling, uncouth appearance (Fig. 147).

The pines do not form buds and branchlets between the annual whorls. If the pruning is done at the right time, before the season's growth is completed, new terminal buds will form at the end of the shortened leader and laterals. If done after the season's growth is complete, the entire leader (or lateral) may die back to the previous season's whorl point. Next spring, the laterals will change their direction of growth to replace any lost leader, and the effect is not what you want. Therefore, the timing of the pruning operation

Fig. 145. A four-year-old Douglas fir in a Christmas-tree plantation in California. Note the tendency to grow too rapidly for the best Christmas-tree form. (*Soil Conservation Service.*)

with pines is highly important. About the middle of the active growing period or as soon as the terminal leader has grown to the length desired is the time to prune the pines. Use pruning shears or a sharp knife. Hedge shears will not do for this job. This is one of the *must* operations. If postponed, the opportunity for that season is gone and some of your trees may be spoiled. It pays to work over the pines systematically every year at about the same time. On a farm, this pruning job probably will interfere with other equally important work. This may be a good reason to grow only spruces and firs. However, unless the plantation is very large, the pruning does not take very long. It must be done to grow first-class pine Christmas trees (Fig. 146).

Using Other Ways of Growing Christmas Trees. Occasionally one hears a good deal about growing conifers from stump sprouts, from layering, or from so-called "turn up" trees. These are all interesting but they are mostly novelties, worth trying a bit for the fun of it, but for steady business, trees can be grown cheaper from planted young trees than by these rather difficult and abnormal methods.

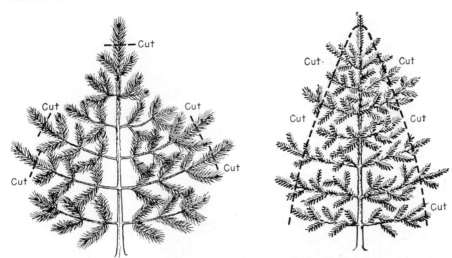

FIG. 146. Method of pruning pines to make well-formed Christmas trees.

FIG. 147. Method of pruning or shearing short-needled conifers to make the best Christmas trees.

Very few conifers produce sprouts. Some conifers have produced stump sprouts under certain conditions. If the stump of a tree 4 in. and larger in diameter is cut high, leaving a cluster of live branches on the stump, dormant buds break through at the top of the stump. These resulting sprouts, if reduced to one or two, will grow into acceptable Christmas trees (Fig. 148).

From the same stump, the live branches left will gradually turn upward, and if the most promising one or two are selected, pruned, and shaped over a period of 5 to 6 years, new trees result.

If the lowest branch of most conifers lies in contact with moist soil for a period of years (reported to be 5 to 10), roots will develop. The growing tip beyond the point of rooting will start growing upright, and a new tree will develop.

There is one possibility of the future that is worth mentioning and

watching for.   Research in plant physiology may develop a hormone
that will cause cuttings from coniferous trees to root, as many hardwoods are able to do.   The planting stock would then be easier and
cheaper to produce, and the grower could take cuttings from the best
trees in his plantation.   Then he would have heredity to help him
improve the quality of his trees.   So far, experiments have not developed a satisfactory method for rooting cuttings from coniferous trees,

Fig. 148. This Montana farmer is about to cut a Christmas tree grown from the stump of a
tree cut several years previously.   (*Soil Conservation Service.*)

but success may come later.   Keep in touch with the forest experiment stations.   They may be able to help you solve many cultural
problems in forestry.

4. Harvesting and Marketing the Crop

You have already decided whether or not you are going to market
all of the trees from a given area in one season or try to sell a few each
year and keep replanting the holes.   The first method is better
adapted to pines than to the short-needle evergreens. The pines grow
fairly evenly, but some are always in the lead.   To cut all in one
season, wait until the sizes run from 4 to 8 ft. high.   If the market
will take these sizes, clear cut and, after ridding the area of the
"foreigners," replant.   If the smaller sizes are not marketable, cut

only the larger ones and wait one or more years before completing the harvest.

If you have decided to try the continuous-yield system, then begin the harvest as soon as a reasonable number reach the appropriate size and follow with replanting the next spring. In this case the "foreigners" must be weeded out at regular intervals.

Inventory the stand in late summer after the season's growth is complete. Make a tally of the trees ready for sale by height classes and, if necessary, by grades, that is, first-class trees and those that will have to sell at less price. With such a list you are ready to negotiate with a commission man if you wish to sell through him. If you plan to sell trees to buyers at the farm, you have the basis for planning your sales program.

The next step (in some cases it can be done at the time of taking inventory) is to tag the selected trees using a printed card with your name and address, the species of tree, its height, and if already sold, the name of the purchaser. This requires time but saves time when cutting the trees because cutters have only to look for the tags. They do not have to wait for someone to select them, and if you do the cutting yourself, it saves your time.

The time to cut the trees depends upon the method of sale and the chance of early snows that might interfere. If sold to a commission man, trees can be cut and stacked out of doors with the butts in contact with the soil. In some climates, a better plan is to stack them in a shed with a dirt floor. Freezing temperatures plus rain or snow will make handling difficult if the trees are piled out of doors. Spruce should not be cut earlier than Dec. 1 and later is better, but very little difference in needle retention is reported between Dec. 1 and later dates. Pine and fir can be cut earlier without risk of needle loss. In the North, severely cold weather may come before Christmas. In temperatures below 10°F. the branches become brittle and easily break in handling, especially in hauling the trees. Some growers try to avoid loading trees for truck hauling when temperatures are below 20°F. The possibility of this kind of weather is a very good reason for early harvest. A curved pruning saw is recommended for cutting Christmas trees.

Selecting a Selling Method. Two methods of selling trees can be recommended to farmers. If several thousand trees are to be sold annually, it is probably best to make arrangements in advance with

a commission man or a dealer who will handle the selling on the
basis of a specified percentage of the price he receives.   The farmer
should cut and haul the trees to market and be ready to cut and haul
additional trees if the dealer asks for them.   It is not necessary to
bundle or wrap the trees for short truck hauls.   If the farmer agrees
that he will be paid only for trees actually sold and thus shares with
the dealer the risk of unsold trees, he can get a larger percentage of the

Fig. 149. A Christmas-tree yard at Kalispell, Montana, where trees are assembled, graded,
and bundled for shipment by rail.   (*Soil Conservation Service.*)

selling price than otherwise.   Sixty to seventy-five percent of the
sale price of the tree probably should go to the farmer under such an
arrangement.

The ideal way for farmers to sell Christmas trees is at the farm or a
near-by roadside stand.   This means devoting most of the farmer's
time to the business with one or more helpers, for perhaps two weeks
before Christmas.   It also means advertising in local and city news-
papers to attract customers and gradually building up a clientele
who will return year after year.   Many farmers successfully sell all
of their trees in this way.   Many people like to drive to the country
and see their Christmas trees and have them tagged before they are
cut and then return a few days before Christmas to get them.   Some

farmers will cut and deliver the selected trees to the doors of their customers.

Selling direct to consumers is the most profitable way to sell Christmas trees and the most satisfactory for farmers. For one thing, it enlarges the circle of friends and customers who may buy other farm

Fig. 150. A truckload of pine Christmas trees cut as thinnings from plantations to be kept for wood products. Destination Detroit, Michigan. (*Soil Conservation Service.*)

products. Not only trees but selected branches that are tied into bundles as Christmas greens can be sold. There are many possibilities of tying in the Christmas-tree sales with those of other farm products and of using the opportunity to know and to serve more people to the mutual advantage of both the farm and the urban population.

The prices a farmer will receive for retail sales depend a great deal upon his product and the service that he renders. City people are used to being "gouged" by salesmen and by some dishonest farmers. When they find a farmer who gives good service, has a good product priced reasonably, and is pleasant to deal with, they are immensely pleased. They tell their friends and if you are that farmer, you will soon build up all the business that you can handle (Figs. 149 and 150).

Applying Special Treatments to Christmas Trees. Some farmers may be interested in trying decorative treatments for Christmas trees or in recommending these and fire-retardant methods to their customers. Recommendations of the Forest Products Laboratory, maintained by the U.S. Forest Service at Madison, Wisconsin, are:

Treating Christmas Trees to Reduce Fire Hazard. After investigating a number of methods considered to have possibilities for making Christmas trees less flammable, the Forest Products Laboratory has concluded that keeping the tree standing in water is about the most practical, satisfactory, and convenient method of those tried for reducing the fire hazard and preventing the needles from discoloring or falling. Additional protection against fire can be provided by the use of fire-retardant coatings in conjunction with the water treatment if the retention of the natural color of the foliage is unimportant.

The procedure recommended for the water treatment is as follows:

1. Obtain a tree that has been cut as recently as possible.
2. Cut off the end of the trunk diagonally at least 1 in. above the original cut end. Stand the tree at once in a container of water and keep the water level above the cut surface during the entire time that the tree is in the house. If the tree is not to be set up for several days, it should be kept standing in water meanwhile in a cool place. If started in time, this treatment not only will prevent the needles from drying out and becoming flammable, but it will also keep them fresh and green. It will, in addition, retard the fall of needles of such species as spruce, which loses needles very easily, in contrast to balsam fir, which retains its needles even after the branches have become dry and the needles brittle. Freshly cut spruce or balsam fir trees standing in water cannot be set on fire by candle or match fires but, of course, will not withstand a large source of heat.[1]

Using Decorative Coatings. Several types of fire-retardant decorative coatings that either prevent or greatly retard flame spread when applied to wood will provide similar protection when applied to Christmas trees. For those willing to undertake the extra trouble and expense in the use of decorative coatings, the following simple formulas are suggested:

---

[1] The average 6- to 8-ft. tree will absorb indoors from 1 to 2 quarts of water a day; so a large container is required.

FORMULA I		FORMULA II	
Produces a shiny, transparent, colorless coating.		Produces a cream-colored coating. May be tinted with suitable dyes.	
INGREDIENT	PARTS BY VOLUME	INGREDIENT	PARTS BY WEIGHT
Sodium silicate (water glass).......	9	Sodium silicate (water glass)......	31
Water, containing a wetting agent...	1	China clay....................	41
(Dreft, Vel, or Breeze—about		Water, containing wetting agent...	28
1 teaspoon per quart)		(about 1 teaspoon per quart)	

FORMULA III
Produces a frosty white coating.   May be tinted with suitable dyes.

INGREDIENT	PARTS BY WEIGHT
Sodium alginate......................	1
Monoammonium phosphate..............	25
China clay...........................	4
Water................................	70

Formula III can be prepared most readily in the following manner: Heat the required amount of water to approximately 180°F., add the sodium alginate, stir until a uniform gel is obtained.   Then add the monoammonium phosphate, heating gently and stirring occasionally until the chemical has dissolved.   Finally, add the china clay and stir until it is uniformly distributed throughout the gel.

In applying any of the foregoing coatings, it must be kept in mind that a heavy coating is necessary in order to reduce the fire hazard. The amount of fire-retardant to be applied depends on the amount of protection desired.   One coat of these formulas will greatly reduce the tendency for flames to spread; two coats are even more effective. The coatings may be applied either by dipping or by spraying.   It may be necessary to thin Formula I for spray application, in which event more applications are necessary.

Silver effects can be had by spraying an aluminum paint on trees coated with either Formula II or Formula III.

If a coating is applied, it is recommended that the water treatment also be used to ensure the added protection against fire that the moisture in the tree provides.   Furthermore, experiments have shown that the water treatment improves the adherence of brittle coatings, such as Formulas I and II, because the moisture-filled needles do not shrink and thus allow brittle coatings to flake off.

Taking Extra Fire Precautions.   Take all possible precautions against fire around the Christmas tree, including the elimination of defective electrical connections and avoidance of the accumulation of combustible decorations on or beneath the tree. *Place the tree so that its accidental burning would not ignite curtains or other combustible furnishings nor trap the occupants of a room or building.*

SUPPLEMENTARY ACTIVITIES

Growing Christmas Trees

1. Locate a farmer who has been growing and selling Christmas trees. (Inquire of the county agent, extension forester, or state forester.)

2. Visit the farmer when he is not too busy. Look at his plantations, ask questions, get information for a report on the business of growing Christmas trees for the market. The following questions will indicate the kind of information to seek: General acreage in plantation? Slope, aspect, soil condition? Species planted? Are they uniformly mixed or separated into blocks? Acres planted to each species? Years trees were planted? How many at each planting? Source and age class of planting stock? Site preparation used? Planting tools used? Was replanting needed because of poor survival?

Management and care:

a. What system of management does he use? Continuous cutting and planting on same area or clear cutting and planting by separate blocks?

b. What fire-protective measures? Fire lines? Special tools? Any troubles with diseases, insects, theft?

c. Does he cultivate trees? Mow weeds? Cut back volunteer growth?

d. Does he prune his trees? How successful is he?

How does he sell trees?

a. To a commission man? What price? At what point? (That is, does the farmer cut and deliver to market, or does the buyer cut and haul to market?)

b. Retail sales at the farm. Do buyers come and select and cut trees? What price?

c. Volume of sales annually? To commission man, to retail buyers, average price.

Costs and profits:

Costs of planting stock; of site preparation; of planting trees; of pruning trees; of protection, weeding, care; and of taxes and interest. Probably the best way to get at costs and profits is to take average yearly expenditures and yearly income. The difference would be profits. How much net income per acre?

3. What conclusions do you reach as to profits and risks in growing Christmas trees on this farm?

Pruning Christmas Trees

1. Locate a place or places where pine and one of the short-needled conifers are growing. At least some of them should be about ready for pruning—about 3 to 5 ft. tall.

2. Get the owner's permission to try some experiments in shaping the trees to make good Christmas trees.

3. Select a dozen specimens of each species that you find. Label and number the trees selected so that you can easily identify them.

4. Visit the pines about the middle of the spring growing period. With a sharp knife, cut back the growth that you think will result in a better-shaped tree. Visit the short-needled trees once a year between September and March, and prune the trees with a knife or shears.

5. Make a record of your work for each species something like this:

Tree number	Date visited	Height, ft.	Species	Remarks—extent of pruning done, accidents, disease, insects, etc.
1				
2				
3				
etc.				

6. Keep this record for three years, or until the trees are cut or accident or disease causes failure. Make a brief report of your work, including your recommendations for pruning, based on this experience. If no pruning was needed, that fact is important. If you worked with one of the southern pines, your experience will be especially interesting and worth while, because little information seems to be available about how to prune these species.

Checking Christmas Trees at the Market Place

1. In December visit a Christmas-tree lot where trees are offered for sale. Get acquainted with the manager; tell him you want to make a study of the business and ask his cooperation.

2. Find out how many species of conifers he has to sell and approximately how many of each.

3. Ask where he gets each species of tree and where they grow, that is, how many and what species come from local plantations and from wilderness areas. How many and what species are shipped by rail? When are they cut?

4. Examine the trees.   What percentage of each species would you accept as satisfactory as to form, color, and dryness of needles?   Get the manager's opinion from the standpoint of his ability to sell them.   Determine by vigorous shaking which species have dry needles.   Tie this in with source and time of harvest.

5. Make a record of prices for different species and sizes.

6. Finally visit the lot after Christmas and count the trees of different species and sizes that were not sold.   What percentage were in the classes that you considered unsatisfactory because of shape, form, or condition of needles?

7. Make a report of your findings.   Perhaps the following form may be helpful in tabulating your figures.

CHRISTMAS-TREE LOT_____ LOCATION_____ MANAGER_____

Species	Source	Date of harvest	Method of transportation	Quantity purchased	Condition of trees	
					Proportion of good trees, percent	Special notes

General remarks:

Prices of trees at retail?   What kinds proved to be most in demand? What proportion of trees sold came from local plantations?   Is species or the form and symmetry of individual trees more important to the individual buyer?   If you learn about the profit or loss of the owner of the business, give the figures.   What, in your opinion, are the possibilities of profit to farmers in growing trees, especially if they are able to produce a large proportion of well-shaped trees?

10. Managing Farm Woods for Naval Stores

IN THE SOUTHEASTERN part of the United States grow two trees, important for wood products and distinct from all other forest trees in the United States in their ability to produce oleoresin in commercial quantities. These trees are two pines, longleaf (*Pinus palustris*) and slash pine (*Pinus caribaea*). From these trees are produced turpentine and rosin, known since the days of wooden ships as "naval stores." Large quantities of the crude gum, from which refined turpentine and rosin are made, are produced from small holdings of timberland including farm woodlands. Markets for all common forest products such as poles, piling, saw logs, pulpwood, and fuel are unusually good.

Gum can be extracted from the pine trees and sold for a nine-month period out of every year. Other wood products can be processed and sold very much as desired by the forest owners. Naval stores operations are the first step in preparing the selected trees for harvest. The first "streak" placed on a tree marks it for cutting, either as an intermediate product in the cultural development of a stand or as a mature tree ready for harvest after having grown to the size designed by the forest manager.

These possibilities of marketing and receiving income from a growing forest offer great opportunities to farmers in a region perhaps more conscious of forest values and more ready to accept wood as a farm crop than any other in the United States. Other factors that make the naval stores region stand out from all others are the peculiar relations of fire and grazing to the job of growing forests. Previously in the text, we have stressed the damage by forest fires to forest soils and to timber growth. We have told the story of forest litter and how it functions in conditioning the soil and supplying it with plant nutrients. We have told about the injury to forest soils due to trampling and to young growth from the grazing of domestic livestock.

317

But here in the flatwoods (the Coastal Plain), the silvicultural world is different. Fire and grazing are accepted, under proper restrictions, not merely as unavoidable evils but as positive measures useful in managing the pine forests.

This chapter is devoted to the story of the naval stores pines. An attempt will be made to resolve the paradox of fire and forest soil and litter in the management of these pine forests and to show that they are the exceptions that prove the rules of good silvicultural practice. The techniques involved in extracting crude gum (oleoresin) from the pine trees are already well known to the farmers and turpentine operators of the region. The subject is also well covered by numerous publications of the forest experiment stations, of the several bureaus of the Department of Agriculture, and of the state forestry departments of the states involved. Things like what trees to tap, when and how often to chip, the application of chemicals to the streaks, the handling and marketing of the crude gum will be discussed here only as they relate to problems of silviculture and management. These matters will be covered under the following headings:

1. Fitting Naval Stores Operations into Farm-woodland Management
2. Holding Fast to Silvicultural Principles
3. Using Fire and Grazing as Tools of Management
4. Using Chipping Practices That Help Develop the Woodland

1. Fitting Naval Stores Operations into Farm-woodland Management

Extracting crude gum from pine trees, as already mentioned, is a destructive process. It is the first step in destroying the tree. As soon as the tree is "worked out" for gum production, it must be removed. This may be in 5 to 10 years, depending upon the size and vigor of the tree at the beginning of operations and upon the plan of management being followed by the forest manager. If conducted without reference to its silvicultural development, a naval stores operation can completely ruin a forest stand. When the worked-out trees are removed, a new forest often must be started from natural reproduction or by planting. The small trees that carry the promise of an adequate growing stock and the production of high-grade wood products are sacrificed for a small output of gum. Total income from the forest is thereby reduced.

The farmer is interested in getting maximum income evenly spread over the years.   To do that he must develop his woodland so that it is capable of producing all forest products.   If the price of crude gum goes down to the point of unprofitable operation (and that does happen), he can stop producing gum for awhile and depend for his income on other products.

Development practices in the naval stores forest are similar to those described for the usual type of pine forest.   They require cultural work, particularly planting, thinning, pruning, and improvement cutting.   Thinning and improvement and harvest cutting are aided by the ability of the trees to produce naval stores products before they are removed for the benefit of the remaining stand.   Tapping the trees for naval stores only means that cutting operations must be scheduled several years in advance of the time when the trees are due to be cut as determined by the growth of the stand.   This may also mean that the years for gum extraction on individual trees will be limited to 5 to 6 years or less, instead of a longer period that might be possible.

If the stand develops as planned, many trees available for chipping will grow to larger and larger sizes before it is advisable to begin chipping.   Thus naval stores operations will make intermediate cuttings profitable; they will enable the forest manager to thin his stand and to conduct improvement cuttings that will result in rapid growth on his crop trees.   Chipping the trees slows the growth in both diameter and height.   If chipping is confined to trees which have already grown as much as the forest manager desires, extraction of gum is no obstacle to forest management.   The income from the crude gum is simply added revenue not available to most forest owners.

The usual practice in the past has been to select trees for naval stores operations on the basis of diameter; that is, all trees 9 in. and larger are tapped regardless of their condition or the effect of their removal on the development of the stand.   This destroys the possibility of developing a well-distributed growing stock capable of producing a balanced income from naval stores and wood products.   It also destroys the capacity of the forest to produce maximum annual income and almost certainly leads to a period when no income is possible, because the growing stock has been ruined.   This type of management, where all of the emphasis is placed on producing crude

gum, may be worth while for naval stores operators who have extensive timber holdings and who are organized solely to conduct this
type of woods operation. It is certainly not good management for
farmers who own relatively few acres of woodland and are chiefly

Fig. 151. Selective cupping in naval stores timber. Only the trees selected for removal are
chipped. The remaining trees are left for further growth and will be chipped later when
harvest size is reached. (*U.S. Forest Service.*)

concerned with woods management that will produce maximum
revenue and a sustained annual income to supplement farm income
from other sources.

The alternative to the diameter-limit system of selecting trees for
naval stores is known as selective "cupping." Under this system, the
trees are selected for cupping in accordance with definite plans for
meeting the silvicultural requirements of the stand. In other words,
it is exactly the plan of stand development which has been advocated
throughout the previous pages of this text. The main objective of

management is to develop a thrifty growing stock capable of yielding wood products of high value. Harvest cuttings are made when crop trees reach the desired size in accordance with a plan of management for a selection forest or more likely some type of clear cutting or shelterwood cutting. Naval stores products make intensive silviculture profitable as soon as trees reach the appropriate size for cupping. The immediate revenue to be obtained from naval stores products must not blind the farmer to the value of saw logs, poles, and piling that will bring revenue if the crop trees are allowed to grow. Naval stores operations in a farmer's woods can be a blight that wipes out his forest or they can be an aid in developing a profitable farm-woodland enterprise. In the naval stores, piney woods, the farm-woodland enterprise, if carefully planned and managed, will overtop all other sources of farm revenue. This statement can be made in very few other sections of rural America (Fig. 151).

2. Holding Fast to Silvicultural Principles

Longleaf pine has for years been the king of the flatwood forests. Like Br'er Rabbit who was "born and bred in the briar patch," longleaf has been "born and bred" in a holocaust of fire. Nature has adapted it to survival in spite of recurrent fires and has enabled it to dominate the forest under conditions where other species are killed. Its seedlings are protected by masses of heavy foliage which insulate them against the heat of ordinary fires. Fire destroys the spores of the brown-spot disease, which is otherwise destructive to the pine seedlings (Figs. 152 and 153). Past the seedling stage, trees make height growth rapidly and develop thick bark which insulates the growing tissues of the trunk from the heat of forest fires. No other tree in the world has developed similar characteristics to the same degree.

Slash pine has not developed the protective insulation for its seedlings, but it has thick bark which resists fire injury once its seedlings escape fire for 10 to 15 years. In the old days, slash pine managed to survive only on sites sufficiently moist that fires seldom occurred. In recent times, the people of the South have stopped enough fires to enable slash pine to spread over a great part of the flatwoods. It is rapidly becoming the dominant tree.

The piney-woods soil generally is a poor soil better adapted to pine than to hardwoods. The hardwoods that encroach on the domain of the pines are mostly scrub oaks and certainly not a desir-

able substitute for the fast-growing and valuable pines.   If the ecological development is toward a climax hardwood forest, the process
will be very long indeed before the soils will support worth-while
hardwoods.

Practically, the transition is impossible anyway because of the
prevalence of wildfire and the efforts of all forest managers to main-

Fig. 152. Longleaf-pine seedling protected by a mass of heavy foliage.   (*U.S. Forest Service.*)

tain the pine trees as the dominant forest cover.   In isolated spots
where soils are good, the transition, with fire control and restricted
grazing, may take place, but by and large the piney woods must be
maintained by management.   The fact that the pines are a temporary
type (if it is a fact) is not purely a theoretical consideration because
it does have a bearing on the scheme of management.

The role of fire in maintaining the piney woods becomes a matter
of vital concern.   Longleaf pine, because of its remarkable ability
to grow and prosper in spite of the constant burning of the forest,
became the dominant tree of the naval stores region.   Now, with a
degree of fire protection, slash pine, which grows more rapidly and
produces more gum, is usurping the ground formerly held by longleaf.   From the standpoint of ease of management, slash pine is much

to be preferred to longleaf.   Practically, the management problem in the piney woods is now concerned with slash pine, with longleaf as only an incidental factor.   The reduction of fire damage through organized fire protection has brought about the change.   Further

Fig. 153. Longleaf-pine seedling after a fire.   The needles are gone but the tree is still alive.   (*U.S. Forest Service.*)

consideration of the role of fire in management will be discussed in the succeeding section.

Thinning.   Slash pine trees at twelve to fifteen years, grown in the open, occasionally produce cones, and at thirty to forty years produce some seed almost every year and fair to good crops at frequent intervals.   If fire is kept out of open places where seed trees are present, dense stands of young seedlings start, often many thousands per acre. The problem is to reduce the number of seedlings so as to make possible rapid growth on relatively few stems.   Unless such stands are

thinned at an early age, stagnation results.   Thin as soon as the seedlings are well established and before the stand reaches an average
diameter of 3 in. (Fig. 154).   Older dense stands benefit from thinning
but the cost is greater.   Hand labor using an ax or a brush hook has

FIG. 154. Dense stand of slash-pine seedlings.   Unless thinned, stagnation results.   (*U.S.
Forest Service.*)

proved satisfactory.   Thin to a spacing of about 8 ft. giving 600 to
800 trees per acre.   Leave fewer trees on poor than on good soils.
In the absence of a forester's help, stick to about $D + 6$ spacing.
If the trees average better than 3 in., fewer than 600 trees will be left.

Mechanical thinning has been tried; it promises to be cheaper but
not very satisfactory.   This is because most stands are spotty, and
mechanical thinners plow through the stand and destroy the young
trees in the thin as well as the dense spots.   Such an early thinning is
known as a "precommercial thinning."   Of course, it produces no

merchantable products, but it is an essential step where these dense stands occur.   Early thinning will put such stands in good growing condition.   All later cutting will produce merchantable products.

The second thinning, 10 years or so later, is usually for pulpwood and fuel when the diameter at breast height (d.b.h.) of the main stand is from 6 to 8 or 9 in.   Thin here on the basis of proper spacing for the dominant and codominant trees, that is, thin from the top. This will sacrifice some trees almost large enough for naval stores, but the advantages in a better growing stock will amply repay the farmer in later forest income. $D + 6$ spacing for dominants and codominants will be a reasonable guide in marking.   The understory trees may be left or cut, depending on their profitable utilization and their usefulness in the stand.   Ten cords of pulpwood per acre is often cut as a thinning at this stage.   The third and succeeding thinnings should follow at 5 to 10-year intervals.   However, if naval stores operations are planned, some trees will be large enough about 5 years after the second thinning.   The procedure then would be to mark the trees for removal, begin chipping those 9 in. and larger, and cut those not suitable for naval stores.   This will give 5 to 6 years for gum operation before the next thinning will be needed.   At this time cut the chipped trees and begin chipping the new lot of trees marked for thinning.   At this point the process becomes a little academic because of unknown factors such as the rate of growth of the stand, diseased trees, and fire damage.   If some such plan is followed as closely as practicable, the naval stores trees will be larger each time new ones are selected from those marked for removal, and the wood products obtained from worked-out trees will be of higher and higher quality.   Natural reproduction will be obtained as the stand is opened up so that the final harvest cut will be made after the new stand is well established.   If this does not happen, a shelterwood or seed-tree cutting will be needed (Figs. 155 and 156).

Making Improvement Cuttings.   Previously unthinned stands grown from natural reproduction to commercial sizes offer two possibilities.   If the stand is lightly stocked, an improvement cutting can be made, removing the rough, limby, dominant trees and reserving the best trees for further growth.   The trees marked for removal may be chipped on at least one face before cutting.   This will often require naval stores cycles of 5 years or less with acid treatment of the streaks to help make the operation profitable.

If the stand is dense, the only choice may be between doing nothing or cutting most of the larger trees.   It is better to cut them, since not to do so will result in slow-growing trees with short crowns.   These are poor producers of either wood products or gum.   If the trees marked for removal are large enough, they first may be chipped for

FIG. 155. This stand is being prepared for a shelterwood cutting.   Trees marked with crosses will be left until reproduction is established; all other trees of sufficient size will be chipped.   Then all trees not marked will be removed.   (*U.S. Forest Service.*)

gum on a short cycle.   Under such conditions thinning cycles of not more than 5 years are recommended.

Managing Plantations.   Slash pine may be planted on old fields, cutover lands, or other open-type areas, on good sites.   This species is much easier to grow than longleaf pine, is a better producer of naval stores, grows faster, especially at first, and hence produces revenue at an earlier age.   Planted slash pine on good sites will have some trees of naval stores size in 15 to 20 years without previous thinning.   On poor sites the growth is often very low.

Plant during the dormant season from about Dec. 1 to Mar. 15. If the planting is well done and there are no adverse weather conditions, a survival of 90 to 95 percent after the first growing season is common.   *Space the trees* 8 by 8 ft.—680 trees per acre.

Preparing the Site.   The preparation of the site almost always should consist of building a fire line around the area to be planted.   Burning the area before planting may be required.   Often a turnplow is used to mark the rows and to facilitate the planting.   Plant the trees on the

Fig. 156.   Natural reproduction of slash pine following a shelterwood cutting.   (*U.S. Forest Service.*)

shoulder of the upturned furrow or on the hard soil adjacent to the furrow—never in the bottom of the furrow.

Cultivating.   The cultivation of the planted trees is not needed except as an added precaution against fire damage or where a temporary crop is to be raised between the rows.   Begin cultivation in the fall following the planting.

Thinning.   The thinning of the planted stand will be needed at the age of 10 to 15 years depending on the quality of the soil.   The trees should reach about 6 in. d.b.h. in this period.   About half the trees can be removed in the first thinning and used or sold for pulpwood, fence posts, or other products. Thinning should be from the top, leaving well-spaced dominant and codominant trees. The understory may be removed if usable, solely from the standpoint of benefit to the reserved trees. Unless you have better advice from a local forester, use $D + 6$ as the guide in spacing the crop trees. Such thinnings usually produce from 5 to 8 cords of merchantable products. The next thinning may be expected 10 to 15 years later when naval stores operations will be feasible.

Pruning. Planted trees or those developed from natural reproduction, when thinned to keep up growth, do not produce clean stems. If the crop trees are being developed for poles and saw logs, they require pruning in order to make high-quality logs. This cultural process is just as essential in the piney woods as it is anywhere else— no farmer can afford to neglect this cultural practice. Prune, if possible, when the trees are about 4 d.b.h. The average height of the trees is then about 30 ft. so that ample crown is left if the stem is cleared to the height of one 16-ft. log. An efficient job can be done in one operation by using a handsaw and a long-handled pruning saw. Pruning adds the convenience of making a thick stand more accessible, reduces the labor of processing, improves the quality of pulpwood, and reduces fire hazard. These are reasons for pruning a large number of trees. Strictly for improving the quality of saw-log trees, however, only those crop trees intended for the final harvest need be pruned. A 4-in. open-grown tree, according to some authorities, can be pruned in 3 min. On this basis, 200 trees per acre would require about 1½ man-days labor (see also Chap. 5).

3. Using Fire and Grazing as Tools of Management

Unquestionably forest fires in the naval stores woods do considerable damage. They kill slash-pine young growth prior to the time the trees reach 3 in. d.b.h. and 20 ft. high. This, of course, is an average and perhaps an arbitrary figure. Obviously, it depends upon the season of burning, the amount of flammable material to burn, the wind, and similar factors that contribute to the destructiveness of any fire. In older stands that are being worked for naval stores, fires injure many and often destroy some trees.

Therefore, as far as slash pine is concerned, fire must be controlled if the young growth is to live. No forestry, no growing stocks, no forest economy is possible without young stands that grow into big trees.   Organized forest-fire protection under the sponsorship of the state forestry department has made possible the promising future which the naval stores forests now have.   Every forest owner and, especially, every farmer needs to support the efforts of the states to provide primary detection and suppression forces.   Many states go further and supply heavy machinery and organized crews to build fire lines for individual forest owners at costs far below what it would otherwise be.   These public undertakings with the active support of individual forest owners have made forestry practice possible.

But these southern forests, protected for a period of years sufficient to establish young stands, build up a tremendous "rough."   This is a local expression meaning accumulation of flammable material in the unburned forest of gallberry, wax myrtle, and palmetto undergrowth, limbs, needles, and grass.   Under such conditions any fire that escapes the vigilance of the protection authorities and gets into the rough does tremendous damage.   Controlled or "prescribed" burning is the remedy advocated by many foresters and practiced by many landowners.   Prescribed burning is the setting of fires at a favorable season, with adequate crews and with the help of prepared fire lines with the intent of reducing the rough without serious damage to the stand.   This seems to be the only way to insure against the damage of a wildfire in a dry season.   In part this system of controlled burning is a recognition of Nature's way of maintaining pine forests as against whatever might eventually come from the ecological process, if fire were entirely excluded.   Most authorities believe that not more than 10 to 15 percent of any woodland area should be control-burned in any year.   This means that usually the same area need be burned only once in 6 to 10 years to give the necessary insurance against wildfire (Fig. 157).

The small owner, the farmer especially, may need to do little or no burning.   It depends upon the local situations—natural barriers, actual accumulation of rough, and the local danger of uncontrolled or incendiary fires.   Even a prescribed fire set in the winter season under most favorable conditions may prove to be more damaging than anticipated.   Any fire will most likely slow the timber growth for one or more years following the fire.   If the same objective could be reached by other means, both the cost and the danger of prescribed burning could be avoided.

For farmers, perhaps grazing of domestic animals offers a partial solution.   Unfortunately, it is only partial because piney-woods grazing of cattle seems likewise to depend upon burning of the forest floor. The wire grasses, which are the chief forage plants, increase in palatability by winter burning.   The increased forage value lasts only from March to the middle of June, but this is important to the farmer who is

FIG. 157. Prescribed burning in the piney woods.   This is the least amount of fire that will consume the rough without serious damage to the timber.   Close watch is kept to prevent the fire from spreading to areas where burning is not needed.   (*U.S. Forest Service.*)

dependent on forest grazing for part of his livelihood.   The forage value of piney-woods grasses is reported to be very low.   Cattle need supplemental feeding on open pastures or from feed troughs.   Many farmers are now using improved open pastures and therefore are becoming less dependent on woods grazing.

How much burning is essential for the benefit of the forest and how much for the cows must be answered by the farmers.   This is the farmer's problem.   A little controlled fire at the right season and after the pine trees have reached 3 in. d.b.h. is, in the opinion of many authorities, good for the forest—good insurance against heavy fire damage.   But for the good of the forest, the prescribed fire must not be repeated on the same area every year—an interval of at least several years free from fire must follow.   If what is good for timber growing is also sufficient for the cattle, then grazing and timber growing can be combined; the two farm enterprises can be operated successfully on the same land.   But if there is conflict, the farmer must decide on the basis of which one is most worth while in his farm economy.   Too much fire will certainly kill young growth or prevent its starting and result in slow-growing, thin, open, unprofitable forests.   A worth-while forestry enterprise integrated with the farm business cannot be developed on that basis.   Foresters can only attempt to show how to manage the woods profitably.   The farmer who owns the land in a free America must make his own decision.

4. Using Chipping Practices That Help Develop the Woodland

Recent research in naval stores practices has shown the way to extract crude gum from pine trees without ruining the valuable lower section of the tree for high-class wood products.   Former methods cut deeply into the wood and left nails, tin, and other metal in the butt section, making a cull of this part of the tree.

The new method is known as bark chipping, aided by an acid spray.   It is a proved and successful practice now being used by many operators.   A farmer who is developing and managing his woodland can use this practice on all trees intended for final utilization as pulpwood, poles, or saw logs.   Since only the bark is chipped, the tree remains round, and very little, if any, degrading results from the naval stores operation.   New methods of attaching cups, aprons, and gutters leave no metal in the wood.   Bark chipping with the use of acid permits chipping every two weeks instead of weekly with no reduction in gum yield; in fact, many operators report increased yield with 14-day chipping.   The labor saving is important to all operators and especially to farmers (Fig. 158).

If, to these practices, there is added short naval stores cycles, 3 to 5 years on one face, the entire stem of the tree remains usable.   This is especially important in chipping trees that have reached a grade 1 log size.   As pointed out in Chap. 5, a considerable part of the value of saw-log trees is in the butt logs.   If gum can be extracted from such trees before cutting, without degrading the butt log, the forest manager has materially increased his income.   Obviously, it would be useless to prune crop trees for the purpose of raising the grade of the butt logs and then ruin the logs by destructive chipping practices.

Fortunately naval stores practices can now be used so that the income from crude gum does not interfere with the development of a profitable growing stock or cause degrading of wood products. This is a negative way of saying that income from naval stores and income from wood products do not conflict if the forest manager so

FIG. 158. Bark chipping with acid treatment.   The acid is in the Nichols' squeeze sprayer. Under this system, trees remain round, which permits the utilization of the butt log for lumber products, and degrading on defects caused by naval stores operation is avoided. (*U.S. Forest Service.*)

wills.   Forest-management research indicates that proper integration of naval stores operations in the development and management of a forest for wood products will result in the highest income to the forest owner.

The integration consists of managing the forest primarily for the highest-grade wood products and taking whatever income from naval stores is available from trees marked for removal.   Farmers must also be satisfied with whatever grazing is obtainable under that system of management.   Naval stores operations are subordinated to wood-products management through careful chipping practices and by holding the cycle of operations to the period of years corresponding to the time set for removal of the chipped trees from the stand.   This latter restriction is necessary because if chipped trees are not promptly removed according to schedule, the growth of the reserved trees would be seriously retarded.   This means not less gum but gum from more trees and greater income from the forestry enterprise.

SUPPLEMENTARY ACTIVITIES

A Study of Method of Applying Streaks on Quality of Wood Products

1. Find and measure 10 trees of harvest size for saw logs 18 in. and up that have been or are being worked for naval stores.
   a. Five trees by the old system of streaks into the wood.
   b. Five trees by the new system of bark chipping with acid treatment. Try to get approximately the same size trees for each group.
2. Take the following measurements on each tree: d.b.h. in inches, estimated total number of 16-ft. saw logs, estimated number of round logs 12 in. top diameter inside bark or larger.   Make a tabulation something like the one shown below.

TABULATION SUGGESTED IN ACTIVITY 2

No.	(1) Species	(2) D.b.h., in.	(3) Total no. of 16 ft. saw logs	(4) No. of round logs, 12-in. top or larger	(5) Vol., ft. b.m., cols. (2) and (3) *	(6) Vol., ft. b.m., cols. (2) and (4) *	(7) Percent of total vol. in col. (6), col. (6) / col. (5)
Trees with streaks into the wood							
1							
2							
3							
etc.							
Total.....							
Trees worked by bark streaks with acid treatments							
1							
2							
3							
etc.							
Total.....							

* In col. (5), use the volume table figures based on d.b.h. and number of logs, but be sure to deduct volume of butt log rendered unmerchantable by turpentine faces.   In col. (6), the board feet (ft. b.m.) in each tree will have to be determined by estimating the top diameter inside bark for each 16-ft. log that is large enough to measure 12 in. or more at the top end; then find the scale of each log from a log-rule table; add together and put the total for each tree in col. (6).

3. What conclusions do you draw from these measurements about the relative value of the two methods of extracting gum?

A Study of a Worked-out Naval Stores Operation

"If conducted without reference to its silvicultural development, a naval stores operation can completely ruin a forest stand. When the worked-out trees are removed, a new forest often must be started by natural reproduction or by planting. The small trees that carry the promise of an adequate growing stock and the production of high-grade products are sacrificed for a relatively small value in gum. The total income from the forest is thereby reduced."

1. Visit a worked-out naval stores operation.

2. How much of a growing stock is left?

3. What is the prospect of immediate income from the forest?

4. How complete is the reproduction of slash or longleaf pine?

5. Should the area be planted to get a full stand?

6. Approximately how long before another naval stores operation is possible?

7. What fire protection measures are needed to get a stand of young slash pine?

8. Write a brief report of your findings with recommendations about planting, fire protection, grazing, and future management.

A Study of Farm-woodland Management and Naval Stores

1. Visit a farm woodland being operated for naval stores.

2. Take a few $\frac{1}{5}$-acre sample plots and make a stand table showing slash and longleaf pine trees from 6 in. d.b.h. and up on an average acre.

3. Indicate on the stand table how many trees of each d.b.h. class support turpentine faces.

4. Is the area grazed? How often is it burned? Are the fires wildfires or prescribed burning?

5. How much young growth below 6 in. d.b.h. is present?

6. Is this woodland being managed so as to produce continuous crops of gum and wood products?

7. Make a brief report giving your opinion of the management policy being followed, from the standpoint of making the woodland contribute most to farm economy. Include your recommendations for changes in practices. If possible, talk to the farmer about his woods, and if he is interested, consider the advisability of giving him a copy of your report.

Appendix I

Bibliography

General References[1]

BAKER, F. S.: *Principles of Silviculture*, McGraw-Hill Book Company, Inc., New York, 1950. (Chaps. 2 to 5)

BARRACLOUGH, K. E.: *The Management of Farm Woodlands in New Hampshire*, New Hampshire Agricultural Extension Service, Extension Bulletin 88, Durham, N.H., June, 1948. (Chaps. 3 and 6)

EYRE, F. H., and P. Z. ZEHNGRAFF: *Red Pine Management in Minnesota*, U.S. Department of Agriculture, Circular 778, May, 1948. (Chaps. 4 and 5)

Forestry Handbook, U.S. Department of Agriculture, Soil Conservation Service, Agriculture Handbook 13, Milwaukee, Wis., September, 1950.
(Preface, Introduction, Chaps. 2, 6 to 9)

GUISE, C. H.: *The Management of Farm Woodlands*, 2d ed., McGraw-Hill Book Company, Inc., New York, 1950. (Chaps. 1, 6 and 7)

HOUGH, A. F., and R. F. TAYLOR: "Response of Allegheny Northern Hardwoods to Partial Cutting," *Journal of Forestry*, vol. 44, pp. 30–38, 1946.
(Chaps. 4 and 6)

JEMISON, G. M., and G. H. HEPTING: *Timber Stand Improvement in the Southern Appalachian Region*, U.S. Department of Agriculture Forest Service, Miscellaneous Publication 693, August, 1949. (Chaps. 3 to 6)

KOROLEFF, A., and J. A. FITZWATER: *Managing Small Woodlands*, The American Forestry Association, Washington, D.C., 1947.
(Chaps. 1 and 6)

Management of Second Growth Forests in the Douglas Fir Region, mimeograph, U.S. Department of Agriculture, Forest Service, Portland, Ore., 1947.
(Chaps. 4 to 6)

Managing the Small Forest, U.S. Department of Agriculture, Farmers' Bulletin 1989, revised January, 1948. (Chaps. 1, 6, and 7)

PRESTON, J. F.: *Farm Wood Crops*, McGraw-Hill Book Company, Inc., New York, 1949. (Preface, Introduction, Chaps. 1 to 7)

[1] The chapter numbers given at the end of each citation refer to the chapters in this book to which the reference is particularly applicable.

335

STOECKELER, J. H., and C. F. ARBOGAST: *Thinning and Pruning Young Second Growth Hardwoods in Northeastern Wisconsin,* Proceedings Society of American Foresters Meeting, 1947. (Chaps. 4 and 5)

WESTVELD, R. H., and R. H. PECK: *Forestry in Farm Management,* 2d ed., John Wiley & Sons, Inc., New York, 1950. (Chaps. 1, 6, and 7)

WILLIAMS, W. K.: *Protect Hardwood Stands from Grazing,* U.S. Department of Agriculture, Leaflet 86, revised 1941. (Chaps. 1 and 6)

Preface and Introduction

ANGELL, G. N.: "Good Money in Farm Woodlots," *Washington Farmer,* No. 74, p. 708, September, 1949.

Cash Crops from Washington Woodlands (Pine Region), Box R, College Station, Pullman, Wash.

COLLINGWOOD, G. H., and W. D. BRUSH: *Knowing Your Trees,* American Forestry Association, Washington, D.C., 1947.

Forestry News, Society of American Foresters, Washington, D.C., October, 1946, p. 8.

McCLOY, T. A.: "Returns from Southern Appalachian Experimental Farm Woodlands," *Southern Lumberman,* Dec. 15, 1949.

MUELLER, C. S.: "Gold in Those Woodlots," *Michigan State Homesteader,* vol. 3, No. 3, p. 6, April, 1950.

Southern Forest Experiment Station: Farm Forestry Compartment, 1949 Cutting Record, New Orleans, La., Oct. 6, 1949.

TRENK, F. B.: *Wisconsin Timber Harvest Forests,* Publication 520, A-46, Wisconsin Conservation Bulletin, vol. 11, No. 2, February, 1946.

ZON, RAPHAEL, and W. A. DUERR: *Farm Forestry in the Lake States,* U.S. Department of Agriculture, Circular 661, November, 1942.

Chapter 1. Growing Wood as a Farm Crop

CHANDLER, J. M.: *The Place of Woodland in the Farm Organization in Coos County, New Hampshire,* New Hampshire Agricultural Experiment Station, Bulletin 337, Durham, N.H., June, 1942.

DEN UYL, D., and R. K. DAY: *Woodland Carrying Capacities and Grazing Injury Studies,* Purdue University Agricultural Experiment Station, Bulletin 391, 1934.

Fire, Friend and Enemy, in *Trees,* U.S. Department of Agriculture Yearbook, 1949, pp. 477–532.

Forests and Wildlife, in *Trees,* U.S. Department of Agriculture Yearbook, 1949, pp. 561–592.

GRAHAM, E. H.: Wild Life in the Small Woodland, in *Trees,* U.S. Department of Agriculture Yearbook, 1949, p. 561.

Insects, Diseases, Parasites, in *Trees*, U.S. Department of Agriculture Yearbook, 1949, pp. 407–476.

LOCKARD, C. R., C. E. BEHRE, H. A. JOHNSON, I. F. FELLOWS, and DONALD RUSH: *Woodland Opportunities on Dairy Farms in New York*, Charles Lothrop Pack Forestry Foundation, Washington, D.C., 1944.

PRESTON, J. F.: *Woodlands in the Farm Plan*, U.S. Department of Agriculture, Farmers' Bulletin 1940, May, 1943.

STOECKELER, J. H., and R. A. WILLIAMS: Windbreaks and Shelterbelts, in *Trees*, U.S. Department of Agriculture Yearbook, 1949, p. 191.

Chapter 2. Starting a Farm Forest

AUTEN, J. T.: *Site Requirements for Black Locust*, U.S. Department of Agriculture, Central States Forest Experiment Station, Station Note 4, Columbus, Ohio, October, 1933.

BULL, HENRY, and H. H. MUNTZ: *Planting Cottonwood on Bottomlands*, Mississippi Agricultural Experiment Station, Bulletin 391, State College, Miss., August, 1943.

DILLER, J. D.: *Planting and Care of Blight Resistant Chestnuts for Forest Trees*, U.S. Department of Agriculture, Division of Forest Pathology, Release No. 15, revised December, 1950.

GIBBS, J. A.: *Erosion Control Tree Planting*, mimeograph, U.S. Department of Agriculture, Soil Conservation Service, Region 2, Field Letter (forestry) No. 37, June 30, 1948.

HEPTING, G. H.: *Reducing Losses from Tree Diseases in Eastern Forests and Farm Woodlands*, U.S. Department of Agriculture, Farmers' Bulletin 1887, January, 1942.

HURSH, C. R., and W. M. CRAFTON: *Plant Indicators of Soil Conditions on Recently Abandoned Fields*, U.S. Department of Agriculture, Appalachian Forest Experiment Station, Technical Note 17, Nov. 6, 1935.

KEEFER, W. O.: "Machine Age Tree Planting," *Pennsylvania Forests and Waters*, vol. 6, No. 8, p. 184, 1949.

McQUILKIN, W. E.: "Use of Fertilizer, Mulch, and Large Stock in Planting Clay Sites," *Journal of Forestry*, vol. 44, No. 1, January, 1946.

MINCKLER, L. S.: *Regeneration Problem Analysis*, mimeograph, U.S. Department of Agriculture, Central States Forest Experiment Station, December, 1949.

ROSS, W. A., and W. R. MATTOON: *Farm Forestry Organized Teaching Material*, U.S. Department of Interior, Office of Education, Bulletin 196, 1939.

RUDOLF, P. O.: *Forest Plantations in the Lake States*, U.S. Department of Agriculture, Technical Bulletin 1010, August, 1950.

TOUMEY, J. W., and C. F. KORSTIAN: *Seeding and Planting in the Practice of Forestry*, 3d ed., John Wiley & Sons, Inc., New York, 1942.

Chapter. 3. Weeding and Releasing Young Trees

BULL, HENRY, and R. S. CAMPBELL: *Recent Research in Poisoning Southern Weed Hardwoods*, mimeograph, U.S. Department of Agriculture, Southern Forest Experiment Station, Jan. 31, 1949.

BULL, HENRY, and R. A. CHAPMAN: *Killing Undesirable Hardwoods in Southern Forests*, U.S. Department of Agriculture, Southern Forest Experiment Station, Occasional Paper No. 50, September, 1935.

CLINE, A. C.: *Forest Weeding with Special Reference to Young Natural Stands in Central New England*, Massachusetts Forestry Association, Boston, Mass., 1929.

DOWNS, A. A.: "Response to Release of Sugar Maple, White Oak, and Yellow Poplar," *Journal of Forestry*, vol. 44, No. 1, January, 1946.

IBBERSON, J. E.: "Chemical Plant Killers Are New Forestry Tools," *Pennsylvania Forests and Waters*, vol. 1, No. 8, 1949.

PEEVY, F. A.: *How to Control Southern Hardwoods with Ammate*, U.S. Department of Agriculture, Southern Forest Experiment Station, M-5296, 1949.

Release Cuttings Needed in Natural Second Growth Stands, U.S. Department of Agriculture, Lake States Forest Experiment Station, Technical Note 61.

TANNEHILL, G. F.: "Control of Hardwood Brush by Bulldozing," *Journal of Forestry*, vol. 49, No. 11, November, 1951.

U.S. Department of Agriculture, Southern Forest Experiment Station, Southern Forestry Notes, No. 58, November, 1948.

U.S. Department of Agriculture, Southern Forest Experiment Station, Southern Forestry Notes, No. 64, November, 1949.

U.S. Department of Agriculture, Southern Forest Experiment Station, Southern Forestry Notes, No. 67, May, 1950.

WESTVELD, M.: *Increased Production of Spruce by Girdling Hardwoods*, U.S. Department of Agriculture, Northeastern Forest Experiment Station, Technical Note 23, April, 1936.

Chapter 4. Thinning Tree Crops

BULL, HENRY: *Recommendations for Thinning Young Slash Pine*, mimeograph, U.S. Department of Agriculture, Southern Forest Experiment Station, May, 1949.

BULL, HENRY: "Thinning Loblolly Pine in Even-aged Stands," *Journal of Forestry*, vol. 33, No. 5, May, 1935.

HOUGH, A. F.: *Improvement of Second Growth Northern Hardwoods by Cordwood Thinnings*, U.S. Department of Agriculture, Northeastern Forest Experiment Station, Forest Management Note 1, Jan. 30, 1946.

MIROV, N. T.: A Tree Is a Living Thing, in *Trees*, U.S. Department of Agriculture Yearbook, 1949, p. 1.

MITCHELL, H. C.: "Regulation of Farm Woodlands by Rule of Thumb," *Journal of Forestry*, vol. 41, No. 4, April, 1943.

ROE, E. I.: *Thinnings in Cedar Swamps*, U.S. Department of Agriculture, Lake States Forest Experiment Station, Technical Note 279, July, 1947.

ROE, E. I., and J. H. STOECKELER: "Thinning Over Dense Jack Pine Seedling Stands in the Lake States," *Journal of Forestry*, vol. 48, No. 12, December, 1950.

Thinnings Assume Commercial Importance, U.S. Department of Agriculture, Lake States Forest Experiment Station, Technical Note 186, March, 1942.

TOUMEY, J. W.: *Foundations of Silviculture*, John Wiley & Sons, Inc., New York, 1928.

Young Plantation Thinnings Yield Merchantable Products, U.S. Department of Agriculture, Central States Forest Experiment Station, Note 51, December, 1948.

Chapter 5.   Pruning Tree Crops

BULL, HENRY: "Pruning Practices in Open-grown Longleaf Pine in Relation to Growth," *Journal of Forestry*, vol. 41, No. 3, March, 1943.

Cost of Producing White Pine Lumber in New England, U.S. Department of Agriculture, Circular 557, 1940.

HELMERS, A. E.: *How Heavily Should Western White Pine Be Pruned?*, U.S. Department of Agriculture, Northern Rocky Mountain Forest and Range Experiment Station, Research Note 41, Apr. 22, 1946.

HUEY, BEN M.: *The Profit in Pruning Western White and Ponderosa Pine*, U.S. Department of Agriculture, Northern Rocky Mountain Forest and Range Experiment Station, Research Note 85, July, 1950.

KOCHIN, THEODORE: "The Hebo Pruning Club," *Journal of Forestry*, vol. 38, No. 7, July, 1940.

MATTOON, W. R.: *Pruning Southern Pines*, U.S. Department of Agriculture, Farmers' Bulletin 1892, January, 1942.

PEARSON, G. A.: *Timber Stand Improvement in the Southwest*, Federal Security Agency, Civilian Conservation Corps, Forestry Publication No. 6, 1940.

REYNOLDS, R. R.: *Some Principles of Farm Woodland Management*, mimeograph, U.S. Department of Agriculture, Southern Forest Experiment Station, 1941.

ROTH, E. R.: "Healing and Defects Following Oak Pruning," *Journal of Forestry*, vol. 46, No. 7, July, 1948.

ROWLAND, C. A., JR.: "Bud Pruning for Better Logs," *Southern Lumberman*, Dec. 15, 1948.

SIMMONS, E. M.: "Pruning and Thinning a White Pine Plantation in Southern Appalachians," *Journal of Forestry*, vol. 33, pp. 519–522, 1935.

Chapter 6. Cutting the Wood Crop

AUTEN, J. T.: "Porosity and Water Absorption of Forest Soils," *Journal of Agricultural Research*, vol. 46, No. 11, pp. 997–1014, June, 1933.

AUTEN, J. T., and T. B. PLAIR, Forests and Soils, in *Trees*, U.S. Department of Agriculture Yearbook, 1949, p. 114.

CHAPMAN, C. H., and D. B. DEMERRITT: *Elements of Forest Mensuration*, J. B. Lyon Company, Albany, N.Y., 1936.

Chemical Killing of Trees to Facilitate Bark Removal, Northeast Research Center, Gorham, N.H., Jan. 10, 1951.

EYRE, F. H., and J. R. NEETZEL: "Practical Cutting Methods for Northern Hardwoods," Michigan Academy of Science, Arts and Letters, vol. 35, part 1, 1938.

GUSTAFSON, A. F.: *Using and Managing Soils*, McGraw-Hill Book Company, Inc., New York, 1948.

JENSEN, V. S.: "Suggestions for the Management of Northern Hardwood Stands in the Northeast," *Journal of Forestry*, vol. 41, No. 3, March, 1943.

LEXEN, BERT: *Alternate Clear-strip Cutting in the Lodgepole Pine Type*, U.S. Department of Agriculture, Rocky Mountain Forest and Range Experiment Station, Station Paper No. 1, April, 1949.

MOWATS, E. L.: *Preliminary Guides for the Management of Lodgepole Pine in Oregon and Washington*, U.S. Department of Agriculture, Pacific Northwest Forest and Range Experiment Station, Research Note 54, Apr. 29, 1949.

MUNSTER, NORMAN, and ARTHUR SPILLERS: Consulting Foresters, in *Trees*, U.S. Department of Agriculture Yearbook, 1949, p. 662.

Peeled Pulpwood, a Year Round Cash Crop, pamphlet by Armstrong Forest Company, Johnsonburg, Pa.

POMEROY, K. B., and N. T. BARON: "Hardwoods vs. Loblolly Pines," *Journal of Forestry*, vol. 48, No. 2, February, 1950.

PUTNAM, J. A., and HENRY BULL: "Improvement Cuttings in the Bottomland Hardwood Forests of Mississippi," *Southern Lumberman*, Dec. 15, 1940.

REYNOLDS, R. R.: "Sidelights on Managing Mixed Pine-Hardwood Stands under the Selection System," *Journal of Forestry*, vol. 48, No. 2, February, 1950.

SIMMONS, F. C.: *Logging Farm Forest Crops in the Northeast*, U.S. Department of Agriculture, Farmers' Bulletin 2008, July, 1949.

SIMMONS, F. C.: *Northeastern Loggers Handbook*, U.S. Department of Agriculture, Agriculture Handbook 6, January, 1951.

SIMS, I. H., E. N. MUNNS, and J. T. AUTEN: Management of Forest Soils, U.S. Department of Agriculture Yearbook, 1938, p. 737.

WACKERMAN, A. E.: *Harvesting Timber Crops*, McGraw-Hill Book Company, Inc., New York, 1949.

WALKER, C. M.: *Your Trees—A Crop. How to Grow and Harvest Them in the Douglas Fir Region*, State of Washington, Division of Forestry, Olympia, Wash., February, 1950.

Chapter 7. Marketing Wood Products

ANDERSON, PARKER: *Markets for Forest Products Grown on Minnesota Farms*, University of Minnesota, Agricultural Extension Service, Pamphlet 69, December, 1940.

BRATTON, A. W.: U.S. Department of Agriculture, Northeastern Forest Experiment Station, Technical Note 50, Feb. 7, 1942.

CARTER, R. M.: *Rapid and Safe Air Seasoning*, U.S. Department of Agriculture, Northeastern Forest Experiment Station, May, 1947.

Chipped Wood Production and Uses, Northeastern Wood Utilization Council, Inc., Bulletin 33, New Haven, Conn., January, 1951.

Factors That Influence the Decay of Untreated Wood in Service and Comparative Decay Resistance of Different Species, U.S. Department of Agriculture, Forest Products Laboratory, No. R-68, Madison, Wis., revised April, 1950.

Gaging the Timber Resources of the United States, U.S. Department of Agriculture, Forest Service, 1946.

GRAHAM, R. D.: *The Soaking Method for the Preservative Treatment of Fence Posts*, Oregon Forest Products Laboratory, Information Circular 4, Oregon State College, Corvallis, Ore., February, 1950.

HICOCK, H. W., A. R. OLSON, and F. M. CALLWARD, *Preserving Wood for Farm Use*, University of Connecticut, College of Agriculture, Extension Service, Bulletin 415, Storrs, Conn., 1949.

HUNT, G. M., and G. A. GARRATT: *Wood Preservation*, 2d ed., McGraw-Hill Book Company, Inc., New York, 1953.

TRIMBLE, G. R., JR., and A. W. BRATTON: U.S. Department of Agriculture, Northeastern Forest Experiment Station, Technical Note 40, June 1, 1943.

WOODS, J. B.: *Report of the Forest Resource Appraisal*, American Forestry Association, Washington, D.C., Jan. 21, 1947.

Chapter 8. Managing the Farm Woods for Maple Sap

BOND, A. D., and J. A. COPE: *Costs and Returns in Producing Maple Syrup*, New York State College of Agriculture, A.E. 661, Albany, N.Y., February, 1948.

CARTER, R. M.: *Woodlot Economics on Vermont Dairy Farms*, Vermont Agricultural Experiment Station, Bulletin 554, Burlington, Vt., January, 1950.

LOCKE, S. S.: "The Sugar Bush Pays Off," *Michigan Farmer*, Jan. 10, 1946.

Report of Proceedings, Conference on Maple Products, U.S. Department of Agriculture, Eastern Research Laboratory, Philadelphia, Pa., Nov. 13–15, 1950.

ROBBINS, P. W.: *Production of Maple Syrup in Michigan*, Michigan State College, Circular Bulletin 213, East Lansing, Mich., February, 1949.

Chapter 9. Managing Farm Woods for Christmas Trees

ABBOTT, R. W., and F. B. TRENK: *Growing and Selling Christmas Trees*, University of Wisconsin, Circular 425, Madison, Wis., October, 1952.

BARRACLOUGH, K. E.: *Christmas Trees, a Cash Crop*, New Hampshire Agricultural Extension Service, Circular 278, Durham, N.H.

COPE, J. A.: *Christmas Tree Farming*, Cornell University, Cornell Extension Bulletin 704, Ithaca, N.Y., revised August, 1949.

DENGLER, H. W.: *Growing Christmas Trees in Maryland*, University of Maryland, College Park, Md., December, 1950.

FENTON, R. H., and F. M. CALLWARD: *Home Grown Christmas Trees for Connecticut*, University of Connecticut, Bulletin 409, Storrs, Conn., October, 1948.

GARIN, G. I., and J. C. MOORE: *Christmas Tree Production*, Alabama Polytechnic Institute, Agricultural Experiment Station, Circular 92, Auburn, Ala., revised December, 1951.

HUEY, B. M. and S. B. HUTCHINSON: *Marketing Montana Christmas Trees*, U.S. Department of Agriculture, Northern Rocky Mountain Forest and Range Experiment Station, Bulletin 2, University of Montana, Missoula, Mont., December, 1949.

LENTZ, A. N.: *Growing Christmas Trees in New Jersey*, Rutgers University, College of Agriculture, Extension Service, Leaflet 30, New Brunswick, N.J., April, 1949.

LOTT, E. J.: *Growing Christmas Trees in Indiana*, Purdue University, mimeograph F-17, Lafayette, Ind., November, 1952.

METCALF, WOODBRIDGE, and R. F. GRAH: *Growing Christmas Trees for California*, University of California, Berkeley, Calif., May, 1952.

MURPHY, F. T.: *Christmas Tree Farming in Pennsylvania*, Pennsylvania State College, Extension Service Bulletin 284, State College, Pa., January, 1948.

SOWDER, A. M.: Christmas Trees, the Industry, in *Trees*, U.S. Department of Agriculture Yearbook, 1949, p. 248.

SOWDER, A. M.: The Farmer and Christmas Trees, in *Trees*, U.S. Department of Agriculture Yearbook, 1949, p. 251.

SOWDER, A. M.: *Christmas Trees, the Tradition and the Trade*, U.S. Department of Agriculture, Agriculture Information Bulletin 94, 1952.

TRYON, E. H., A. W. GOODSPEED, R. P. TRUE, and C. J. JOHNSON: *Christmas Trees, Their Profitable Production in West Virginia*, Agricultural Experiment Station, Circular 82, Morgantown, W. Va., June, 1951.

U.S. Department of Agriculture, Forest Service, Forest Products Laboratory, Technical Note 250, November, 1949.

Chapter 10.   *Managing Farm Woods for Naval Stores*

DYER, C. D.: *Working Trees for Naval Stores*, Georgia Agricultural Extension Service, Bulletin 582, Athens, Ga., revised July, 1952.

McCULLEY, R. D.: *Management of Natural Slash Pine Stands in the Flatwoods of South Georgia and North Florida*, U.S. Department of Agriculture, Circular 845, June, 1950.

Appendix II

Glossary[1]

age class. Even-aged stands are commonly grouped by 20- to 40-year age intervals, *e.g.*, 0 to 20, 21 to 40, etc. Each group is referred to as an age class. In all-aged forests a similar rough classification is sometimes made.

allowable cut. The estimated amount of timber to be cut from a forest under management, calculated on the basis of building up or maintaining the growing stock. Usually, it is the estimated growth of the forest for the next five years. It can be expressed in terms of volume (cords, cubic feet, board feet) or in terms of number of trees of specified sizes.

bark chipping. Naval stores term. Applying a streak with a bark hack. Only the bark is removed leaving the tree round. *See* chipping.

basal area. For a tree, the area of its cross section at $4\frac{1}{2}$ feet from the ground; area is expressed in square feet. For an acre, the sum of the basal areas of all trees or all trees of specified sizes or species. Basal area times the average merchantable height in feet gives a rough indication of volume in cubic feet.

board foot. A board 1 by 12 by 12 in. This is the common unit of lumber measurement. Logs to be cut into lumber are measured in board feet by a log scale by means of which the board-foot contents are estimated. Board foot is abbreviated ft. b.m. or bd. ft.; 1,000 board feet is abbreviated M ft. b.m., MBM, or MBF.

bole. The trunk of a tree; often the merchantable or usable length is meant.

bucking. A logger's term for cutting a felled tree into suitable lengths for utilizing the contents. Considerable skill and knowledge of market requirements are needed in order to get logs of greatest value.

blocks. *See* compartments.

bud pruning. *See* pruning.

cambium. The layer of living cells between the wood and bark of a tree.

cant hook. A tool for rolling logs and timbers. It has a stout wooden handle and a hinged, curved steel hook near the lower end that works

---

[1] Definitions are largely taken from "Forestry Terminology," Society of American Foresters, Washington, D.C., 1944.

on a bolt. The end of the handle that contacts the log or timber is a steel toe ring instead of a spike, as in a peavey.

canopy, crown. All of the crown or tops of the trees in a woodland, except the understory.

chipping. Naval stores term. Refers to wound or streak made into the wood of a tree beginning near the ground and with each succeeding streak being made just above the last one. Chipping is done with a tool called a "hack."

climax type. *See* forest type.

colloidal. Characteristic of a colloid. Colloidal soil means one of very even, smooth texture, with separate particles of minute size.

compartments. Divisions of a forest for purposes of management.

conifers. Cone-bearing trees—pine, spruce, cedar, cypress, etc. Most, but not all, are also evergreen.

coppice. A woods originating as sprouts from stump or root of trees cut. Most of the hardwoods sprout readily when cut young. Very few conifers will sprout from the stump.

crop trees. In immature stands, the best trees, evenly spaced, are often selected for development into sizes appropriate for utilization of the final products desired, *e.g.*, saw logs. These are called crop trees, and trees interfering with the growth of crop trees are removed. Usually many more crop trees are selected than can finally mature so as to allow for further selection and for accidents.

crown. The upper part of a tree, including the branches with their foliage.

crown class. *See* page 105, Fig. 48.

cruise, cruising. A systematic survey to determine the volume of products, the number of tree species and sizes, etc., on a specific woodland area. It is most often done by sample plots, sample strips, and the total calculated from the samples.

cull factor. The amount by which the estimated volume of standing timber is reduced to cover hidden defects, breakage in falling, etc. It is usually expressed as a percentage of the gross volume.

cultural treatment. Silvicultural operations such as pruning, thinning, and weeding, primarily intended to increase the growth or improve the quality of the stand remaining.

cupping. Naval stores term. Installation of tins and cups on a tree to catch the gum. Sometimes used as synonomous with chipping.

cutting cycle. The planned intervals between major cutting operations on a unit of woodland under management. Five years is usually recommended for farm woodlands.

cuttings. Short pieces of twigs cut from living trees or shrubs intended to grow by sprouting when placed in moist soil; usually they are about $\frac{1}{2}$

in. thick at the butt and 8 to 12 in. long.   Normally only deciduous trees and shrubs will grow from cuttings.

deciduous.   Plants that drop their leaves annually.   Most hardwood trees are in this class, while most conifers are evergreen; *i.e.*, their leaves or needles are 2 or more years old before they are dropped.

d.b.h.   Diameter at breast height ($4\frac{1}{2}$ ft. from the ground).

ecology.   The study of plants in relation to their environment and the factors that control their distribution.

face.   The wound area of a tree worked for naval stores.   A, front: the first face on a tree extending from 90 to 100 in. up the tree.   B, back: the second or third face on a tree extending from 90 to 100 in. up the tree.

farmstead windbreak.   Trees and shrubs maintained for the protection of the farmstead.

farm woodland, or woods.   Natural or planted forest trees maintained as part of the farm; shelter belts and windbreaks are included.   The woodland is not necessarily a physical part of the farm if it is maintained for the benefit of the farm.

felling.   A logger's term for cutting trees at stump height and placing them on the ground to be utilized for their products.

firebreak.   An existing barrier, or one constructed before a fire occurs, from which all or most of the flammable materials have been removed; designed to stop or check creeping or running but not spotting fires, or to serve as a line from which to work and to facilitate the movement of men and equipment in fire suppression.

forest type.   A descriptive term used to group stands of similar character as regards composition and development due to certain ecological factors, by which they may be differentiated from other groups of stands.   The term suggests repetition of the same character under similar conditions. A type is temporary if its character is due to passing influences such as logging or fire; permanent if no appreciable change is expected and the character is due to ecological factors alone; climax if it is the ultimate stage of a succession of temporary types.   A cover type is a forest type now occupying the ground, no implication being conveyed as to whether it is temporary or permanent.

group selection.   A modification of the selection method whereby the mature timber is removed in groups rather than by single trees.

growing stock.   All of the trees in a stand maintained as the capital from which growth in the form of wood products can be cut.   Growing stock obviously varies greatly with age, treatment, and objectives of management.

gum.   The oleoresin or liquid produced by a living pine tree from which turpentine and rosin are produced; also called dip.

hardwood. A general term that may refer merely to the characteristics of the wood of any tree. Generally, however, it refers to wood of trees belonging to the botanical group with broad leaves, in contrast to conifers. *See* softwood.

harvest cutting. *See* page 166.

humus. Plant and animal residues of the soil that are undergoing decomposition.

improvement cutting. *See* page 159.

intolerant. *See* tolerance.

jack pine. A general term applied to low-grade pine trees usually of the pioneer class ecologically. Almost synonymous with scrub. Also the common name of *Pinus banksiona*, a Lake states pine.

line and plot. *See* page 197.

litter. The uppermost layer of the forest floor, composed of freshly fallen or slightly decomposed organic material.

log rule. A table showing the estimated or calculated amount of lumber that can be sawed from logs of given length and diameter; commonly divided into four groups upon the basis of derivation: (1) diagram rules, (2) formula rules, (3) rules based on actual average output, and (4) hybrid rules.

log scale. The lumber contents of a log or of a number of logs considered collectively, based on a specific log rule.

lumber. Timber sawed or split for use; logs cut into materials suitable for buildings, bridges, and similar structures.

lumber tally. The result of measuring the actual output of lumber from logs; contrasted with log scale.

mature. In timber, the size or rotation age, decided by the forest manager to be the maximum that he wishes to grow. Often used loosely to refer to trees or timber believed to be fully grown.

merchantable. Term used to designate the portion of trees or stands that can be profitably marketed under given economic conditions.

mine timbers. The class of round and sawed wood products used in mines, including stulls, props, ties, and lagging.

mulch. A layer of organic matter spread on top of the soil to retain moisture and prevent erosion.

naval stores. The products obtained from the pitch of longleaf and slash pine—mostly turpentine and rosin.

partial cutting. *See* page 186.

peeled wood. Logs or bolts from which the bark has been removed. During late spring and early summer (usually May to July), bark can be removed easily. At other seasons the bark is tight and must be removed with knives or rossing machines. With pulpwood, peeled wood is contrasted with rough wood, *i.e.*, wood with the bark on.

permanent type. *See* forest type.

piling. Round timbers to be driven into the ground to support other structures.

plots, sample. Measured areas by which the entire mass is judged. In forestry, samples to judge entire timber stand as to stocking, species, volume, quality, or other characteristics. Plots usually are $\frac{1}{4}$ to $\frac{1}{5}$ or $\frac{1}{10}$ acre, or they may be square rods or even smaller for some purposes.

pole. A young tree 4 in. d.b.h. or more. The maximum size of poles is usually though not invariably taken to be some d.b.h. between 8 and 12 in. *See* sapling.

poles. Timbers in the round, usually used to support power or telephone lines.

post. Timber used for supporting fencing. It may be round, split, or sawed.

processed products. Manufactured or partly manufactured products; processed wood products are fuel, posts, logs, poles, piling, pulpwood, and similar products. Also called "converted timber products."

pruning. *Timber trees*—(1) removal of living or dead branches from the lower part of the stems of living trees to enable the trees to produce knot-free wood on the outside of the bole; (2) removal of buds which form the lateral branches of young trees to prevent the lateral from forming. This is known as "bud pruning". *See* page 148. *Christmas trees*—shaping the trees by cutting with a knife or by shearing to improve the quality of the trees for the market.

pulpwood. Wood cut or prepared primarily for manufacture into wood pulp, for subsequent manufacture into paper, fiberboard, or other products, depending largely on the species cut and pulping process.

release cutting. *See* page 85.

reproduction. Naturally established tree seedlings or sprouts. Usually less than 2 in. d.b.h. Young trees larger than this are usually classed as saplings or poles.

rotation. The period of years required to establish and grow timber crops to a specified condition of maturity.

rough wood. Usually means bolts of wood with bark attached. *See* peeled wood.

sapling. A young tree less than 4 in. d.b.h. The minimum size of saplings is usually though not invariably placed at 2 in. d.b.h. *See* pole.

saw log. A log large enough to produce lumber or other products that can be sawed. Its size and quality vary with the utilization practices of the region.

scale. (1) The estimated sound contents in terms of a given log rule of a log or group of logs. (2) To estimate the sound contents of a log or group of logs. *See* log rule.

scrub pine. *See* jack pine.

second growth. A stand of timber following the removal of mature timber.

seedling. (1) A tree grown from seed. (2) In nursery practice, a tree which has not been transplanted in the nursery.

selection method of cutting. Removal of mature timber, usually the oldest or largest trees, either as single scattered trees or in small groups at relatively short intervals, commonly 5 to 20 years, repeated indefinitely, by means of which the continuous establishment of natural reproduction in the stand is encouraged and an uneven-aged arrangement of ages is maintained. Also called "selective cutting."

shelter belt. A wind barrier of living trees and shrubs maintained for the purpose of protecting farm fields. As applied to individual farmsteads, termed "windbreak."

shelterwood cutting. The system whereby the forest canopy is opened up to admit light but a large number of trees are left standing until reproduction is established.

silviculture. The art of producing and tending a forest; the application of the knowledge of silvics in the treatment of a forest.

site. An area considered as to its ecological factors with reference to capacity to produce forests or other vegetation; the combination of biotic, climatic, and soil conditions of an area.

skid. (1) To drag logs on the ground from stump to skidway or landing. (2) A log or pole, commonly used in pairs, on which logs are rolled or piled.

skidway. Two skids laid parallel at right angles to a road, usually raised above the ground at the end nearest the road. Logs are usually piled upon a skidway as they are brought from the stump for loading upon sleds, wagons, or cars.

slash. Branches, bark, tops, chunks, cull logs, uprooted stumps, and broken or uprooted trees left on the ground after logging; also a large accumulation of debris after wind or fire.

softwood. Usually wood from some species of conifers; or it may refer merely to the characteristics of the wood. *See* hardwood.

soil-conservation district. A local unit of government organized and operated under state law by landowners and operators for the purpose of conservation of soil and water resources and the control and prevention of soil erosion.

sprout. A tree that has grown from a stump or a root.

stocking. The coverage of an area with trees. Usually used in connection with the degree of coverage; excellent, medium, or poor stocking.

stumpage. (1) The value of timber as it stands uncut in the woods. (2) In a general sense, the standing timber itself.

temporary type. *See* forest type.

thinning. A cutting made in an immature stand for the purpose of increasing the rate of growth or improving the form of the trees that remain and increasing the total production of the stand.

timber. A term loosely applied to forest stands or their products; often to wood in forms suitable for heavy construction, as for houses, ships, and bridges. Specifically, sawed lumber 4 by 4 in. or more in breadth and thickness; or, in English markets, sawed material more than 4½ in. thick and 6 in. wide.

tolerance. The capacity of a tree to develop and grow in the shade of and in competition with other trees. Trees are commonly classified as tolerant (or shade enduring), intermediate, and intolerant (or light demanding). Examples of tolerant trees are hemlock and sugar maple; of intermediate trees, white pine and red oak; of intolerant trees, southern pine and white ash.

tree farm. A term used to designate a forest area formally dedicated by the private forest industries and other forest owners to the continuous production of forest crops, which is protected from fire and harvested in such a manner as to furnish economic and social benefits to the community at large. An area is eligible for the designation "tree farm" when the owner pledges himself to meet specific standards of forest management. The designation "tree farm" applies to private lands.

type, forest. *See* forest type.

veneer. A thin sheet of wood cut on a veneer machine. There are three kinds of veneers: sawed, sliced, and rotary cut.

weeding. *See* page 76.

windbreak. A wind barrier of living trees and shrubs maintained for the purpose of protecting the farm home, other buildings, garden, orchard, or feed lots.

wolf tree. A tree that occupies more than its fair share of growing space in a woodland.

yarding. Gathering together products at a yard or skidway. Often used in connection with donkey logging.

Appendix III
Volume Tables

TABLE 32. AMOUNT OF SAW TIMBER IN TREES, BY DIAMETER AND MERCHANTABLE HEIGHT, INTERNATIONAL ¼-IN. RULE

D.b.h., in.	Volume (ft. b.m.) according to number of usable 16-ft. logs *										
	1	1½	2	2½	3	3½	4	4½	5	5½	6
10	39	51	63	72	80						
11	49	64	80	92	104						
12	59	78	98	112	127	136	146				
13	71	96	120	138	156	168	181				
14	83	112	141	164	186	201	216				
15	98	132	166	194	221	240	260				
16	112	151	190	223	256	280	305				
17	128	174	219	258	296	325	354				
18	144	196	248	292	336	369	402				
19	162	222	281	332	382	420	457				
20	181	248	314	370	427	470	512	546	580		
21	201	276	350	414	478	526	575	616	656		
22	221	304	387	458	528	583	638	685	732		
23	244	336	428	507	586	646	706	761	816		
24	266	368	469	556	644	708	773	836	899		
25	290	402	514	610	706	779	852	922	992		
26	315	436	558	662	767	849	931	1,008	1,086		
27	341	474	606	721	836	925	1,014	1,100	1,185		
28	367	510	654	779	904	1,000	1,096	1,190	1,284	1,368	1,453
29	396	551	706	842	977	1,080	1,184	1,289	1,394	1,491	1,588
30	424	591	758	904	1,050	1,161	1,272	1,388	1,503	1,613	1,723
31	454	634	814	973	1,132	1,254	1,376	1,497	1,618	1,740	1,862
32	485	678	870	1,042	1,213	1,346	1,480	1,606	1,733	1,867	2,001
33	518	724	930	1,114	1,298	1,442	1,586	1,722	1,858	2,005	2,152
34	550	770	989	1,186	1,383	1,537	1,691	1,838	1,984	2,144	2,304
35	585	820	1,055	1,266	1,477	1,642	1,806	1,965	2,124	2,291	2,458
36	620	870	1,121	1,346	1,571	1,746	1,922	2,093	2,264	2,438	2,612
37	656	922	1,188	1,430	1,672	1,858	2,044	2,230	2,416	2,600	2,783
38	693	974	1,256	1,514	1,772	1,970	2,167	2,368	2,568	2,761	2,954
39	732	1,031	1,330	1,602	1,874	2,087	2,300	2,507	2,714	2,920	3,127
40	770	1,086	1,403	1,690	1,977	2,204	2,432	2,646	2,860	3,080	3,300

* Data from Mesavage and Girard, tables for estimating board-foot volume of timber (Form class 80), U.S. Department of Agriculture, Forest Service, 1946. For exceptionally tall, slender trees add 10 percent. For exceptionally short, stubby trees deduct 10 percent.

TABLE 33. AMOUNT OF SAW TIMBER IN TREES, BY DIAMETER AND MERCHANTABLE HEIGHT, DOYLE LOG RULE

D.b.h., in.	Volume (ft. b.m.) according to number of usable 16-ft. logs*										
	1	1½	2	2½	3	3½	4	4½	5	5½	6
10	16	20	23	24	26						
11	24	30	35	38	42						
12	31	39	47	52	57	60	62				
13	42	53	64	72	80	84	88				
14	52	67	82	93	104	109	114				
15	64	84	104	118	132	141	150				
16	77	101	125	143	161	174	186				
17	92	122	152	175	198	214	230				
18	108	144	179	206	234	254	273				
19	126	168	210	244	278	301	324				
20	144	193	242	282	321	348	374	396	417		
21	164	221	278	324	370	403	436	462	489		
22	185	250	315	368	420	458	497	529	561		
23	208	282	356	417	478	521	564	604	643		
24	231	314	397	466	536	583	630	678	725		
25	256	350	443	522	600	655	710	764	818		
26	282	386	489	576	663	727	791	852	912		
27	310	425	540	638	735	806	877	946	1,015		
28	339	466	592	700	807	885	963	1,040	1,118	1,188	1,258
29	370	509	648	766	884	970	1,056	1,144	1,232	1,315	1,398
30	400	552	703	832	961	1,055	1,149	1,248	1,346	1,442	1,537
31	434	599	764	906	1,049	1,154	1,260	1,364	1,469	1,576	1,684
32	467	646	824	980	1,137	1,254	1,370	1,481	1,592	1,712	1,831
33	502	696	889	1,060	1,230	1,356	1,483	1,604	1,726	1,860	1,994
34	538	746	954	1,138	1,322	1,459	1,596	1,728	1,861	2,008	2,156
35	576	801	1,026	1,225	1,424	1,573	1,722	1,867	2,012	2,167	2,322
36	615	857	1,099	1,312	1,526	1,688	1,849	2,006	2,163	2,326	2,488
37	656	915	1,174	1,406	1,638	1,811	1,984	2,157	2,330	2,502	2,675
38	697	973	1,249	1,499	1,749	1,934	2,119	2,308	2,496	2,679	2,862
39	740	1,036	1,332	1,598	1,864	2,065	2,266	2,462	2,658	2,855	3,052
40	784	1,099	1,414	1,696	1,979	2,196	2,413	2,616	2,819	3,030	3,241

*Data from Mesavage and Girard, tables for estimating board-foot volume of timber (Form class 80), U.S. Department of Agriculture, Forest Service, 1946. For exceptionally tall, slender trees add 10 percent. For exceptionally short, stubby trees deduct 10 percent.

Form Class

Volume tables (the samples in this appendix) are based on form class 80. "Form class" is the term used by foresters to define precisely the taper of the bole of timber trees. Rapid taper means less volume in the bole than where the taper is slight.

By "form class" is meant the percentage ratio between the diameter inside the bark at the top of the first 16-ft. log and the diameter outside the bark at breast height ($4\frac{1}{2}$ ft. above ground). For example, a tree 20 in. d.b.h. and measuring 16 in. inside the bark at the top of the first 16-ft. log has a form class of $(16/20 \times 100) = 80$ percent, known as form class 80.

Volume tables are available[1] giving volumes of trees by log rules for various form classes from 65 to 90. For the highest degrees of accuracy in estimating volumes of standing timber, it is essential to determine the form class of the trees and use the appropriate form-class tables, or use tables made for specific species grown under conditions similar to those in your woodland.

Form class 80 (in sample tables) indicates good timber with moderate taper.

Rules of Thumb

Rules of thumb for determining volumes of standing trees that are even approximately accurate are difficult to find. Here is one that may be of some help for quick approximation.

For *form class* 80:

1. International $\frac{1}{4}$-in. rule. *Volume of 3-log trees in board feet is approximately equal to the square of the d.b.h. of the tree.* (Good up to 24 in. d.b.h.; *above* that results are 10 to 15 percent low.)

2. Scribner rule. Same rule applies. (Fairly good results for trees 20 in. d.b.h. and larger; *below* that results are 15 to 20 percent high.)

TABLE 34. INFLUENCE OF AVERAGE TREE SIZE (D.B.H.) ON NUMBER OF BOLTS PER CORD AND CUBIC-FOOT VOLUME*

Average tree, d.b.h., in.	Cubic-foot volume per cord	Number of bolts per cord
4	104.7	155
5	105.1	141
6	105.9	126
7	108.1	111
8	112.4	94
9	117.6	75

* From A. C. McIntyre: "A Cordwood Study," *Journal of Forestry*, vol. 32, p. 588, 1934.

[1] From the U.S. Forest Service.

TABLE 35. APPROXIMATE NUMBER OF TREES REQUIRED TO YIELD
SPECIFIC VOLUMES OF MATERIAL (HARDWOODS) *

D.b.h., in.	1 cord† fuel wood	1 tie‡ 6 × 8 in.	1 fence post, 4-in. top	M ft. b.m. lumber	
				Med. ht. trees	Tall trees
6	20	....	0.50		
8	10	....	0.25		
10	6	....	0.10		
12	4	1	0.06	20	15
14	3	0.75	0.04	12	8
16	2	0.50	....	9	6
18	1.5	0.33	....	7	4
20	1.3	....	....	6	3.5
22	....	....	....	5	3
24	....	....	....	4	2
26	....	....	....	2.5	1.5
28	....	....	....	2	1.3

* From *Forestry Handbook*, U.S. Department of Agriculture, Soil Conservation Service, Agriculture Handbook 13, Milwaukee, Wis., September, 1950.

† 3-in. sticks and larger.

‡ Side lumber taken from larger bolts in addition to ties. Also, 1 cord of top wood and ⅛ cord of slabs are obtainable for every ten ties.

TABLE 36. VOLUME IN TREE TOPS (HARDWOODS)
(Fuelwood above merchantable stem *,†)

D.b.h., in.	Height above merchantable stem, ft.—Total height minus merchantable height					
	20	30	40	50	60	70
	Cords					
12	...	...	$\frac{1}{10}$	$\frac{1}{10}$	$\frac{1}{6}$	$\frac{1}{6}$
14	...	$\frac{1}{10}$	$\frac{1}{6}$	$\frac{1}{6}$	$\frac{1}{4}$	$\frac{1}{4}$
16	$\frac{1}{10}$	$\frac{1}{10}$	$\frac{1}{6}$	$\frac{1}{4}$	$\frac{1}{3}$	$\frac{1}{3}$
18	$\frac{1}{10}$	$\frac{1}{6}$	$\frac{1}{4}$	$\frac{1}{3}$	$\frac{1}{3}$	$\frac{1}{2}$
20	$\frac{1}{10}$	$\frac{1}{4}$	$\frac{1}{3}$	$\frac{1}{2}$	$\frac{1}{2}$	$\frac{2}{3}$
22	$\frac{1}{6}$	$\frac{1}{4}$	$\frac{1}{3}$	$\frac{1}{2}$	$\frac{2}{3}$	$\frac{3}{4}$
24	$\frac{1}{6}$	$\frac{1}{3}$	$\frac{1}{2}$	$\frac{2}{3}$	$\frac{3}{4}$	1
26	$\frac{1}{4}$	$\frac{1}{2}$	$\frac{2}{3}$	$\frac{3}{4}$	1	$1\frac{1}{6}$
28	$\frac{1}{3}$	$\frac{1}{2}$	$\frac{3}{4}$	1	$1\frac{1}{6}$	$1\frac{1}{4}$
30	$\frac{1}{3}$	$\frac{2}{3}$	$\frac{3}{4}$	1	$1\frac{1}{4}$	

* For estimating *approximate* volume of stacked fuelwood in tops and branches above merchantable height. Merchantable height is the distance above the stump to an 8 in. top or where the merchantable stem is otherwise limited by large branches or defects.

† From *Forestry Handbook*, U.S. Department of Agriculture, Soil Conservation Service, Agriculture Handbook 13, Milwaukee, Wis., September, 1950.

TABLE 37. VOLUME IN TERMS OF TREES PER CORD: WOOD WITH BARK SUITABLE
FOR PULPWOOD*

For trees up to 75 ft. total height.   Minimum size of bolts 4 in. small end

Trees, d.b.h., in.	Number of trees to make one standard cord			
	Pine: loblolly, shortleaf	Spruce	Hardwood types	
			Beech, birch, maple	Oak, hickory
5	30	40	35	25
6	20	24	20	17
7	14	16	15	13
8	9	12	11	9
9	7	9	8	7
10	6	7	6	6
12	4	4		
14	3	3		
16	2	2.5		
18	1.5	2		

* NOTE: This table was compiled by the author from various sources.   It is suitable for use where a quick answer is needed and a high degree of accuracy is not required.   It does not include limb wood.   For fuel wood that includes top wood, increase results by 10 to 15 percent.   For peeled pulpwood, decrease results by 10 to 15 percent.

TABLE 38. CORDWOOD VOLUME TABLE FOR SECOND-GROWTH DOUGLAS FIR TREES*

D.b.h., in.	Total height of tree, ft.												
	30	40	50	60	70	80	90	100	110	120	130	140	150
	Cords per tree												
6	0.02	0.03	0.04	0.05	0.06	0.07							
8	0.05	0.07	0.08	0.10	0.12	0.14	0.15						
10	0.08	0.11	0.13	0.16	0.19	0.21	0.23	0.26	0.29	0.31			
12	0.12	0.16	0.19	0.23	0.26	0.30	0.33	0.36	0.41	0.44			
14	0.16	0.20	0.25	0.30	0.35	0.40	0.45	0.49	0.54	0.59	0.64	0.70	
16	....	0.26	0.32	0.38	0.45	0.51	0.57	0.62	0.67	0.74	0.80	0.88	0.95
18	....	....	0.40	0.48	0.55	0.62	0.70	0.77	0.83	0.90	0.98	1.07	1.17
20	....	....	0.48	0.57	0.66	0.75	0.83	0.92	0.98	1.07	1.17	1.28	1.39
22	....	....	0.57	0.66	0.76	0.86	0.96	1.05	1.13	1.24	1.35	1.46	1.60
24	....	....	....	0.76	0.87	0.98	1.08	1.17	1.27	1.39	1.50	1.63	1.79

* NOTE: Volume of unpeeled stem between stump height equal to d.b.h. and a 4-in. top diameter inside bark; cordwood assumed to be cut in 8-ft. lengths.   By Staebler and Shaw, Pacific Northwest Forest and Range Experiment Station, February, 1949.

Appendix IV

Log Rules

TABLE 39. INTERNATIONAL LOG RULE*

Top diam. of log inside bark, in.	Volume of log by length, ft. b.m.						
	8 ft.	10 ft.	12 ft.	14 ft.	16 ft.	18 ft.	20 ft.
4	. . .	5	5	5	5	5	10
5	5	5	10	10	10	15	15
6	10	10	15	15	20	25	25
7	10	15	20	25	30	35	40
8	15	20	25	35	40	45	50
9	20	30	35	45	50	60	70
10	30	35	45	55	65	75	85
11	35	45	55	70	80	95	105
12	45	55	70	85	95	110	125
13	55	70	85	100	115	135	150
14	65	80	100	115	135	155	175
15	75	95	115	135	160	180	205
16	85	110	130	155	180	205	235
17	95	125	150	180	205	235	265
18	110	140	170	200	230	265	300
19	125	155	190	225	260	300	335
20	135	175	210	250	290	330	370
21	155	195	235	280	320	365	410
22	170	215	260	305	355	405	455
23	185	235	285	335	390	445	495
24	205	255	310	370	425	485	545
25	220	280	340	400	460	525	590
26	240	305	370	435	500	570	640
27	260	330	400	470	540	615	690
28	280	355	430	510	585	665	745
29	305	385	465	545	630	715	800
30	325	410	495	585	675	765	860
31	350	440	530	625	720	820	915
32	375	470	570	670	770	875	980
33	400	500	605	715	820	930	1,045
34	425	535	645	760	875	990	1,110
35	450	565	685	805	925	1,050	1,175
36	475	600	725	855	980	1,115	1,245
37	505	635	770	905	1,040	1,175	1,315
38	535	670	810	955	1,095	1,245	1,390
39	565	710	855	1,005	1,155	1,310	1,465
40	595	750	900	1,060	1,220	1,380	1,540

* Saw kerf, $\frac{1}{4}$ in. Allowance for shrinkage in thickness, $\frac{1}{8}$ in. per inch. Taper allowance, $\frac{1}{2}$ in. per 4-ft. section. Formula for volume of 4-ft. section, $V = (0.22D^2 - 0.71D)0.9048$.

TABLE 40. SCRIBNER DECIMAL *C* LOG RULE

Top diam. of log inside bark, in.	Volume of log, ft. b.m. in tens, by length									
	6 ft.	8 ft.	10 ft.	12 ft.	14 ft.	16* ft.	18 ft.	20 ft.	22 ft.	24 ft.
6	0.5	0.5	1	1	1	2	2	2	3	3
7	0.5	1	1	2	2	3	3	3	4	4
8	1	1	2	2	2	3	3	3	4	4
9	1	2	3	3	3	4	4	4	5	6
10	2	3	3	3	4	6	6	7	8	9
11	2	3	4	4	5	7	8	8	9	10
12	3	4	5	6	7	8	9	10	11	12
13	4	5	6	7	8	10	11	12	13	15
14	4	6	7	9	10	11	13	14	16	17
15	5	7	9	11	12	14	16	18	20	21
16	6	8	10	12	14	16	18	20	22	24
17	7	9	12	14	16	18	21	23	25	28
18	8	11	13	16	19	21	24	27	29	32
19	9	12	15	18	21	24	27	30	33	36
20	11	14	17	21	24	28	31	35	38	42
21	12	15	19	23	27	30	34	38	42	46
22	13	17	21	25	29	33	38	42	46	50
23	14	19	23	28	33	38	42	47	52	57
24	15	21	25	30	35	40	45	50	55	61
25	17	23	29	34	40	46	52	57	63	69
26	19	25	31	37	44	50	56	62	69	75
27	21	27	34	41	48	55	62	68	75	82
28	22	29	36	44	51	58	65	73	80	87
29	23	31	38	46	53	61	68	76	84	91
30	25	33	41	49	57	66	74	82	90	99
31	27	36	44	53	62	71	80	89	98	106
32	28	37	46	55	64	74	83	92	101	110
33	29	39	49	59	69	78	88	98	108	118
34	30	40	50	60	70	80	90	100	110	120
35	33	44	55	66	77	88	98	109	120	131
36	35	46	58	69	81	92	104	115	127	138
37	39	51	64	77	90	103	116	129	142	154
38	40	54	67	80	93	107	120	133	147	160
39	42	56	70	84	98	112	126	140	154	168
40	45	60	75	90	105	120	135	150	166	181

* When smooth values for 16-ft. logs are needed, use should be made of the formula $V = 0.79D^2 - (2D + 4)$, in which D is top diameter inside bark in inches.

TABLE 41. DOYLE LOG RULE*

Top diam. of log inside bark, in.	Volume of log by length, ft. b.m.						
	8 ft.	10 ft.	12 ft.	14 ft.	16 ft.	18 ft.	20 ft.
8	8	10	12	14	16	18	20
9	13	16	19	22	25	28	31
10	18	23	27	32	36	41	45
11	25	31	37	43	49	55	61
12	32	40	48	56	64	72	80
13	41	51	61	71	81	91	101
14	50	63	75	88	100	113	125
15	61	76	91	106	121	136	151
16	72	90	108	126	144	162	180
17	85	106	127	148	169	190	211
18	98	123	147	172	196	221	245
19	113	141	169	197	225	253	281
20	128	160	192	224	256	288	320
21	145	181	217	253	289	325	361
22	162	203	243	284	324	365	405
23	181	226	271	316	361	406	451
24	200	250	300	350	400	450	500
25	221	276	331	386	441	496	551
26	242	303	363	424	484	545	6C5
27	265	331	397	463	529	595	661
28	288	360	432	504	576	648	720
29	313	391	469	547	625	703	781
30	338	423	507	592	676	761	845
31	365	456	547	638	729	820	911
32	392	490	588	686	784	882	980
33	421	526	631	736	841	946	1,051
34	450	563	675	788	900	1,013	1,125
35	481	601	721	841	961	1,081	1,201
36	512	640	768	896	1,024	1,152	1,280
37	545	681	817	953	1,089	1,225	1,361
38	578	723	867	1,012	1,156	1,301	1,445
39	613	766	919	1,072	1,225	1,378	1,531
40	648	810	972	1,134	1,296	1,458	1,620

* Formula: $V = 0.75D^2 - 6D + 12$.

Appendix V

Modified Acreage Grid

Area Determinations with the Modified Acreage Grid[1]

Land managers frequently find it necessary to use maps and aerial photographs for locating certain areas and determining their acreage. Time and facilities are not always available for making base maps of a given scale. Enlargements of aerial photographs to the scale of 8 in. to the mile are common but not always available. Much time is saved by use of the following quick, though accurate, method of determining acreages of areas on whatever scale or kind of maps or photographs is available.

The ordinary and most accurate method of determining acreages from maps and aerial photographs is by the use of the planimeter. However, it is time consuming, and planimeters are often not available in the field. A practical method of measuring acreages is by the use of grids. Here the principle is the same as plotting a map to scale on cross-section paper and counting the squares, each representing a number of acres. Portions of squares within the boundary of the area to be measured have to be "balanced" off.

It is time consuming and often impractical to plot on cross-section paper each area to be measured. By an improved method grids or squares have been drawn on transparent celluloid, which is used as an overlay for determining acreage directly from the original map or aerial photograph. For increased accuracy, speed, and convenience in the field, the grid method has been modified by placing evenly spaced dots within each square on the transparent overlay. In measuring it is then only necessary to *count dots* and compute acreage instead of counting squares and estimating portions of squares that fall within the boundary of the woodland area.

This modified grid method is based on the principle that, if a square inch on a map equals 160 acres (scale 2 in. per mile), the square inch can be divided into 16 squares each having a value of 10 acres; then by placing four equally spaced dots within each of the 16 squares, each dot will have a value

[1] Reprinted from *Journal of Forestry*, vol. 41, No. 9, September, 1943. Grids can be obtained from Milton M. Bryan, Forest Service, Washington, D.C.

of 2½ acres. By counting the dots that fall within the boundary of the woodland or other area to be measured, a more accurate determination of acreage can be made than by estimating whether ¼, ½, or ¾ of the 10-acre square falls within the boundary. *When two dots fall exactly on the boundary line of the area being measured, one dot is counted and the second is skipped;* that is, only alternate boundary-line dots are counted. When considerable accuracy is desired, several separate counts should be made, changing the position of the grid over the area each time. The average number of dots is used for computing acreage. Greater accuracy results with each additional count.

The modified acreage grid shown in the accompanying illustration has been prepared on the basis of 64 dots per square inch. It can be used on maps of *any* scale if the fractional scale of the map is known. The value of each dot (converting factor) can be determined by dividing the acres per square inch on the map by 64; the number of dots inside the woodland or field to be measured multiplied by this converting factor will give the acreage of the area. Map scales and equivalents for nine of the most common scales in use are shown on the modified grid. Most enlargements of aerial contact prints available in field offices are on the scale of 8 in. to the mile; reference to the modified grid will show that, for this scale, each dot on the grid equals 0.156 acre. Thus, if there are 100 dots in the woodland or field being measured, the total acreage will be 100 × 0.156, or 15.6 acres. With but little practice, one can become proficient in the use of this modified grid for acreage determinations.

TABLE 42. MAP SCALES AND EQUIVALENTS

Fractional scale, in.	Inches per mile	Acres per square inch	Converting factor, each dot equals
1 = 7,920	8.00	10.000	0.156 acre
1 = 9,600	6.60	14.692	0.230 acre
1 = 15,840	4.00	40.000	0.625 acre
1 = 20,000	3.168	63.769	0.996 acre
1 = 31,680	2.00	160.000	2.500 acres
1 = 63,360	1.00	640.000	10.000 acres
1 = 125,000	0.507	2,490.980	38.922 acres
1 = 250,000	0.253	9,963.906	155.686 acres
1 = 500,000	0.127	39,855.627	622.744 acres

MODIFIED ACREAGE GRID*
(64 dots per square inch)
To be used for acreage determinations on maps of any scale.

Place grid over area to be measured; count dots and multiply by converting factor to compute total acreage. When dots fall on area boundary, count alternate dots.

Appendix VI

Growth and Returns from a Black Locust Fence-post Lot[1]

Field data show that under average conditions plantations will attain a height of 30 ft. in 15 years and 40 ft. in 20 years. The number of 7-ft. posts that can be cut from tree boles is shown in the table.

TABLE 43. NUMBER OF 7-FT. POSTS, BLACK LOCUST

D.b.h., in.	Total height, ft.	Top diameter of posts		
		4 in.	5 in.	6 in.
		Number of round or split 7-ft. posts		
6	30	1		
	50	2		
8	30	3	1	
	50	4	2	1
10	40	6	4	2
	60	11	6	3
12	40	9	6	3
	60	16	9	5
	80	24	14	7

TABLE 44. NUMBER OF SPLIT POSTS PER ROUND POST

Average size split post, in.	Diameter at small end of round post			
	6 in.	8 in.	10 in.	12 in.
	Number of split posts			
4	2	4	6	8
5	1	2	4	5
6	1	1	2	4

[1] From U.S. Department of Agriculture, Forest Service, Central States Forest Experiment Station, Note 13, 1934.

Appendix VII

Sample Timber Sale Contract[1]

Timber Contract

Agreement entered into this _____ day of November, 19__, between James Boyd, of Centerdale, Ohio, hereinafter called the seller, and Thomas B. McCord, of New Albany, Ohio, hereinafter called the purchaser.

Witnesseth:

Article 1. The seller agrees to sell to the purchaser, upon the terms and conditions hereinafter stated, all the living timber marked or designated by the seller and all merchantable dead timber, standing or down, estimated to be 84,000 ft. b.m., more or less, on a certain tract of land situated in the township of Centerdale, county of Tompkins, state of Ohio, and located on the farm belonging to the seller, and about one-half mile west of his farmhouse.

Article 2. The purchaser agrees to pay the seller the sum of seven hundred dollars ($700), more or less, as may be determined by the actual scale, at the rate of fourteen dollars ($14) per thousand board feet for white oak and white ash, twelve and $^{50}/_{100}$ dollars ($12.50) for red oak and hickory, eight dollars ($8) for sugar maple and beech, and six dollars ($6) for black gum, blue beech, and ironwood, payable prior to the date of removal of material, in installments of two hundred dollars ($200) each.

Article 3. The purchaser further agrees to cut and remove said timber in strict accordance with the following conditions:

1. Unless extension of time is granted, all timber shall be cut, paid for, and removed on or before March 30, 19__.

2. Saw timber shall be scaled by the _____ log rule, and measured at the small end along the average diameter inside the bark to the nearest inch.

3. The maximum scaling length of logs shall be 16 ft.; greater lengths shall be scaled as two or more logs. Upon all logs an additional length of 4 in. shall be allowed for trimming. Logs overrunning this allowance shall be scaled not to exceed the next foot in length.

[1] From U.S. Department of Agriculture, Farmers' Bulletin No. 1210.

4. No unmarked timber of any kind shall be cut, except black gum, blue beech, and ironwood.

5. Stumps shall be cut so as to cause the least possible waste; stumps of trees up to 16 in. in diameter not higher than 12 in. above the ground, and those of trees above this size at a distance above the ground not greater than three-fourths of their diameter.

6. All trees shall be utilized in their tops to the lowest possible diameter for commercially salable material.

7. Young trees shall be protected against unnecessary injury; only dead trees and the less valuable kinds may be used for construction purposes in connection with lumbering operations.

8. Care shall be exercised at all times by the purchaser and his employees against the starting and spread of fire.

Article 4.   It is mutually understood and agreed by and between the parties hereto as follows:

1. All timber included in this agreement shall remain the property of the seller until paid for in full.

2. In case of dispute over the terms of this contract, final decision shall rest with a reputable person to be mutually agreed upon by the parties to this contract; and in case of further disagreement, with an arbitration board of three persons, one to be selected by each party to this contract and a third to be the state forester or his chosen representative.

In witness whereof the parties hereto have hereunto set their hands and seals this _____ day of _____, 19__.

Witnesses:

    ------------------------------   ------------------------------

    ------------------------------   ------------------------------

Other clauses which might be included are those requiring that the timber shall be scaled in the presence of the seller or his authorized agent; that the log lengths shall be varied so as best to utilize the timber; that unmarked trees, if cut, shall be paid for at double the regular price; that tops left in logging shall remain on the tract for the use of the seller (or, if desired, shall be utilized by the purchaser).

Appendix VIII

List of Forest and Range Experiment Stations[*] U.S. Forest Service

California Forest and Range Experiment Station
347 Forestry Building
University of California
Berkeley 1, California

Central States Forest Experiment Station
111 Old Federal Building
Columbus 15, Ohio

Intermountain Forest and Range Experiment Station
Forest Service Building
Ogden, Utah

Lake States Forest Experiment Station
University Farm
St. Paul 1, Minnesota

Northeastern Forest Experiment Station
102 Motors Avenue
Upper Darby, Pennsylvania

Northern Rocky Mountain Forest and Range Experiment Station
Federal Building
Missoula, Montana

Pacific Northwest Forest and Range Experiment Station
423 U.S. Courthouse
Portland 5, Oregon

Rocky Mountain Forest and Range Experiment Station
Forestry Building
Fort Collins, Colorado

Southeastern Forest Experiment Station
223 Federal Building
Asheville, North Carolina

Southern Forest Experiment Station
704 Lowich Bldg.
2026 St. Charles Avenue
New Orleans 13, Louisiana

[*] July, 1951.

Southwestern Forest and Range
   Experiment Station
Tumamoc Hill
P.O. Box 951
Tucson, Arizona

Alaska Forest Research Center
P.O. Box 740
Juneau, Alaska

Tropical Forest Experiment Station
P.O. Box 577
Rio Piedras, Puerto Rico

Forest Products Laboratory
North Walnut Street
Madison 5, Wisconsin

Appendix IX

A Summary of Forest Taxation Laws by States

By **Carl A. Newport**[1]

For many years it has been recognized that forest properties have certain characteristics which in many cases demand for them special tax laws in order to distribute equitably the tax burden among all types of property. Several forms of special taxation or other legislation have been suggested and attempted. The merits of these various forest tax principles have been written and discussed at length and no attempt will be made to do so here. The intent of this paper is to indicate to what extent the various forms of forest tax laws have been applied by state governments.

Questionnaires were sent to state tax commissions and state foresters requesting information in regard to any special legislation in force or recently enacted with respect to forest properties. In many cases copies of the laws or reports in connection with them were returned. Using the above sources and the *State Forest Tax Law Digest of* 1945 prepared by the Division of Forest Economics, U.S. Forest Service, it was possible to compile a table of the forest tax laws (Table 45), if any, for all of the states as of Dec. 31, 1949.

This table is published as a general source of information on state tax laws applying specifically to forest property. The points of interest in each law are outlined only briefly. The provisions are in no way to be considered official in any state. Copies of the laws may be obtained by writing to the state tax commission of any state in question.

[1] Journal of Forestry, vol. 49, No. 3, March, 1951.

TABLE 45. A SUMMARY OF FOREST TAXATION BY STATES

State	Type of law and date	Classification of land			Tax rates or assessments	
		Eligible land	Method	Required conditions	Timber	Land
Alabama	Yield 1923	Any suited to forest culture	Owner applies for contract with state	Nothing must hinder growth. Utilization under state rules	Yield tax at 8 percent of value of timber cut	Under 160 acres is exempt. Other, assessed as other property but on value of land alone
Arizona	None					
Arkansas	None					
California	Exemption 1926	Any land not previously bearing merchantable timber or from which 70 percent of merchantable timber has been removed	Action by assessor. Owner may request	Timber is considered immature for 40 years after planting or cutting	Exempt	Subject to property tax
Colorado	Exemption 1911	Planted land stocked with immature timber	Action by assessor	Must not be mature nor be more than thirty years of age	Exempt	Subject to property tax which must not be increased due to planting
Connecticut	Exemption 1929	Land having a stand of trees	Owner applies to state forester	Stand of trees that will be valuable as lumber in future	Exempt	Taxed as other real property

TABLE 45. A SUMMARY OF FOREST TAXATION BY STATES.—(Continued)

State	Type of law and date	Classification of land			Tax rates or assessments	
		Eligible land	Method	Required conditions	Timber	Land
Connecticut	Yield 1913	5 acres or more. Land worth less than $25 per acre. Fully stocked with approved species	Owner must apply to state forester	No grazing. Must not be cleared for other use	Over 10 years old:* 2 percent of value of cut during first 10 years. 1 percent increase every 10 years to 7 percent max. Under 10 years old:† 10 percent of value of cut	Tax levy not to exceed 20 mills on full value at time of classification. Value includes timber under Class 1
Delaware	Exemption 1931	5 acres or more. Sufficient trees under 5 ft. in height to ensure merchantable crop	Owner must apply to State Forest Commission	Protect from fire, grazing, and other damage. Cut only trees marked by State Forestry Dept.	Exempt for 30 years	Exempt for 30 years
Florida	None					
Georgia	None					
Idaho	Yield 1929	Must be within a reforestation district. Chiefly valuable for forestry. Timber must be removed under regulation	Owner must present a verified petition to Board of Forestry for contract	Must be managed according to regulations	Yield tax at 12½ percent of stumpage value	$1 per acre fixed assessment

* Class 1. † Class 2.

TABLE 45. A SUMMARY OF FOREST TAXATION BY STATES.—(*Continued*)

| State | Type of law and date | Classification of land | | | Tax rates or assessments | |
		Eligible land	Method	Required conditions	Timber	Land
Idaho	Exemption 1937	Must be within a cooperative sustained-yield district. Owner must be planning to cut	Owner must file notice of intent to cut	Filing of intent to cut makes owner subject to regulation in cutting	Young growth and seed trees exempt	Taxed as other real property
Illinois	None					
Indiana	Fixed assessment 1921	3 acres or more. Land must be well stocked with approved species	Owner must apply and pay for accurate survey	Stand must be kept fully stocked. No grazing. Owner must make annual written report	Fixed assessment of $1 per acre	Fixed assessment includes land
Iowa	Fixed assessment 1906	2 acres or more. Must be not less than 200 trees of approved species on each acre	Owner must apply	Stand must be kept fully stocked. No grazing. Not more than ⅕ of the total number of trees may be cut in a single year	Fixed assessment of $4 per acre	Fixed assessment includes land
Kansas	Exemption 1941	One acre or more of approved shelter belt or windbreak between 60 and 120 ft. wide	County commissioners determine each year what land is used for shelter-belt purposes under law	Must be maintained in accordance with good farm forestry practice. No grazing	Trees are exempt from taxation	Certain of the lands are eligible for an 80 percent reduction in assessed value
Kentucky	None					

TABLE 45. A SUMMARY OF FOREST TAXATION BY STATES.—(*Continued*)

State	Type of law and date	Classification of land			Tax rates or assessments	
		Eligible land	Method	Required conditions	Timber	Land
Louisiana	Yield 1910	Denuded land suited to the practice of forestry. Average actual value must be from $3 to $8 per acre	Owner must apply for contract not to exceed 40 years	Owner must plant suitable timber trees, protect from fire, and maintain thrifty growing conditions	Yield tax at 6 percent of value of products cut	Assessed at value which must average from $3 to $8 per acre
Maine	Exemption 1872	Cleared land which has been planted with 640 forest trees per acre and cultivated for 3 years	Owner must apply to the assessors	Trees must remain thrifty during the 20-year exemption period	Exempt for 20 years	Exempt for 20 years
Maryland	None					
Massachusetts	Yield 1914	At least 10 acres of forest land not used for grazing or purposes other than forest production. Worth $25 or less per acre	Action of local assessors. Owner may refuse	Used for forest production and not have a higher value for other use	Yield tax in year of classification: 1 percent of stumpage 1st year after—2 percent 2nd year after—3 percent 3rd year after—4 percent 4th year after—5 percent 5th year after—6 percent	Assessment in year of classification and 1st year after—75 percent of value of land and timber. 2nd and 3rd years after—50 percent of value. 4th and 5th years after—25 percent of value. None of these adjusted values must be less the $5 per acre

TABLE 45. A SUMMARY OF FOREST TAXATION BY STATES.—*(Continued)*

State	Type of law and date	Classification of land			Tax rates or assessments	
		Eligible land	Method	Required conditions	Timber	Land
Michigan	Yield 1914 (wood lot)	Land must be a part of an agricultural tract of not over 160 acres, but must be less than ¼ of it. Desirable species	Owner applies to county treasurer	Maintain full stocking. Grazing by permission	Timber is taxed at 5 percent of stumpage value when cut	Land and timber assessed annually at $1 or less per acre
Michigan	Yield 1925 (commercial)	Land must be capable of producing commercial timber. Must not contain natural resources other than timber	Owner applies to Dept. of Conservation	Nothing must hinder timber growth. Need permit to cut	Yield tax at 2 percent of stumpage when cut, increasing 1 percent each year after classification to a maximum of 10 percent	Specific tax of 5 cents per acre
Minnesota	Yield 1927	35 acres or more suitable for commercial forestry. 5 to 40 acres also if owner or tenant lives thereon	Owner applies to county board. Contract with state up to 50 years	Must be maintained according to contract	Yield tax on cut made in 1st year of classification is 40 percent of stumpage. Tax is reduced 2 percent annually until 10 percent. Exempt if merchantable at time of contract	Specific tax of 6 cents per acre

TABLE 45. A SUMMARY OF FOREST TAXATION BY STATES.—*(Continued)*

| State | Type of law and date | Classification of land | | | Tax rates or assessments | |
		Eligible land	Method	Required conditions	Timber	Land
Minnesota	Bounty 1871	State pays $2.50 per acre for 6 successive years (not to exceed $25 in any one year)				
Mississippi	Yield 1940	All timber is subject to this tax.	Nonoptional		All growing timber is exempt from ad valorem taxes. Products are taxed when cut at set rates per unit	Property taxes apply to value of land only
Missouri	Yield 1946	At least 40 acres not valued at more than $10 per acre without timber	Owner applies to district forester for 25 years of classification	Proper forest conditions and practices must be maintained. Grazing with permission	Yield tax on cut made 1 to 10 years after classification is 4 percent of stumpage. 11 to 20 years is 5 percent, 21 to 25 years is 6 percent	Assessed at $1 per acre
Montana	None					
Nebraska	None					
Nevada	None					
New Hampshire	Yield 1950	All timberland	Nonoptional	Owner or operator must give notice of intent to cut. Mature timber must be cut or will be taxed at ad valorem	Yield tax at 10 percent of stumpage value. Owner may apply for 30 percent abatement of tax for good practices	Ad valorem tax on land value only

TABLE 45. A SUMMARY OF FOREST TAXATION BY STATES.—(Continued)

| State | Type of law and date | Classification of land | | | Tax rates or assessments | |
		Eligible land	Method	Required conditions	Timber	Land
New Jersey	None					
New Mexico	None					
New York	Yield 1912	15 acres or more of forest land; planted, partially cut, or within 30 years of maturity	Owner applies to assessors and Conservation Dept.	Thinnings with permission. Forests must be kept below certain volumes per acre by good cutting practices	Yield tax at 6 percent of stumpage value	Assessed a value in common with other lands and not more than at time of classification
North Carolina	Exemption 1939	Trees planted for reforestation purposes	Assessor takes action	Maintain good growing conditions for 10 years	Planted trees are exempt for 10 years	Assessed at value without regard to trees
North Dakota	None					
Ohio	Differential assessment 1925	Any land bearing a stand of trees	Owner applies to state forester	Adequate stocking of valuable timber trees. No grazing. Must protect from fire	See Rate—land →	Forest land may be taxed at 50 percent of local tax rate
Oklahoma	None					
Oregon	Yield 1939	Suitable for forest crops but timber not presently mature in sufficient quantity	State Board of Forestry determines what lands are eligible and may enter into contract with owner	Protected and used primarily for forest production. Permit needed to cut and assurance of tax payment given	Yield tax at 12½ percent of value before cutting	Specific tax at 5 cents per acre, west of Cascade Summit. 2½ cents per acre east of Cascade Summit

TABLE 45. A SUMMARY OF FOREST TAXATION BY STATES.—(Continued)

| State | Type of law and date | Classification of land | | | Tax rates or assessments | |
		Eligible land	Method	Required conditions	Timber	Land
Pennsylvania	None					
Rhode Island	Exemption 1878	1 to 300 acres worth less than $25 per acre and planted to 500 specified trees per acre	Owner must file affidavit with assessors	Maintain good growing conditions for 15 years. Fire loss must be replaced	Exempt from taxation for 15 years after planting	Exempt for 15 years after planting
South Carolina	None					
South Dakota	Bounty 1890	Land must be planted to 300 trees per acre	Owner must apply to the county auditor	Must maintain 170 trees per acre for 10 years	State pays $5 per acre per year for not over 10 acres of each owner	Ad valorem tax on land only
Tennessee	None					
Texas	None					
Utah	None					
Vermont	None					
Virginia	None					
Washington	Deferred tax 1941	Forest land used chiefly for timber production and not classified under yield tax law. No wood lots under 40 acres	Owner must give petition to county assessor	Continued use for timber production	Assessed as other personal property when classified. Tax levy is diminished 7½ percent each year after classification until 75 percent reduction is reached. Deferred amount is payable when timber is cut	Assessed as other personal property but as if timber had been removed

TABLE 45. A SUMMARY OF FOREST TAXATION BY STATES.—(Continued)

State	Type of law and date	Classification of land			Tax rates or assessments	
		Eligible land	Method	Required conditions	Timber	Land
Washington	Yield 1931	Immature or unforested lands chiefly valuable for timber production	State Forestry Board must determine what lands eligible. Owner may enter into contract	Land must be used for forest production and protected as law requires	Products taxed at 1 percent of market value for each year of classification with maximum of 12½ percent	Assessed at $1 per acre west of Cascades and 50 cents per acre east of Cascades
West Virginia	Forestry amendment of 1946 makes a forest tax law possible but none has been enacted as yet					
Wisconsin	Exemption 1935	Any fenced wood lot not more than ⅕ of the farm of which it is a part. Any slopes in excess of 30 percent	Sworn statement by owner to the assessor is needed	Protect from grazing, mowing, cultivation, and burning. Maintain forest conditions. Promote growth of grass, trees, or shrubs on slopes to prevent erosion	Exempt	Exempt
Wisconsin	Yield 1927	40 acres or more capable of supporting merchantable timber. 50 percent of timber removed since 1915	Owner must send petition to Conservation Commission stating intention of practicing forestry. Contract may be made for 50 years and is renewable	Notice of intent to cut needed. Commission may limit cutting on any classified land, and inspects every 5 years. Must be kept open for hunting and fishing	Taxed at 10 percent of stumpage value on private land and at 10 percent of half the stumpage value on county land	Specific tax of 10 cents per acre. Management costs may be deducted under state income tax law. County land exempt
Wyoming	None					

Appendix X

Correlated List of Visual Aids

THE VISUAL AIDS listed below and on the following pages can be used to supplement the material in this book. Both motion pictures and filmstrips are included, and the character of each one is indicated by the self-explanatory abbreviations "MP" and "FS." Immediately following this identification is the name of the producer; and if the distributor is different from the producer, the name of the distributor follows the name of the producer. Abbreviations are used for the names of producers and distributors, and these abbreviations are identified in a directory of sources at the end of the bibliography. In most instances, the films can be borrowed or rented from local or state 16mm film libraries. (A nationwide list of these local sources is given in *A Directory of 2002 16mm Film Libraries*, available from the Superintendent of Documents, Washington 25, D.C.) Unless otherwise indicated, the motion pictures are 16mm sound black-and-white films. The filmstrips are all 35mm black-and-white and silent. The length of the motion pictures is given in minutes (min), that of the filmstrips in frames (fr).

This bibliography is suggestive only, and film users should examine the latest catalogues of the U.S. Forest Service and the annual edition and quarterly supplements of *Educational Film Guide*, a catalogue of some 12,000 films, published by the H. W. Wilson Company, New York. The *Guide*, a standard reference book, is available in most college and public libraries.

Better Timber (MP Ga Ag Ext 11min color). Shows what trees should be cut so that the average farm wood lot will produce the highest continuous yield.

Birth of a Southern Pine (MP So Pulp 15min color). Pictures the process of reproducing a pine tree including the biological functions of the male and female flowers that result in the pine bur, followed by the seed, and finally the seedling growing in the grass.

Easier Ways of Logging (MP USDA 26min color). Demonstrates recommended logging practices with particular emphasis on methods for farmers and small woodland owners in the eastern United States. Explains the sources of information on logging.

377

The Farm and the Farm Woods (FS USDA/Photo 48fr). Explains the values of farm woodlands and illustrates some points of proper care and management.

Farm Forestry Extension in the United States (FS USDA/Photo 69fr). Illustrates the benefits of farm woodlands and surveys the work of state extension foresters and county agents in promoting the proper care of such woodlands.

Forests Forever (MP USDA 25min color). Shows what should be done to stop destructive tree-cutting practices and to restore and maintain a growing stock of healthy trees.

Green Harvest (MP Weyerhaeuser/MTP 29min color). Shows the relationship between wildlife and forestation, how scientific harvesting of trees is practiced, how proper planning and selection ensure natural reforestation, and how logs and lumber are handled mechanically.

Indian Forests of the Southwest (MP USIS 18min color). Explains the principles of forest management and of sustained yield and the need for forest cover to protect grazing lands, prevent erosion and floods, and furnish refuge for game and fish.   Describes fire-control methods.

Living Forest (MP series EBF 11min each color). Consists of a series of motion pictures produced in affiliation with the Conservation Foundation in association with the New York Zoological Society.   Titles of the individual films are:

Forest Conservation
Forest Grows
Forest Produces

Lonnie's New Crop (MP So Pulp 10min color). Encourages the small farmer to plant pines on land that is neither productive nor in use. Explains the procedure for obtaining assistance in securing nursery seedlings and in planting and marketing the trees.

Making the Most of Your Woodlot (FS CNFB/Bowmar 64fr). Explains wood-lot management including thinning and cutting, reforestation, crop rotation, and marketing.

Operation of a Forest Nursery (MP USDA 11min). Shows the operations of a large nursery including treatment and storage of seeds, germination tests, sowing seeds, and protection and care of seedlings until they are ready for field planting.

Pine Ways to Profit (MP USDA 20min). Shows the industrial uses of southern pine and emphasizes the importance of sustained-yield cutting and proper conservation methods.   Includes scenes of the making of paper and the distillation of turpentine.

Pines from Seedlings (MP Va Ed Dept 23min). Acquaints vocational agriculture students with reforestation problems; shows lands best suited to forest crops; and illustrates two methods of seeding, natural and artificial, used for reforestation.

River Run (MP USDA 16min color). Shows the values of the proper management of privately owned forests, illustrating particularly the continued productivity of the forests of the Machias River watershed in Maine, which culminates each year in a log drive down the Machias River.

Timber Growing Today (MP TVA 15min color). Explains that the sustained-yield management of forests is economically sound and shows how woodland owners in the Tennessee Valley are beginning to adopt such practices.

A Tree Grows for Christmas (MP USDA 11min color). Tells the story of the Christmas tree in history and legend and of the Christmas tree industry today. Shows how trees are cut and marketed and how a tree should be handled in the home.

Trees Are a Crop (MP CNFB 23min color). Demonstrates efficient wood-lot management by telling how a farmer can make the maximum yearly income from his woodlands. Gives information on which trees to cut and advice on marketing.

Trees Today and Tomorrow (MP Miss Ag Ext 22min color). Describes the steps necessary in marking and cutting a small wood lot, determining a market for the wood, and replanting to preserve the wood lot.

When a Fellow Needs a Forester (MP So Pulp 23min color). Demonstrates forest-management practices necessary to assure full tree growth on farm woodlands.

White Pine Blister Rust (MP series USDA). Consists of a series of six motion pictures showing the effects of white pine blister rust and the control measures being used to stop its spread. The first film deals with national aspects and the other five deal with regional problems. All are in color and run approximately 15 minutes. They are:

Blister Rust: Enemy of the Pines
A Destructive Invader (Northwest)
King of the Softwoods (California and Oregon)
Our White Pine Heritage (New England)
Paul Bunyan Had a Son (Great Lakes)
Return of the Pines (Southern Appalachians)
Woods and a Way (MP So Pulp 30min color). Tells the story of a young farmer in need of money who learns from his county agent how to cut and manage his wood lot.

Sources of Films Listed

Bowmar—Stanley Bowmar Company, 513 West 166th St., New York 32, N.Y.

CNFB—Canadian National Film Board, 1270 Avenue of the Americas, New York, N.Y.

EBF—Encyclopaedia Britannica Films, Inc., Wilmette, Ill.

Ga Ag Ext—Georgia Agricultural Extension Service, Athens, Ga.

Miss Ag Ext—Mississippi Agricultural Extension Service, State College, Miss.

MTP—Modern Talking Pictures Service, Inc., 45 Rockefeller Plaza, New York, N.Y.

Photo—Photo Lab, Inc., 3825 Georgia Ave., Washington 11, D.C.

So Pulp—Southern Pulpwood Conservation Association, 1224 Peachtree St., N.E., Atlanta 5, Ga.

TVA—Tennessee Valley Authority, Knoxville, Tenn.

USDA—U.S. Department of Agriculture, Motion Picture Service, Washington 25, D.C. (Motion pictures distributed through depository film libraries, filmstrips through Photo Lab, Inc., Washington.)

USIS—U.S. Indian Service, Intermountain School, Brigham City, Utah.

Va Ed Dept—Virginia Department of Education, Richmond, Va.

Index